Complete MathSmart

Revised and Updated!

Grade 5

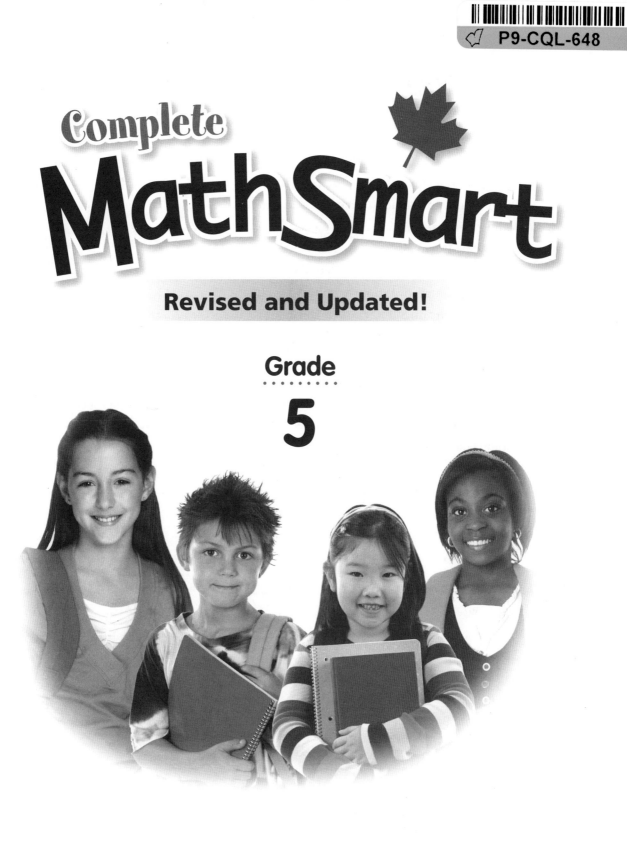

ISBN: 978-1-897164-15-0

ontents

ISBN: 978-1-897164-15-0

ISBN: 978-1-897164-15-0

 ISBN: 978-1-897164-15-0

Section I

Overview

In Grade 4, fraction skills were introduced. In this section, these skills are practised and expanded upon.

Concepts of equivalent fractions, improper fractions and mixed numbers are consolidated. Students learn how to add and subtract fractions with the same denominator. Ample practice in converting fractions to decimals and adding and subtracting decimals are provided.

Other skills include multiplying and dividing decimals by whole numbers.

Introducing Decimals

1. $0.94 = \frac{94}{100}$ or $\frac{9}{10} + \frac{4}{100} = 9$ tenths and 4 hundredths

2. $0.4 = \frac{4}{10}$ or $\frac{40}{100} = 4$ tenths or 40 hundredths

3. $0.02 = \frac{2}{100} = 2$ hundredths

4. $1.43 = 1 + 0.43$

$= 1 + \frac{43}{100}$

$= 1$ and 43 hundredths

Complete the chart below.

	Decimal	Fraction
①	0.52	
②		$\frac{5}{100}$
③		$\frac{3}{10}$
④	0.09	
⑤		$7\frac{2}{10}$
⑥	4.1	

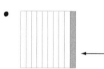

HINTS:

ones
↓ ┌─ decimal point
- **2.94 is a decimal number.**
↑ └─ hundredths
tenths

Read as two point nine four.

- The square is divided into 10 equal parts.
$\frac{1}{10} = 0.1$

- The square is divided into 100 equal parts.
$\frac{1}{100} = 0.01$

- 1 tenth is the same as 10 hundredths.

- Deleting the zeros at the end of a decimal number will not affect the numerical value of a decimal number.
e.g. $2.30 = 2.3$

- When rounding decimal numbers, round up if the last digit is 5 or more; otherwise, round down.

Place the numbers on the number line below.

⑦

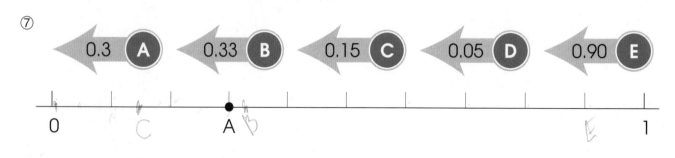

| 0.3 A | 0.33 B | 0.15 C | 0.05 D | 0.90 E |

0   C   A B   E   1

Write the numbers in order from least to greatest.

⑧   0.2, 0.15, 0.1, 0.02, 0.01

_____

⑨   1.45, 1.50, 1.4, 1.54, 1.05

_____

Write the numbers in order from greatest to least.

⑩   5.08, 5.80, 5.88, 0.58, 0.55, 0.50

_____

⑪   2.9, 2.09, 3.2, 2.39, 2.93, 2.3

_____

Write the quantities in decimal form.

⑫   5 cents = $ _____   ⑬   2 nickels = $ _____

⑭   3 quarters = $ _____   ⑮   4 dimes = $ _____

⑯   316 cm = _____ m   ⑰   37 mm = _____ cm

Write True (T) or False (F) in the ( ).

⑱   0.7 = 0.70   (T)   ⑲   1.02 = 1.2   (   )

⑳   3.0 = 3   (   )   ㉑   0.5 = .5   (   )

㉒ $9.1 = 9\frac{1}{100}$ (   )   ㉓ $2.3 = 2\frac{3}{100}$ (   )

Complete the expanded forms using decimals.

㉔ $7 + \frac{2}{100}$ = _____   ㉕ $3 + \frac{5}{10} + \frac{7}{100}$ = _____

㉖ $\frac{1}{10} + \frac{6}{100}$ = _____   ㉗ $2 + \frac{3}{10} + \frac{5}{100}$ = _____

Write an approximate decimal value for each of the numbers on the number line below.

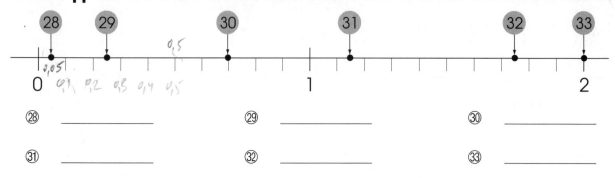

28 _____   29 _____   30 _____

31 _____   32 _____   33 _____

Write the place value and meaning of each underlined digit.

34   0.5<u>1</u>   _____   means _____

35   2.4<u>7</u>   _____   means _____

36   <u>2</u>3.46   _____   means _____

37   1<u>3</u>.21   _____   means _____

38   0.2<u>6</u>   _____   means _____

39   <u>1</u>47.31   _____   means _____

Round each of the following numbers to the nearest tenth.

40   5.72   _____   41   0.88   _____

42   1.99   _____   43   12.34   _____

Round each of the following numbers to the nearest hundredth.

44   5.938   _____   45   2.704   _____

46   3.097   _____   47   6.006   _____

Place < or > between each pair of decimal numbers.

48   0.3   0.32   49   0.09   0.9

50   0.22   0.2   51   23.1   23.01

ISBN: 978-1-897164-15-0

Answer the following questions.

㊾ Ron finished a marathon race in 3 hours 57.8 minutes. John took 0.7 minutes longer.

   a. How long did John take to finish the race? _____

   b. Did they both finish under 4 hours? _____

㊼ Ann spent $47.99 on a pair of jeans and $15.75 on a T-shirt. How much did she spend to the nearest dollar?

_____

㊽ Janice paid $0.80 for a chocolate bar. Write 2 different ways she could pay with 8 coins.

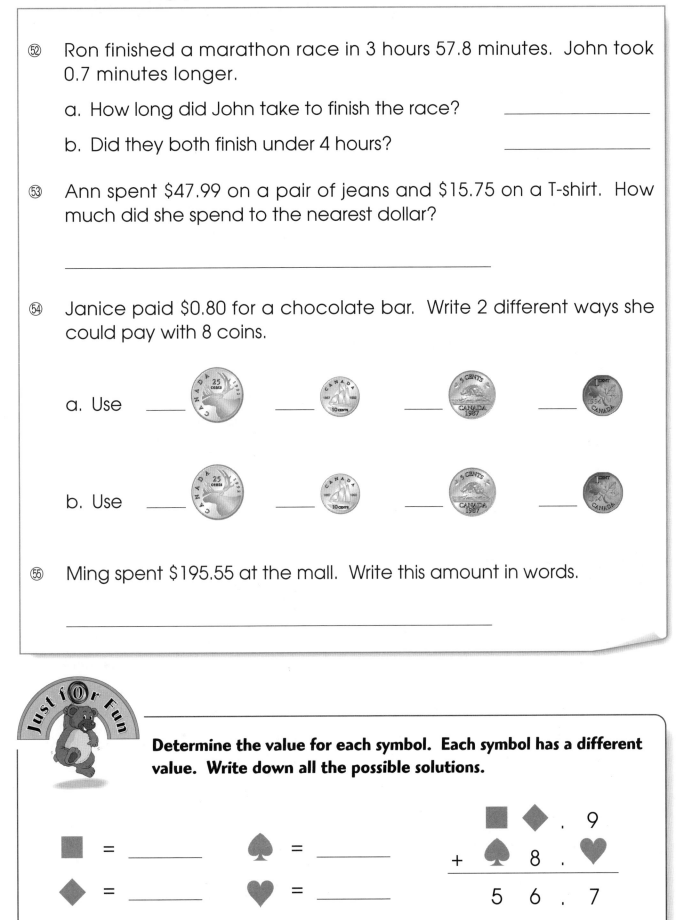

   a. Use ____ ____ ____ ____

   b. Use ____ ____ ____ ____

㊾ Ming spent $195.55 at the mall. Write this amount in words.

_____

Just for Fun

Determine the value for each symbol. Each symbol has a different value. Write down all the possible solutions.

■ = _____   ♠ = _____

♦ = _____   ♥ = _____

$$
\begin{array}{r}
\blacksquare\ \blacklozenge\ .\ 9 \\
+\ \spadesuit\ 8\ .\ \heartsuit \\
\hline
5\ 6\ .\ 7
\end{array}
$$

ISBN: 978-1-897164-15-0

Operations with Whole Numbers

EXAMPLES

1. Find the sum of 4297 and 970 and the difference between them.

$$
\begin{array}{r}
{}^{1}\ {}^{1} \\
4297 \\
+\ \ 970 \\
\hline
\text{sum} \rightarrow 5267
\end{array}
\qquad
\begin{array}{r}
{}^{3}\ {}^{12} \\
\cancel{4}297 \\
-\ \ 970 \\
\hline
\text{difference} \rightarrow 3327
\end{array}
$$

2. Find the product of 296 and 4.

$$
\begin{array}{r}
{}^{2} \\
296 \\
\times\ \ \ 4 \\
\hline
4
\end{array}
\quad \longrightarrow \quad
\begin{array}{r}
{}^{3}\ {}^{2} \\
296 \\
\times\ \ \ 4 \\
\hline
84
\end{array}
\quad \longrightarrow \quad
\begin{array}{r}
{}^{3} \\
296 \\
\times\ \ \ 4 \\
\hline
1184
\end{array}
\leftarrow \text{product}
$$

$6 \times 4 = 24$ $9 \times 4 + 2 = 36 + 2 = 38$ $2 \times 4 + 3 = 8 + 3 = 11$

3. Find the quotient when 511 is divided by 7.

$$
\begin{array}{r}
73 \quad \leftarrow \text{quotient} \\
7\overline{)511} \\
49 \quad \leftarrow 7 \times 7 = 49 \\
\hline
21 \quad \leftarrow \text{bring down 1} \\
21 \quad \leftarrow 7 \times 3 = 21 \\
\hline
\end{array}
$$

$51 - 49 = 2$

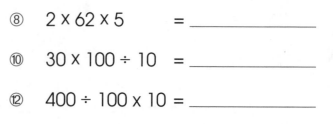

HINTS:

- Align all numbers on the right-hand side when doing vertical addition, subtraction and multiplication.

- In doing addition or multiplication, remember to carry groups of 10 to the column on the left if the sum or product of a column is greater than 10.

- In doing subtraction, borrow 10 from the column on the left if you can't take away.

- Continue to divide until the remainder is smaller than the divisor.

- Multiplication and division are done in order from left to right.

Find the answers mentally.

① $2 \times 7 \times 50$ = _____

② $5700 \div 10$ = _____

③ $5 \times 8 \times 20$ = _____

④ 2000×35 = _____

⑤ $5 \times 29 \times 2$ = _____

⑥ $27000 \div 300$ = _____

⑦ $1000 \times 20 \div 100$ = _____   ⑧ $2 \times 62 \times 5$ = _____

⑨ $2000 \div 100 \times 5$ = _____   ⑩ $30 \times 100 \div 10$ = _____

⑪ $500 \div 50 \times 100$ = _____   ⑫ $400 \div 100 \times 10$ = _____

ISBN: 978-1-897164-15-0

Do the calculation.

⑬ 2784 + 3796	⑭ 999 − 888
⑮ 2784 + 4370 − 401	⑯ 4983 + 3974 − 728

⑰ 595 ÷ 7	⑱ 314 × 8	⑲ 438 ÷ 6

⑳ 5) 325	㉑ 3) 873	㉒ 8) 736

㉓ 5 3 7 × 9	㉔ 8 5 4 × 6	㉕ 2 1 3 × 5

Find the answers.

㉖ The sum of seven thousand two and four hundred ninety-nine.

㉗ The difference between nine hundred eighty-four and five hundred seventy-eight.

ISBN: 978-1-897164-15-0

Write your answers in the puzzle below.

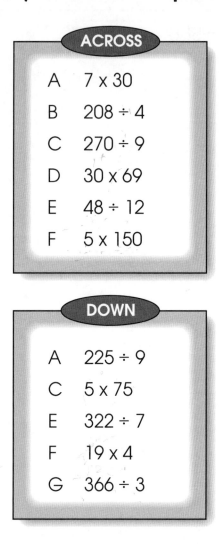

ACROSS

A	7 x 30
B	208 ÷ 4
C	270 ÷ 9
D	30 x 69
E	48 ÷ 12
F	5 x 150

DOWN

A	225 ÷ 9
C	5 x 75
E	322 ÷ 7
F	19 x 4
G	366 ÷ 3

㉘

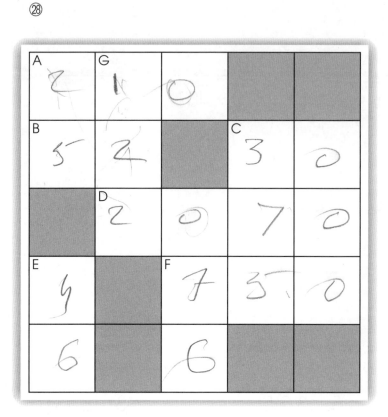

Do the division and write down the remainder in each case. The sum of the remainders is equal to the number of coconuts in the tree.

㉙ 218 ÷ 3   remainder = _____

㉚ 497 ÷ 7   remainder = _____

㉛ 100 ÷ 3   remainder = _____

㉜ 200 ÷ 5   remainder = _____

㉝ 124 ÷ 8   remainder = _____

㉞ 874 ÷ 4   remainder = _____

㉟ Sum of remainders   = _____

There are _____ coconuts in the tree.

ISBN: 978-1-897164-15-0

Solve the problems. Show your work.

㊱ Jane is 7 years older than Jeff. Jane is 11 years old. How old is Jeff?

Jeff is _____ years old.

㊲ What is the perimeter of the rectangle?

12 m

2 m [rectangle] 2 m

12 m

㊳ Dan's heart beats 66 times a minute. How many times does it beat in an hour?

㊴ Farmer Fred's chickens lay 240 eggs per day. If he gets $2 for one dozen eggs, how much does he earn per day?

Just for Fun

Solve the problems.

① Write the next 3 numbers in each of the following sequences.

a. 77 88 99 _____ _____ _____

b. 72 84 96 _____ _____ _____

② A number is divisible by 3 if the sum of its digits is divisible by 3. Circle the numbers which are divisible by 3. (Do not divide!)

1234   5790   2927   9980   4563

ISBN: 978-1-897164-15-0

Adding Decimals

1. $57.23 + 85.9 + 0.78 + 30$

     $= 173.91$

2.   Write 219.57 in expanded form.

     $219.57 = 200 + 10 + 9 + 0.5 + 0.07$

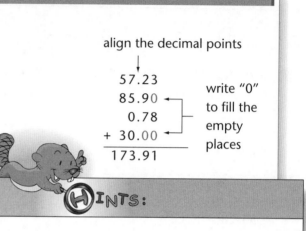

align the decimal points

```
  57.23
  85.90  ←  write "0"
   0.78     to fill the
+ 30.00  ←  empty
  ───────   places
 173.91
```

HINTS:

- Align the decimal points when doing vertical addition.

- Write zeros to fill the empty places.

- Add decimal numbers the same way we add whole numbers.

- Don't forget to add the decimal point in the answer.

Add these decimals in tenths.

①
$$\begin{array}{r} 0.7 \\ + \ 0.8 \\ \hline \end{array}$$

②
$$\begin{array}{r} 1.9 \\ + \ 8.7 \\ \hline 9.18 \end{array}$$

③
$$\begin{array}{r} 30.2 \\ + \ 16.6 \\ \hline \end{array}$$

④
$$\begin{array}{r} 23.4 \\ + \ 41.6 \\ \hline \end{array}$$

⑤ $10.2 + 12.7 = $ _____

⑥ $0.9 + 12.8 = $ _____

Add these decimals in hundredths.

⑦
$$\begin{array}{r} 50.93 \\ + \ \ 7.28 \\ \hline 58.21 \end{array}$$

⑧
$$\begin{array}{r} 6.54 \\ + \ 27.69 \\ \hline 34.23 \end{array}$$

⑨
$$\begin{array}{r} 27.84 \\ + \ \ 3.07 \\ \hline 30.91 \end{array}$$

⑩
$$\begin{array}{r} 100.30 \\ + \ \ 6.84 \\ \hline 107.14 \end{array}$$

⑪ $5.83 + 3.0 \ \ = $ __8.83__

⑫ $99.01 + 9.09 \ = $ __108.10__

⑬ $5.50 + 0.9 \ \ = $ __6.40__

⑭ $324.78 + 1.22 = $ __326.00__

⑮ $123.45 + 34.56 = $ __158.01__

⑯ $13.59 + 12.64 = $ __26.23__

ISBN: 978-1-897164-15-0

Add these decimals.

⑰ 5 + 7.8 = _____	⑱ 5.9 + 0.78 = _____
⑲ 2.73 + 4.9 = _____	⑳ 7 + 1.23 = _____
㉑ 5.9 + 8.73 = _____	㉒ 5.03 + 2.9 = _____
㉓ 11.67 + 40.9 = _____	㉔ 22.45 + 6.7 = _____
㉕ 52.93 + 109.2 = _____	㉖ 809 + 2.82 = _____
㉗ 141.05 + 26.4 = _____	㉘ 17.42 + 353 = _____
㉙ 0.98 + 3.2 + 12 = _____	㉚ 9 + 61.4 + 45.5 = _____

㉛   14.07 + 6.67 + 9.91   = _____

㉜   4.5 + 2.77 + 1.82   = _____

㉝   5 + 4.23 + 12.6   = _____

㉞   4.97 + 9.3 + 1.87 + 5 = _____

㉟   902 + 77.13 + 0.87   = _____

Write these decimals in expanded form.

㊱   25.87 = _____

㊲   12.93 = _____

Write the decimals.

㊳   500 + 70 + 0.8 = _____

㊴   100 + 8 + 0.6 + 0.04 = _____

Add the money. If the sum is larger than the amount in the previous question, write it on the line in ㊼ and add the sums to find Sally's savings.

㊵ $9.32 + $0.95   = _____

㊶ $9.85 + $1.32   = _____

㊷ $5.23 + $6.09   = _____

㊸ $10.93 + $0.21 = _____

㊹ $53.29 + $6.78 = _____

㊺ $70.94 + $0.50 = _____

㊻ $29.84 + $39.99 = _____

㊼   _____

㊽   sum =
     _____

㊾   Sally saves _____ .

Do the following addition. Write + or − in the ◯ to show the relation of P, Q, R and S.

㊿   5.9 + 12.8 = (P)   51   15.2 + 9.4 = (R)

52   19.4 + 3.9 = (Q)   53   7.8 + 9.6 = (S)

54   (P) ◯ (Q) = (R) ◯ (S)

ISBN: 978-1-897164-15-0

Solve the problems. Show your work.

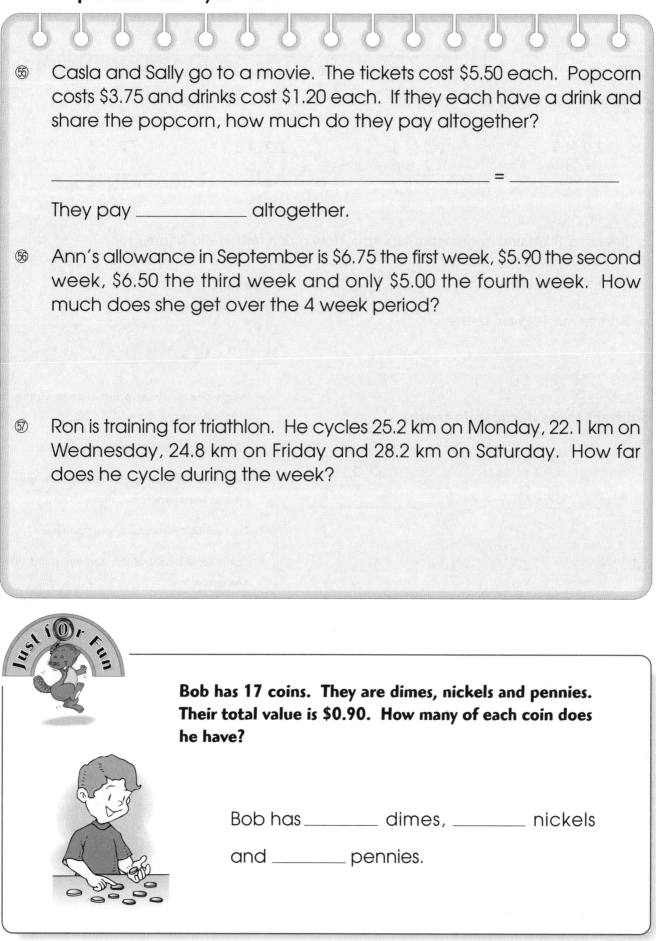

55 Casla and Sally go to a movie. The tickets cost $5.50 each. Popcorn costs $3.75 and drinks cost $1.20 each. If they each have a drink and share the popcorn, how much do they pay altogether?

_____ = _____

They pay _____ altogether.

56 Ann's allowance in September is $6.75 the first week, $5.90 the second week, $6.50 the third week and only $5.00 the fourth week. How much does she get over the 4 week period?

57 Ron is training for triathlon. He cycles 25.2 km on Monday, 22.1 km on Wednesday, 24.8 km on Friday and 28.2 km on Saturday. How far does he cycle during the week?

Just for Fun

Bob has 17 coins. They are dimes, nickels and pennies. Their total value is $0.90. How many of each coin does he have?

Bob has _____ dimes, _____ nickels

and _____ pennies.

4 Subtracting Decimals

1. $29.43 - 17.86 = \ ?$

$$
\begin{array}{r}
29.\overset{3\ 13}{\cancel{4}\cancel{3}} \\
-\ 17.86 \\
\hline
7
\end{array}
\quad \rightarrow \quad
\begin{array}{r}
29.\overset{8\ 13}{\cancel{4}3} \\
-\ 17.86 \\
\hline
.57
\end{array}
\quad \rightarrow \quad
\begin{array}{r}
2\overset{8}{\cancel{9}}.43 \\
-\ 17.86 \\
\hline
1.57
\end{array}
\quad \rightarrow \quad
\begin{array}{r}
29.43 \\
-\ 17.86 \\
\hline
11.57
\end{array}
$$

2. Jim ran 5.8 km and Andrea ran 7.25 km. How much farther did Andrea run?

$7.25 - 5.8 = 1.45$

$$
\begin{array}{r}
\overset{6\ 12}{\cancel{7}.\cancel{2}5} \\
-\ 5.80 \\
\hline
1.45
\end{array}
$$

Andrea ran 1.45 km farther.

HINTS:

- Align the decimal points when doing vertical subtraction.
- Write zeros to fill the empty places.
- Subtract decimal numbers the same way we subtract whole numbers.
- Use addition to check your answer.
- Don't forget to add the decimal point in the answer.

Subtract these decimals in tenths.

①
$$
\begin{array}{r}
0.7 \\
-\ 0.2 \\
\hline
\end{array}
$$

②
$$
\begin{array}{r}
58.3 \\
-\ 1.8 \\
\hline
\end{array}
$$

③
$$
\begin{array}{r}
9.2 \\
-\ 2.9 \\
\hline
\end{array}
$$

④
$$
\begin{array}{r}
5.0 \\
-\ 3.8 \\
\hline
\end{array}
$$

⑤ $45.3 - 16.9 =$ _____

⑥ $72.4 - 38.6 =$ _____

Subtract these decimals in hundredths.

⑦
$$
\begin{array}{r}
17.04 \\
-\ 12.00 \\
\hline
\end{array}
$$

⑧
$$
\begin{array}{r}
1.57 \\
-\ 0.88 \\
\hline
\end{array}
$$

⑨
$$
\begin{array}{r}
8.04 \\
-\ 4.98 \\
\hline
\end{array}
$$

⑩ $704.23 - 125.07 =$ _____

⑪ $32.16 - 8.45 =$ _____

ISBN: 978-1-897164-15-0

Subtract these decimals.

⑫ $2.0 - 0.02$ = _____ ⑬ $9.03 - 4$ = _____

⑭ $7.9 - 4.13$ = _____ ⑮ $10.4 - 2.13$ = _____

⑯ $8.1 - 5.08$ = _____ ⑰ $15 - 3.62$ = _____

⑱ $12.1 - 4.23$ = _____ ⑲ $9.5 - 7.68$ = _____

⑳ $0.96 - 0.08$ = _____ ㉑ $0.72 - 0.5$ = _____

㉒ $1.1 - 0.84$ = _____ ㉓ $2.3 - 1.49$ = _____

㉔ $0.26 - 0.26$ = _____ ㉕ $0.36 - 0.3$ = _____

㉖ $42.1 - 9.63$ = _____ ㉗ $98 - 71.6$ = _____

㉘ $206.37 - 55.6$ = _____ ㉙ $58.9 - 8.9$ = _____

㉚ $42.48 - 22.7$ = _____ ㉛ $1200 - 1000.6$ = _____

Round each of the following differences to the nearest whole number.

㉜ $8.4 - 5.7$ = _____ ㉝ $3.1 - 1.7$ = _____

㉞ $58.9 - 19.2$ = _____ ㉟ $14.2 - 5.4$ = _____

㊱ $22.4 - 8.9$ = _____ ㊲ $36.4 - 22.8$ = _____

Round each of the following differences to the nearest tenth.

㊳ $9.23 - 6.57$ = _____ ㊴ $7.63 - 5.87$ = _____

㊵ $28.97 - 17.85$ = _____ ㊶ $32.04 - 13.68$ = _____

㊷ $45 - 10.73$ = _____ ㊸ $19.4 - 6.83$ = _____

Complete the number sentences and colour the boxes containing your answers in the number chart below.

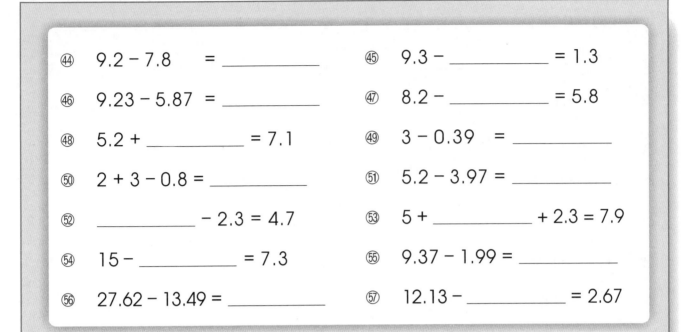

㊽   9.2 – 7.8   = _____

㊺   9.23 – 5.87 = _____

㊽   5.2 + _____ = 7.1

㊿   2 + 3 – 0.8 = _____

㊾   _____ – 2.3 = 4.7

㊴   15 – _____ = 7.3

㊶   27.62 – 13.49 = _____

㊺   9.3 – _____ = 1.3

㊼   8.2 – _____ = 5.8

㊾   3 – 0.39   = _____

㊿   5.2 – 3.97 = _____

㊼   5 + _____ + 2.3 = 7.9

㊼   9.37 – 1.99 = _____

㊼   12.13 – _____ = 2.67

㉘

11.4	7.7	7.38	7.0	6.94
17.0	5.8	1.4	10.6	9.17
7.5	0.2	14.13	5.2	3.61
15.1	9.3	4.2	14.0	15.2
14.8	3.63	9.46	41.11	12.3
12.3	22.3	2.61	2.60	11.36
2.63	0.6	8.0	1.23	3.27

㉙   What is the letter formed by the coloured boxes?

The letter formed by the coloured boxes is _____ .

 ISBN: 978-1-897164-15-0

Solve the problems. Show your work.

⑥⓪ Bill pays $35 for his groceries. How much change does he get if the total is $32.85?

_____ = _____

He gets _____ change.

⑥① Sue weighs 45.2 kg. Her sister weighs 41.5 kg. How much heavier is Sue than her sister?

⑥② The CN Tower in Toronto is 0.55 km high. The Calgary Tower is 0.19 km high. How much taller is the CN Tower?

⑥③ At a high school track meet, Ben ran 100 m in 11.87 seconds and Carl ran the same distance in 12.13 seconds. How much longer did Carl take?

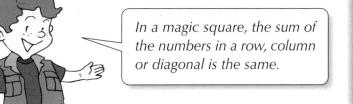

Just for Fun

Fill in the missing numbers in the magic square. All numbers from 1 to 9 must be used.

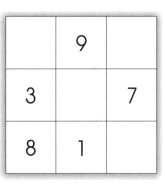

In a magic square, the sum of the numbers in a row, column or diagonal is the same.

	9	
3		7
8	1	

ISBN: 978-1-897164-15-0

5 Multiplying Decimals by Whole Numbers

EXAMPLES

1. 7.3 x 9 = 65.7

$$
\begin{array}{r}
\overset{2}{7}.3 \\
\times \quad 9 \\
\hline
65.7
\end{array}
$$
← 1 decimal place
← align the numbers
← 1 decimal place in product

2. Danielle buys 5 books at $5.95 each. How much does she pay altogether?

   $5.95 x 5 = $29.75

   She pays $29.75 altogether.

$$
\begin{array}{r}
\overset{4}{5}.\overset{2}{9}5 \\
\times \quad 5 \\
\hline
29.75
\end{array}
$$
← 2 decimal places
← align the numbers
← 2 decimal places in product

3. 0.75 x 10 = 7.5 ← move the decimal point one place to the right

4. 0.75 x 100 = 75. ← move the decimal point two places to the right

HINTS:

- Align all numbers on the right-hand side.

- Multiply the decimals as with whole numbers, from right to left.

- The number of decimal places in the product is the same as that in the question.

- Multiplying a decimal number

  by 10 → move the decimal point one place right

  by 100 → move the decimal point two places right

  and so on.

- Check if your answer is reasonable by rounding the decimal to the nearest whole number and estimate the answer.

Find the products mentally.

① 0.2 x 5 = _____

② 3.2 x 10 = _____

③ 0.1 x 7 = _____

④ 0.01 x 8 = _____

⑤ 3.0 x 4 = _____

⑥ 1.1 x 9 = _____

⑦ 4.01 x 6 = _____

⑧ 5.4 x 100 = _____

⑨ 9.15 x 10 = _____

⑩ 0.01 x 10 = _____

⑪ 0.1 x 100 = _____

⑫ 9.3 x 10 = _____

⑬ 100.4 x 2 = _____

⑭ 0.08 x 100 = _____

⑮ 0.62 x 10 = _____

⑯ 0.1 x 10 = _____

⑰ 24.8 x 10 = _____

⑱ 0.01 x 100 = _____

ISBN: 978-1-897164-15-0

Write the decimal point in each product.

⑲
```
    4.7
×     3
  1 4 1
```

⑳
```
    2.6 9
×       4
  1 0 7 6
```

㉑
```
    1 0.9
×       5
    5 4 5
```

㉒ 6.47 × 7 = 4 5 2 9

㉓ 5.55 × 8 = 4 4 4 0

Find the products. Show your work.

㉔
```
      7.3
×       9
```

㉕
```
      4.9
×       7
```

㉖
```
    1 2.2
×       8
```

㉗
```
    5.7 2
×       5
```

㉘
```
    9.8 9
×       6
```

㉙
```
      2.7
×       4
```

㉚
```
    0.9 8
×       4
```

㉛
```
    4.8 3
×       7
```

㉜
```
    0.1 8
×       9
```

㉝
```
    3.2 5
×       9
```

㉞
```
    1.3 8
×       7
```

㉟
```
      2.9
×       8
```

㊱
```
    7 2.3
×       7
```

㊲
```
    9.9 9
×       3
```

㊳
```
    0.7 6
×       6
```

Estimate. Then find the exact products.

		Estimate	Exact Product
㊴	5.2 x 7		
㊵	3.7 x 2		
㊶	9.81 x 5		
㊷	8.23 x 6		
㊸	3.75 x 3		
㊹	0.36 x 8		
㊺	0.17 x 9		
㊻	8.44 x 4		

Check the answers of the following multiplication. Put a ✓ in the box if the answer is correct; otherwise, write the correct answer in the box.

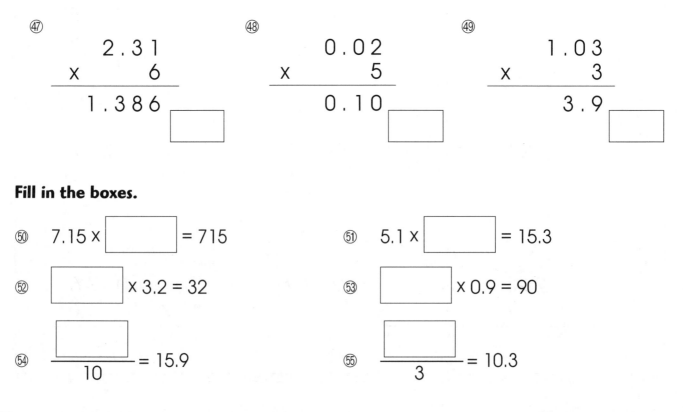

㊼
$$\begin{array}{r} 2.31 \\ \times\quad 6 \\ \hline 1.386 \end{array}$$ ☐

㊽
$$\begin{array}{r} 0.02 \\ \times\quad 5 \\ \hline 0.10 \end{array}$$ ☐

㊾
$$\begin{array}{r} 1.03 \\ \times\quad 3 \\ \hline 3.9 \end{array}$$ ☐

Fill in the boxes.

(50) 7.15 x ☐ = 715

(51) 5.1 x ☐ = 15.3

(52) ☐ x 3.2 = 32

(53) ☐ x 0.9 = 90

(54) $\dfrac{\square}{10} = 15.9$

(55) $\dfrac{\square}{3} = 10.3$

ISBN: 978-1-897164-15-0

Solve the problems. Show your work.

㊶ Sina buys 3 CDs at $23.99 each. How much does she pay altogether?

_____ = _____

She pays _____ altogether.

㊷ Ron buys 4 trees at $89.50 each. Calculate the total cost.

㊸ Adam walks 2.3 km each day to school. How far does he walk in a 5-day week?

㊹ How much space do 8 textbooks occupy on a book shelf if each is 3.2 cm thick?

㊺ Susanne buys 3 T-shirts at $12.95 each and 2 pairs of jeans at $39.99 each. How much does she pay altogether to the nearest dollar?

Help Bob solve the problem.

How can I add four + signs in the following number sentence to make it true?

4   4   4   4   4   4   4   4   =   500

Dividing Decimals by Whole Numbers

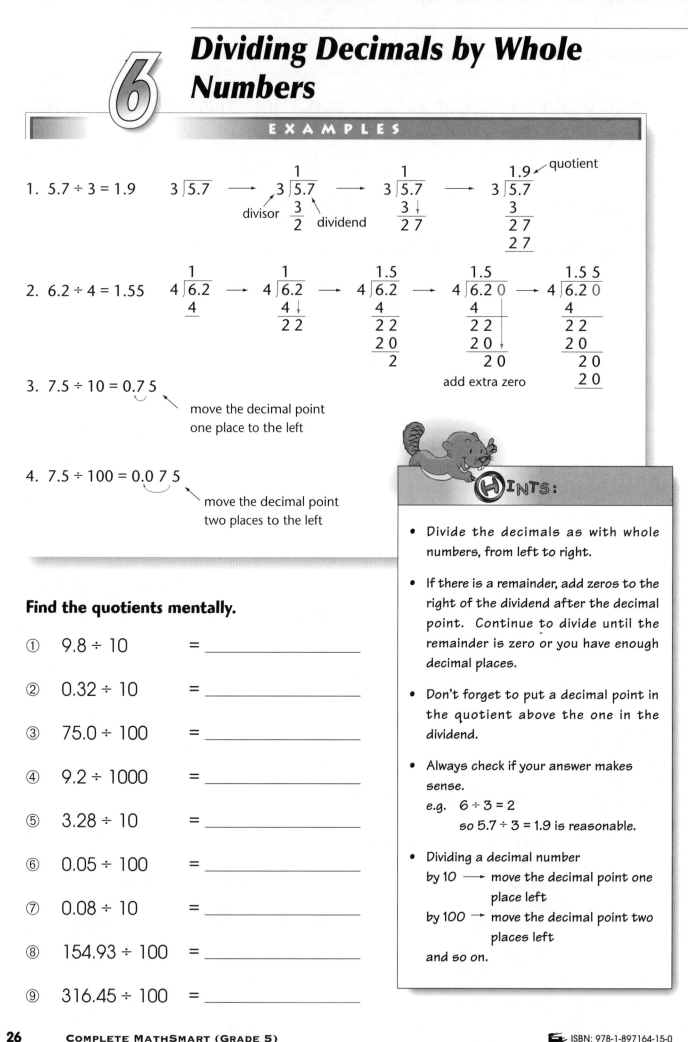

1. $5.7 \div 3 = 1.9$

2. $6.2 \div 4 = 1.55$

add extra zero

3. $7.5 \div 10 = 0.75$

move the decimal point one place to the left

4. $7.5 \div 100 = 0.075$

move the decimal point two places to the left

HINTS:

- Divide the decimals as with whole numbers, from left to right.

- If there is a remainder, add zeros to the right of the dividend after the decimal point. Continue to divide until the remainder is zero or you have enough decimal places.

- Don't forget to put a decimal point in the quotient above the one in the dividend.

- Always check if your answer makes sense.
  e.g. $6 \div 3 = 2$
  so $5.7 \div 3 = 1.9$ is reasonable.

- Dividing a decimal number
  by 10 ⟶ move the decimal point one place left
  by 100 ⟶ move the decimal point two places left
  and so on.

Find the quotients mentally.

① $9.8 \div 10$ = _____

② $0.32 \div 10$ = _____

③ $75.0 \div 100$ = _____

④ $9.2 \div 1000$ = _____

⑤ $3.28 \div 10$ = _____

⑥ $0.05 \div 100$ = _____

⑦ $0.08 \div 10$ = _____

⑧ $154.93 \div 100$ = _____

⑨ $316.45 \div 100$ = _____

ISBN: 978-1-897164-15-0

Write the decimal point in each quotient. Add zeros where necessary.

⑩ $52.8 \div 3$ $=$ 1 7 6   ⑪ $0.84 \div 7$ $=$ 1 2

⑫ $14.28 \div 7$ $=$ 2 0 4   ⑬ $2.08 \div 4$ $=$ 5 2

Find the quotients. Show your work.

⑭ $7 \overline{)8.05}$	⑮ $9 \overline{)66.6}$	⑯ $7 \overline{)73.5}$
⑰ $6 \overline{)8.52}$	⑱ $4 \overline{)0.24}$	⑲ $8 \overline{)160.8}$
⑳ $3 \overline{)12.09}$	㉑ $5 \overline{)52.65}$	㉒ $8 \overline{)36.4}$
㉓ $4 \overline{)70.4}$	㉔ $5 \overline{)10.4}$	㉕ $9 \overline{)19.35}$

ISBN: 978-1-897164-15-0

Divide. Show your work. Match the letters with the numbers in the boxes. What is the message?

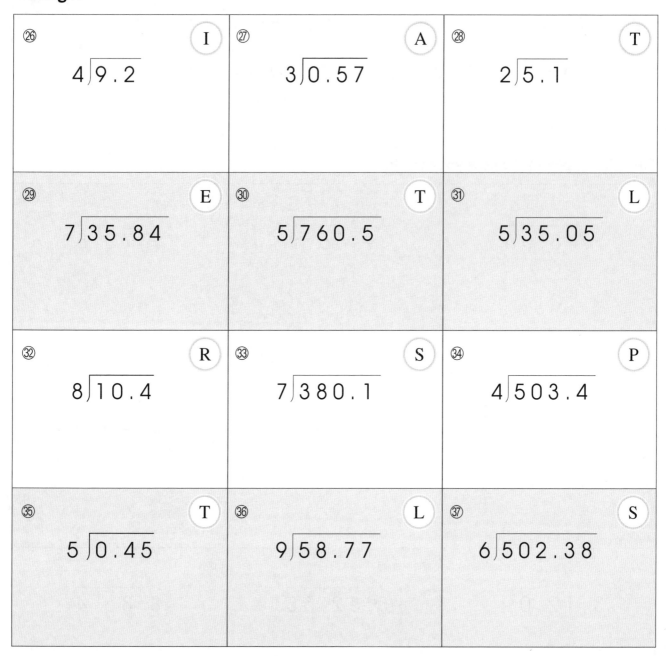

㉖   Ⓘ

$$4\overline{)9.2}$$

㉗   Ⓐ

$$3\overline{)0.57}$$

㉘   Ⓣ

$$2\overline{)5.1}$$

㉙   Ⓔ

$$7\overline{)35.84}$$

㉚   Ⓣ

$$5\overline{)760.5}$$

㉛   Ⓛ

$$5\overline{)35.05}$$

㉜   Ⓡ

$$8\overline{)10.4}$$

㉝   Ⓢ

$$7\overline{)380.1}$$

㉞   Ⓟ

$$4\overline{)503.4}$$

㉟   Ⓣ

$$5\overline{)0.45}$$

㊱   Ⓛ

$$9\overline{)58.77}$$

㊲   Ⓢ

$$6\overline{)502.38}$$

㊳   What does Sally see in the night sky?

7.01	2.3	2.55	152.1	6.53	5.12

54.3	0.09	0.19	1.3	83.73

ISBN: 978-1-897164-15-0

Solve the problems. Show your work.

③⑨　John mails 10 equal packages. The total weight is 32.5 kg. How much does each package weigh ?

_____ = _____

Each package weighs   _____ .

④⓪　On his summer holidays Bob drove 7350 km in 100 hours. How far did he travel each hour?

④①　Sam divides 36.4 metres of phone cable into 8 equal parts. How long is each part?

④②　8 students share the cost of a trip. If the total cost of the trip is $394.00, how much does each student pay?

④③　An equilateral triangle has all sides equal. If the perimeter is 13.5 cm, what is the length of each side?

Just for Fun

Look for the pattern. What are the next 3 numbers?

1 , 1 , 2 , 3 , 5 , 8 , 13 , ◯ , ◯ , ◯

ISBN: 978-1-897164-15-0

7 More Addition and Subtraction of Decimals

1. $5.93 + 17.29 - 3.74$ or $5.93 + 17.29 - 3.74$
   $= 23.22 - 3.74$ $= 5.93 - 3.74 + 17.29$ ⟵ order of operations changed
   $= 19.48$ $= 2.19 + 17.29$
                          $= 19.48$ ⟵ still the same answer

2. $2 - 3.1 + 1.93$
   $= 2 + 1.93 - 3.1$ ⟵ Order of operations is changed because
   $= 3.93 - 3.1$ you can't take away 3.1 from 2.
   $= 0.83$

$$\begin{array}{r} 2.00 \\ +\ 1.93 \\ \hline 3.93 \end{array} \qquad \begin{array}{r} 3.93 \\ -\ 3.10 \\ \hline 0.83 \end{array}$$

Find the answers mentally.

① $5.2 - 3.2 + 17.5$ = _____

② $3.75 - 1.25 - 0.5$ = _____

③ $5.99 - 3.99 + 4.99$ = _____

④ $12 - 0.5 + 2.5$ = _____

⑤ $7.55 + 3.45 - 0.50$ = _____

⑥ $3 - 0.75 - 0.75$ = _____

⑦ $1.9 - 0.5 - 1.4$ = _____

⑧ $9.99 + 10.01 - 5.00$ = _____

⑨ $13.25 - 5.5 + 2.25$ = _____

⑩ $26.5 - 2 + 3.5$ = _____

⑪ $45.85 - 70.5 + 25.15$ = _____

⑫ $175.5 - 155.5 - 2.5$ = _____

⑬ $115.50 - 100.00 - 5.50$ = _____

⑭ $125.75 + 25.25 - 51.0$ = _____

HINTS:

- To change the order of operations in multi-step operations, move the number together with the sign immediately in front of it.

  e.g. $5.1 + 3.2 - 4.9$

       $= 5.1 + 4.9 - 3.2$

       $= 10 - 3.2$

       $= 6.8$ ✗

       $5.1 + 3.2 - 4.9$

       $= 5.1 - 4.9 + 3.2$

       $= 0.2 + 3.2$

       $= 3.4$ ✓

- Remember to add zeros for missing decimal places in vertical addition or subtraction.

Find the answers. Show your work.

⑮ 19.2 − 3.75

= _____

⑯ 7 − 3.72

= _____

⑰ 22 − 3.5 − 9.7

= _____

⑱ 7.1 + 3 − 5.09

= _____

⑲ 1 − 0.09 + 3.78

= _____

⑳ 7.3 + 2.9 − 5.4

= _____

㉑ 123.55 − 17.55 + 3.25

= _____

㉒ 125 − 100.95 − 3.72

= _____

㉓ 197.8 + 188.7 − 142.9

= _____

㉔ 1000 − 1.2 + 5.00

= _____

㉕ 0.09 + 0.92 − 0.08

= _____

㉖ 77 + 29.2 − 5.93

= _____

㉗ 26.94 − 47.86 + 35.48

= _____

㉘ 6.73 − 28.45 + 32.38

= _____

ISBN: 978-1-897164-15-0

Show your work for the following money problems.

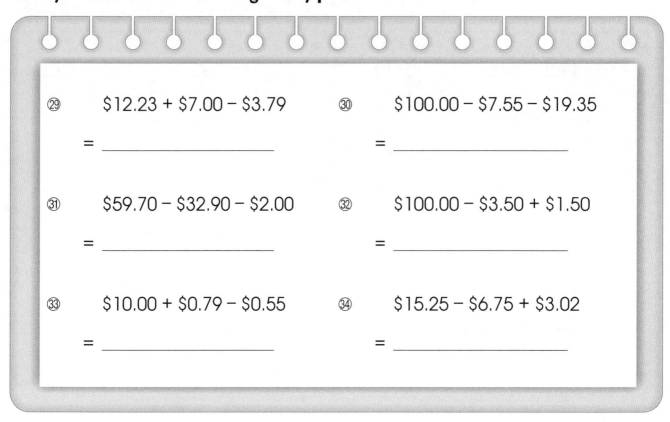

㉙ $12.23 + $7.00 − $3.79

= _____

㉚ $100.00 − $7.55 − $19.35

= _____

㉛ $59.70 − $32.90 − $2.00

= _____

㉜ $100.00 − $3.50 + $1.50

= _____

㉝ $10.00 + $0.79 − $0.55

= _____

㉞ $15.25 − $6.75 + $3.02

= _____

Round each answer to the nearest cent.

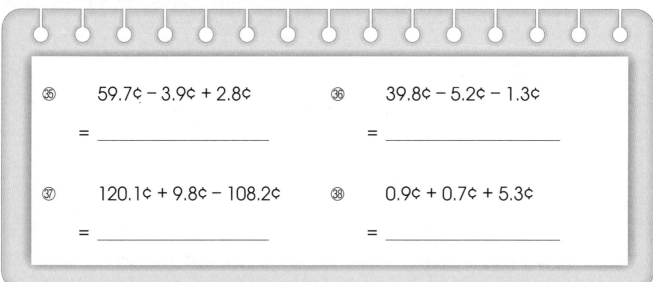

㉟   59.7¢ − 3.9¢ + 2.8¢

= _____

㊱   39.8¢ − 5.2¢ − 1.3¢

= _____

㊲   120.1¢ + 9.8¢ − 108.2¢

= _____

㊳   0.9¢ + 0.7¢ + 5.3¢

= _____

Fill in the missing number in each of the following number sentences.

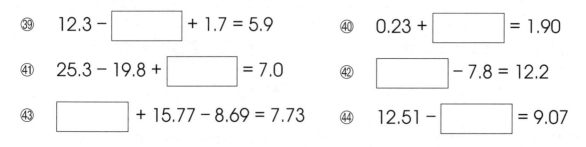

㊴ $12.3 - \boxed{} + 1.7 = 5.9$

㊵ $0.23 + \boxed{} = 1.90$

㊶ $25.3 - 19.8 + \boxed{} = 7.0$

㊷ $\boxed{} - 7.8 = 12.2$

㊸ $\boxed{} + 15.77 - 8.69 = 7.73$

㊹ $12.51 - \boxed{} = 9.07$

ISBN: 978-1-897164-15-0

Solve the problems. Show your work.

㊺   Sam has saved $25.00 for a trip to town. He spends $4.55 on transportation and $6.99 on lunch. How much does he have left?

_____ = _____

He has _____ left.

㊻   Rebecca earns $35.00 from a baby-sitting job. She uses the money to buy gifts for Clara and Debbie. Clara's gift costs $5.95 and Debbie's gift costs $17.45. How much does Rebecca have left?

㊼   Adam, Bob & Colin went to the CNE together. The fare cost them $6.50 each and a 1-day pass cost $19.95 each.   Lunch cost $7.50 each and they each had a discount coupon worth $2.00. How much did each of them spend?

㊽   Penny, Peter and Pam contribute $17.50 each to buy a birthday gift for Sue. They decide to buy 2 CDs which cost $20.95 each. The tax for 2 CDs is $6.30. Do they have enough money?

Just for Fun

Answer Sally's question.

If you put 1¢ in your piggy bank on Monday, 2¢ on Tuesday, 4¢ on Wednesday, 8¢ on Thursday and so on, how much will you have saved at the end of 1 week?

I will have saved _____ at the end of 1 week.

8 More Multiplying and Dividing of Decimals

EXAMPLES

1. $7.92 \times 5 = 39.6$

$$
\begin{array}{r}
\overset{4}{}\overset{1}{} \\
7.9\,2 \\
\times \quad 5 \\
\hline
3\,9.6\,\cancel{0}
\end{array}
$$
← delete the zero at the last decimal place

put a zero in the quotient →

2. $10.25 \div 5 = 2.05$

$$
\begin{array}{r}
2.5 \\
5\,\overline{)10.25} \\
10 \\
\hline
25 \\
25 \\
\hline
\end{array} \; ✗
\qquad
\begin{array}{r}
2.05 \\
5\,\overline{)10.25} \\
10 \\
\hline
25 \\
25 \\
\hline
\end{array} \; ✓
$$

HINTS:

- The number of decimal places in the product is the same as that in the question, but a zero at the last decimal place can be deleted.

  e.g. $7.92 \times 5 = 39.6$ ←

  only one decimal place in the product because the zero in the hundredths place is deleted

- Remember to put a zero in the quotient when the dividend is smaller than the divisor.

  e.g. $10.25 \div 5 = 2.05$ but not 2.5

  a zero is put at the tenths place because 2 in the dividend is smaller than the divisor 5

Find the answers mentally.

① 7.34×10 = _____

② $9.23 \div 10$ = _____

③ $123.4 \div 100$ = _____

④ $2.42 \div 2$ = _____

⑤ $36.9 \div 3$ = _____

⑥ 1.2×100 = _____

⑦ $0.15 \div 5$ = _____   ⑧ $80.8 \div 8$ = _____

⑨ $342.9 \div 100$ = _____   ⑩ 34.29×1000 = _____

⑪ 1.25×100 = _____   ⑫ $0.02 \div 10$ = _____

⑬ 0.4×10 = _____   ⑭ 1.18×10 = _____

⑮ 0.04×100 = _____   ⑯ $1.25 \div 100$ = _____

⑰ 0.02×10 = _____   ⑱ 63.5×10 = _____

ISBN: 978-1-897164-15-0

Do the calculation. Show your work.

⑲ $4\overline{)94.4}$	⑳ $7\overline{)7.28}$	㉑ $3\overline{)45.09}$
㉒ $\begin{array}{r} 3.92 \\ \times \quad 4 \\ \hline \end{array}$	㉓ $\begin{array}{r} 10.3 \\ \times \quad 7 \\ \hline \end{array}$	㉔ $\begin{array}{r} 5.91 \\ \times \quad 6 \\ \hline \end{array}$
㉕ $6\overline{)7.92}$	㉖ $9\overline{)17.1}$	㉗ $5\overline{)6.2}$
㉘ $\begin{array}{r} 0.47 \\ \times \quad 8 \\ \hline \end{array}$	㉙ $\begin{array}{r} 18.2 \\ \times \quad 9 \\ \hline \end{array}$	㉚ $\begin{array}{r} 36.7 \\ \times \quad 2 \\ \hline \end{array}$

Find the answers.

㉛ 1.25 × 8   = _____   ㉜ 1.75 × 4   = _____

㉝ 1.19 ÷ 7   = _____   ㉞ 10.4 ÷ 4   = _____

㉟ 3.08 × 9   = _____   ㊱ 76.8 ÷ 3   = _____

㊲ 89 × 10 ÷ 10 = _____   ㊳ 1.9 × 10 × 10 = _____

ISBN: 978-1-897164-15-0

Estimate. Then complete only those questions with a product greater than 15.

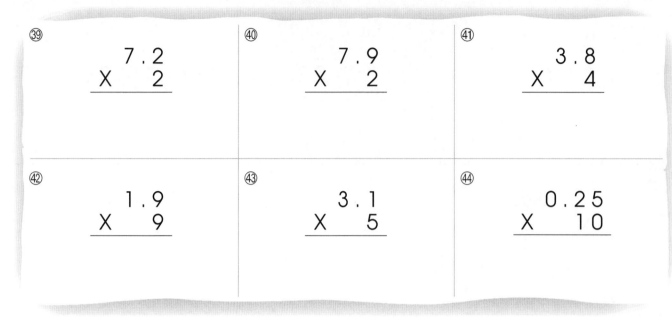

㊴ 7.2×2	㊵ 7.9×2	㊶ 3.8×4
㊷ 1.9×9	㊸ 3.1×5	㊹ 0.25×10

Estimate. Then complete only those questions with a quotient smaller than 2.

㊺ $9\overline{)12.6}$	㊻ $3\overline{)7.2}$	㊼ $10\overline{)23.4}$
㊽ $3\overline{)5.7}$	㊾ $6\overline{)10.8}$	㊿ $7\overline{)13.3}$

Fill in the blanks.

51. 12.7 ÷ ________ = 0.127
52. 3.92 x ________ = 39.2
53. ________ ÷ 3 = 1.14
54. 5.8 x ________ = 11.6
55. 2 x ________ = 12.4
56. ________ ÷ 7 = 1.3
57. 0.18 x ________ = 18
58. 54 ÷ ________ = 5.4

ISBN: 978-1-897164-15-0

Answer the questions. Show your work.

(59) The Grade 5 class collects $58.20 to buy gifts for 3 children in a needy family. How much can they spend on each gift if the money is divided evenly?

____________ = ____________

They can spend ____________ on each gift.

(60) Mrs Ling buys plants for her patio. She buys 3 plants at $19.95 each, 2 plants at $12.45 each and 10 plants at $1.25 each. How much does she pay altogether?

(61) 5 friends buy 2 pizzas at $12.99 each, 2 cans of juice at $1.29 each and 2 packets of chips at $1.49 each. They divide the total cost among them. How much must they each pay? Give the answer to the nearest cent.

(62) Carol is buying food for her dog. She can buy a 3-kg bag for $29.40 or a 5-kg bag for $39.50. Calculate the cost per kg for each bag. Which is the better buy?

What number am I?

I am a decimal number. Multiply me by 35. Divide the product by 7. The result is 2.5.

____

Calculate. Show your work.

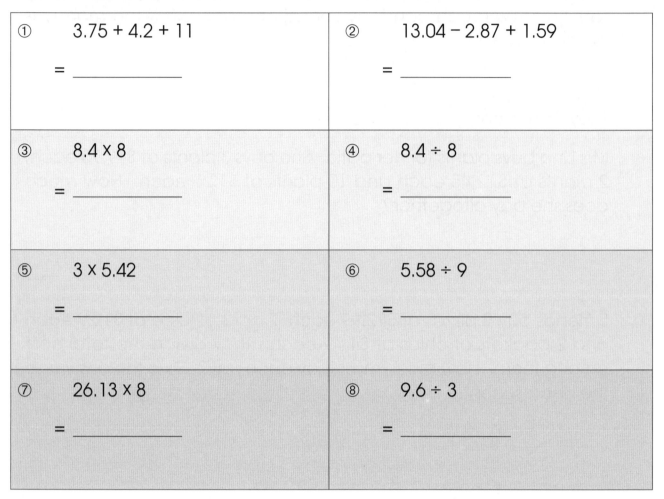

①   3.75 + 4.2 + 11

= _____

②   13.04 − 2.87 + 1.59

= _____

③   8.4 × 8

= _____

④   8.4 ÷ 8

= _____

⑤   3 × 5.42

= _____

⑥   5.58 ÷ 9

= _____

⑦   26.13 × 8

= _____

⑧   9.6 ÷ 3

= _____

Help Sally put the digits and decimal point in the right order to solve the problems.

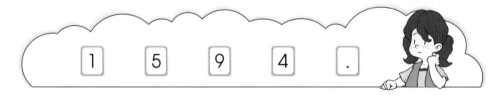

$$\boxed{1} \quad \boxed{5} \quad \boxed{9} \quad \boxed{4} \quad \boxed{.}$$

⑨   The largest decimal number with one decimal place   _____

⑩   The smallest decimal number with two decimal places   _____

⑪   The sum of the two decimals in ⑨ and ⑩   _____

⑫   The smallest decimal number with one decimal place and 9 at the ones place   _____

⑬   The largest decimal number with two decimal places and 9 at the hundredth place   _____

⑭   The difference of the two decimals in ⑫ and ⑬   _____

Complete the chart.

	Number	Number x 10	Number ÷ 10
⑮	52.0		
⑯	0.7		
⑰	0.12		
⑱		75.0	
⑲		3.0	
⑳			0.8
㉑			15.0

Circle the letter which represents the correct answer to each problem.

㉒ John earns $15.00 per hour. He works 9 hours a day, 5 days a week. How much does he earn per week?

    A. $135.00   B. $630.00   C. $450.00   D. $675.00

㉓ If $1.00 U.S. is worth $1.50 Canadian, how much is $7.00 U.S. worth in Canadian money?

    A. $8.50   B. $4.75   C. $10.50   D. $7.35

㉔ Mrs Wing earns 1.5 times her regular hourly wage on Sundays. She earns $8.00 per hour on weekdays. How much is her hourly wage on Sundays?

    A. $6.00   B. $10.00   C. $12.00   D. $16.00

㉕ John reads 10 pages per hour. How many pages does he read in 2.5 hours?

    A. 20   B. 22.5   C. 25   D. 27.5

㉖ If 1 cm = 0.39 inch, how many inches are there in 100 cm?

    A. 3.9   B. 39   C. 390   D. 3900

㉗ Mandy's mother buys her 2 new T-shirts at $9.50 each, 1 pair of jeans at $29.95 and 1 pair of sandals at $19.95. How much does Mandy's mother pay to the nearest dollar?

A. $60   B. $70   C. $68   D. $69

㉘ In August, Toronto's highest temperature is 35.5°C and the lowest temperature is 16.2°C. What is the difference between these temperatures?

A. 51.7 °C   B. 19.3 °C   C. 26 °C   D. 29 °C

㉙ The product of 1.6 and 2 is

A. 3.6   B. 0.8   C. 3.2   D. 1.4

㉚ When 1.2 is divided by 4, the quotient is

A. 0.3   B. 3.0   C. 4.8   D. 5.6

㉛ To calculate the average of 2 numbers is to add them up and then divide the sum by 2. The average of 13 and 10.2 is

A. 23.2   B. 11.6   C. 1.6   D. 3.2

㉜ When you divide a number by 10, the result is the same as multiplying the number by

A. 10   B. 0.1   C. 0.01   D. 100

㉝ When you multiply a number by 100, you move the decimal point

A. 3 places to the right   B. 3 places to the left

C. 2 places to the right   D. 2 places to the left

㉞ Which of the following statements is correct?

A. $5 \div 2 = 0.5 \div 20$ B. $5 \div 2 = 2 \div 5$

C. $5 \div 2 = 50 \div 20$ D. $5 \div 2 = 50 \div 0.2$

ISBN: 978-1-897164-15-0

Ken's dog likes to run around in the backyard. Answer the questions using the measurements given in the diagram.

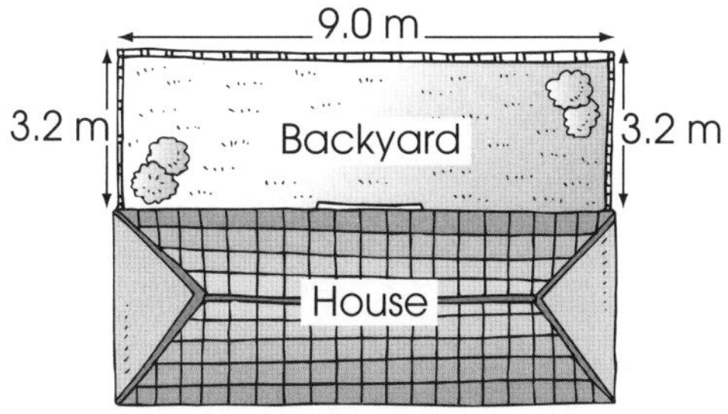

9.0 m

3.2 m Backyard 3.2 m

House

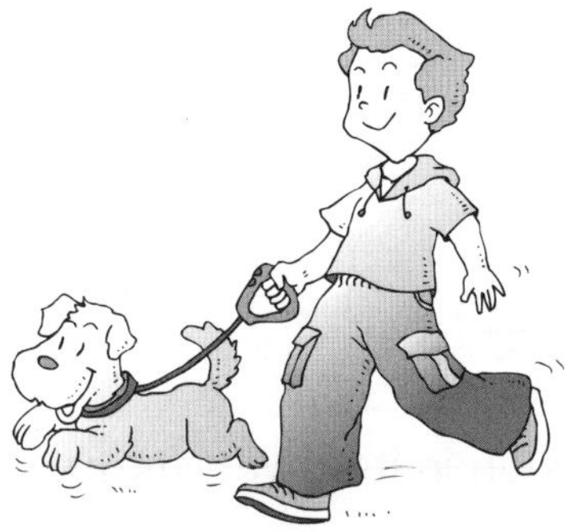

㉟ How much fencing is needed to enclose the backyard on 3 sides?

_____ m fencing is needed.

㊱ The fencing costs $20 per m. What is the total cost of the fencing?

㊲ What is the perimeter of the backyard?

㊳ What is the area of the backyard?

㊴ If both the width and the length of the backyard are doubled, what effect would this have on the perimeter and the area of the backyard?

a. perimeter

b. area

9 Introducing Fractions

EXAMPLES

1. Write a fraction for the shaded area in each diagram.

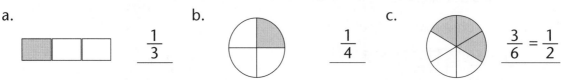

   a. $\dfrac{1}{3}$

   b. $\dfrac{1}{4}$

   c. $\dfrac{3}{6} = \dfrac{1}{2}$

2. Write the fraction in its lowest terms.

$$\frac{10}{15} = \frac{10 \div 5}{15 \div 5} = \frac{2}{3}$$

3. Label each of the divisions on the number line below. Write the fractions in lowest terms.

0 — 1

$\dfrac{1}{8}$ $\dfrac{2}{8} = \dfrac{1}{4}$ $\dfrac{3}{8}$ $\dfrac{4}{8} = \dfrac{1}{2}$ $\dfrac{5}{8}$ $\dfrac{6}{8} = \dfrac{3}{4}$ $\dfrac{7}{8}$

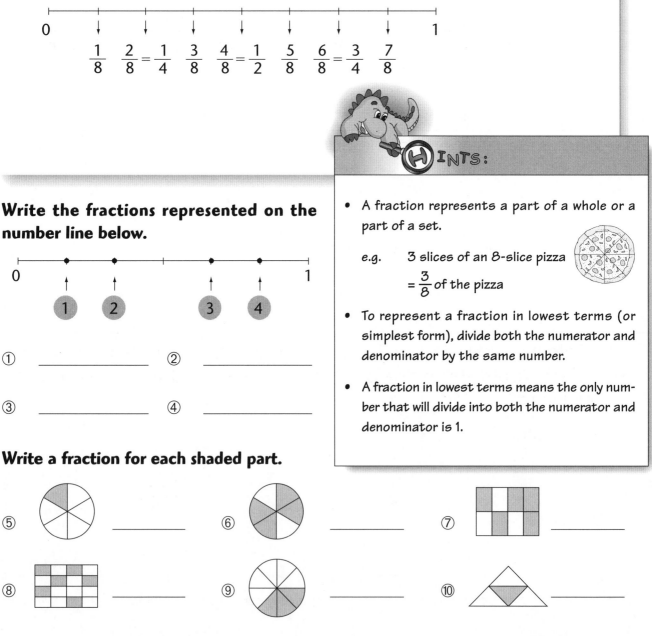

Write the fractions represented on the number line below.

0 — 1

① _____   ② _____

③ _____   ④ _____

Write a fraction for each shaded part.

⑤ _____   ⑥ _____   ⑦ _____

⑧ _____   ⑨ _____   ⑩ _____

HINTS:

- A fraction represents a part of a whole or a part of a set.

  e.g.   3 slices of an 8-slice pizza
  $= \dfrac{3}{8}$ of the pizza

- To represent a fraction in lowest terms (or simplest form), divide both the numerator and denominator by the same number.

- A fraction in lowest terms means the only number that will divide into both the numerator and denominator is 1.

ISBN: 978-1-897164-15-0

Colour the diagrams to show each fraction.

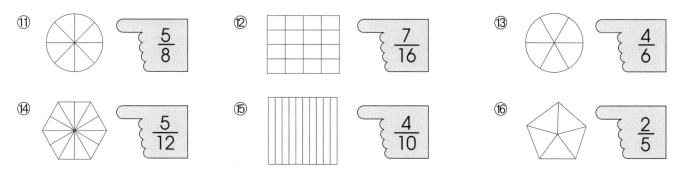

⑪ $\frac{5}{8}$ ⑫ $\frac{7}{16}$ ⑬ $\frac{4}{6}$

⑭ $\frac{5}{12}$ ⑮ $\frac{4}{10}$ ⑯ $\frac{2}{5}$

Place the following fractions on the number line below.

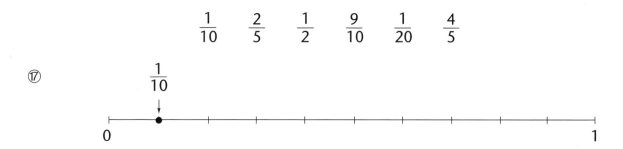

$\frac{1}{10}$ $\frac{2}{5}$ $\frac{1}{2}$ $\frac{9}{10}$ $\frac{1}{20}$ $\frac{4}{5}$

⑰ $\frac{1}{10}$

0 1

Write a fraction for the grey shapes of each set.

⑱ ⑲ ⑳

_____ _____ _____

Colour the correct number of shapes grey to show each fraction.

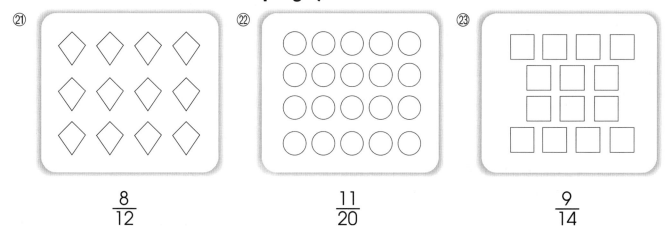

㉑ $\frac{8}{12}$ ㉒ $\frac{11}{20}$ ㉓ $\frac{9}{14}$

ISBN: 978-1-897164-15-0

Use the pictures to write the numbers.

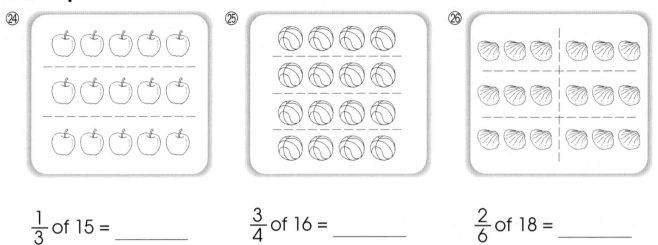

㉔ $\frac{1}{3}$ of 15 = _____

㉕ $\frac{3}{4}$ of 16 = _____

㉖ $\frac{2}{6}$ of 18 = _____

Fill in the boxes to express the following fractions in lowest terms.

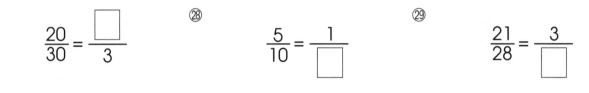

㉗ $\frac{20}{30} = \frac{\boxed{}}{3}$

㉘ $\frac{5}{10} = \frac{1}{\boxed{}}$

㉙ $\frac{21}{28} = \frac{3}{\boxed{}}$

Write the following fractions in lowest terms.

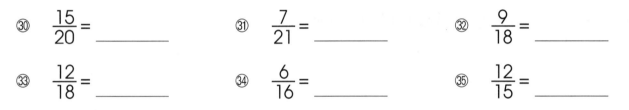

㉚ $\frac{15}{20}$ = _____

㉛ $\frac{7}{21}$ = _____

㉜ $\frac{9}{18}$ = _____

㉝ $\frac{12}{18}$ = _____

㉞ $\frac{6}{16}$ = _____

㉟ $\frac{12}{15}$ = _____

Answer the following questions.

㊱ List any 3 fractions which lie between 0 and $\frac{1}{2}$. _____

㊲ What fraction of a dollar is represented by

   a. 7 nickels? _____

   b. 6 dimes? _____

㊳ Bill watches TV for 3 hours a day. What fraction of a day does he spend watching TV? _____

㊴ Margaret has 8 pairs of shoes. 6 pairs are black. What fraction of her shoes are not black? _____

㊵ Rick has finished reading 50 pages of a 250-page book. What fraction of the book has he read? _____

ISBN: 978-1-897164-15-0

㊶ Pam is a rock climber. After she has climbed 30 m up a 45 m cliff, what fraction of the cliff must she climb to reach the top? _____

㊷ 5 letters of the 26 letters in the alphabet are vowels. The others are consonants. What fraction of the alphabet do consonants make up? _____

㊸ Tom worked 18 out of the 30 days in September. What fraction of the month did he work? _____

㊹ Carol earns $7 per hour as a waitress. One weekend she worked for 10 hours and got $50 in tips. What fraction of her total earnings that day did her tips make up? _____

㊺ Every day, Suzie sharpens her 16 cm long pencil and it loses 1 cm of its length. After 4 days, what fraction of its length remains? _____

㊻ An ant crawls 50 cm along a 100-cm log the first day. The second day the ant crawls 25 cm and the third day it crawls 12 cm.

a. What fraction of the log has it covered in three days? _____

b. What fraction of the log remains to be covered till it reaches the end? _____

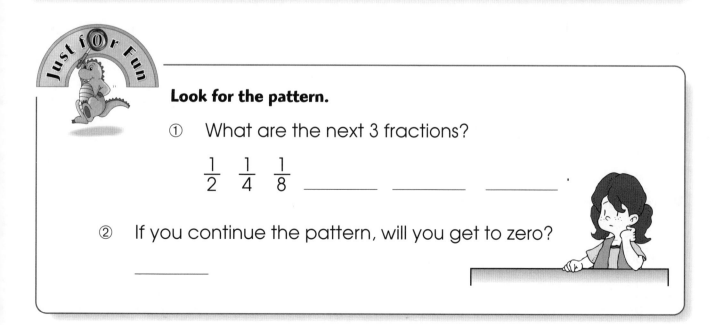

Look for the pattern.

① What are the next 3 fractions?

$$\frac{1}{2} \quad \frac{1}{4} \quad \frac{1}{8} \quad \text{\_\_\_\_\_} \quad \text{\_\_\_\_\_} \quad \text{\_\_\_\_\_} .$$

② If you continue the pattern, will you get to zero?

_____

ISBN: 978-1-897164-15-0

Equivalent Fractions and Ordering of Fractions

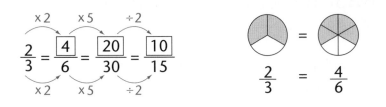

1. Fill in the boxes to find the equivalent fractions of $\frac{2}{3}$.

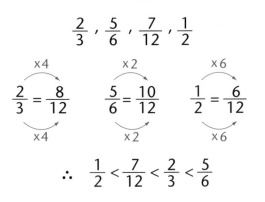

$$\frac{2}{3} = \frac{4}{6} = \frac{20}{30} = \frac{10}{15}$$

$$\frac{2}{3} = \frac{4}{6}$$

2. Order the following fractions from least to greatest.

$$\frac{2}{3}, \frac{5}{6}, \frac{7}{12}, \frac{1}{2}$$

$$\frac{2}{3} \xrightarrow{\times 4} \frac{8}{12} \qquad \frac{5}{6} \xrightarrow{\times 2} \frac{10}{12} \qquad \frac{1}{2} \xrightarrow{\times 6} \frac{6}{12}$$

$$\therefore \quad \frac{1}{2} < \frac{7}{12} < \frac{2}{3} < \frac{5}{6}$$

 INTS:

- To find an equivalent fraction, multiply or divide the numerator and denominator by the same number.

- To compare the fractions, find their equivalent fractions with the same denominator first. Then compare their numerators.

- Equivalent fractions are fractions that are equal in value.

Fill in the boxes to find the equivalent fractions.

① $\frac{1}{2} = \dfrac{\boxed{}}{50}$

② $\frac{5}{6} = \dfrac{\boxed{}}{30}$

③ $\frac{5}{7} = \dfrac{\boxed{}}{21}$

④ $\frac{3}{4} = \dfrac{\boxed{}}{100}$

⑤ $\dfrac{\boxed{}}{8} = \dfrac{14}{56}$

⑥ $\frac{11}{12} = \dfrac{\boxed{}}{84}$

Write each fraction in lowest terms.

⑦ $\frac{25}{30} = $ _____

⑧ $\frac{19}{38} = $ _____

⑨ $\frac{22}{121} = $ _____

⑩ $\frac{36}{84} = $ _____

⑪ $\frac{250}{1000} = $ _____

⑫ $\frac{32}{48} = $ _____

ISBN: 978-1-897164-15-0

Circle the smaller fraction in each pair of fractions.

⑬ $\dfrac{3}{4}$ $\dfrac{7}{8}$ ⑭ $\dfrac{1}{3}$ $\dfrac{1}{2}$ ⑮ $\dfrac{1}{5}$ $\dfrac{1}{6}$

⑯ $\dfrac{5}{6}$ $\dfrac{2}{3}$ ⑰ $\dfrac{3}{7}$ $\dfrac{8}{21}$ ⑱ $\dfrac{4}{5}$ $\dfrac{11}{15}$

Order the fractions from least to greatest using < .

⑲ $\dfrac{3}{5}$ $\dfrac{4}{5}$ $\dfrac{1}{2}$ $\dfrac{1}{5}$ $\dfrac{1}{10}$ $\dfrac{7}{10}$ _____

⑳ $\dfrac{1}{3}$ $\dfrac{1}{4}$ $\dfrac{3}{4}$ $\dfrac{2}{3}$ $\dfrac{2}{4}$ _____

Write True (T) or False (F) for each statement.

㉑ $\dfrac{2}{3} < \dfrac{4}{5}$ (   )   ㉒ $\dfrac{5}{9} < \dfrac{1}{2}$ (   )

㉓ $\dfrac{21}{28} < \dfrac{6}{7}$ (   )   ㉔ $\dfrac{24}{27} < \dfrac{7}{9}$ (   )

Fill in the boxes.

㉕ $\dfrac{9}{15} = \dfrac{\Box}{5} = \dfrac{\Box}{20}$ ㉖ $\dfrac{9}{45} = \dfrac{1}{\Box} = \dfrac{\Box}{10}$

㉗ $\dfrac{14}{35} = \dfrac{\Box}{5} = \dfrac{\Box}{10}$ ㉘ $\dfrac{11}{\Box} = \dfrac{1}{5} = \dfrac{\Box}{20}$

Write 3 equivalent fractions for each of the following fractions.

㉙ $\dfrac{1}{8} = \Box = \Box = \Box$ ㉚ $\dfrac{2}{3} = \Box = \Box = \Box$

㉛ $\dfrac{1}{4} = \Box = \Box = \Box$ ㉜ $\dfrac{5}{7} = \Box = \Box = \Box$

ISBN: 978-1-897164-15-0

Order each group of fractions from greatest to least using > .

㉝ $\frac{3}{4}$ $\frac{7}{8}$ $\frac{1}{2}$ $\frac{5}{8}$ $\frac{3}{16}$ $\frac{1}{4}$ $\frac{3}{8}$

____

㉞ $\frac{2}{3}$ $\frac{1}{6}$ $\frac{7}{18}$ $\frac{1}{2}$ $\frac{5}{6}$ $\frac{13}{18}$ $\frac{1}{3}$

____

Compare each pair of fractions and write > , < or = between them.

㉟ $\frac{5}{6}$ $\frac{7}{8}$

㊱ $\frac{14}{18}$ $\frac{7}{9}$

㊲ $\frac{11}{12}$ $\frac{9}{10}$

㊳ $\frac{2}{3}$ $\frac{11}{15}$

㊴ $\frac{5}{16}$ $\frac{3}{8}$

㊵ $\frac{15}{30}$ $\frac{7}{16}$

Write each fraction in lowest terms and order the fractions from least to greatest.

㊶ $\frac{15}{20}$ = ________

㊷ $\frac{75}{125}$ = ________

㊸ $\frac{45}{54}$ = ________

㊹ $\frac{200}{450}$ = ________

㊺ $\frac{14}{18}$ = ________

㊻ $\frac{150}{175}$ = ________

㊼ ________ < ________ < ________ < ________ < ________ < ________

Find the missing numbers.

㊽

x □

$\frac{2}{3} = \frac{28}{42}$

x □

㊾

÷ □

$\frac{24}{32} = \frac{3}{4}$

÷ □

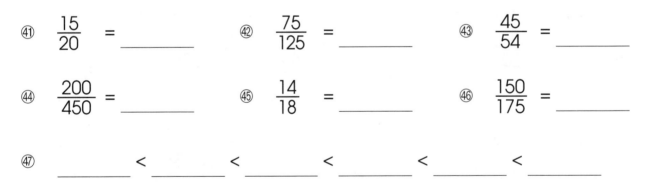

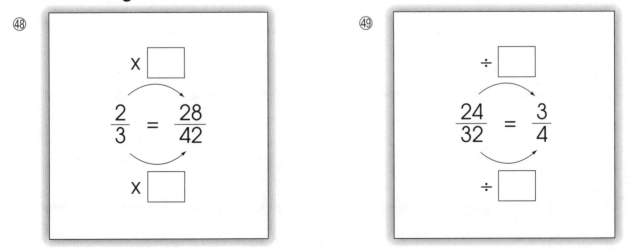

ISBN: 978-1-897164-15-0

Answer the questions.

50 John gets 22 out of 25 on a test. What is his mark out of 100?

$\dfrac{22}{25} = \dfrac{}{100}$ His mark is _____.

51 Nadine gets 9 out of 12 in a quiz. Danielle gets 14 out of 18 in another quiz. Who has the better score?

_____ has the better score.

52 The table below shows the world population in 1994 and the projected value in 2025. (Use your calculator to calculate, if necessary.)

World Population (in millions)		
	1994	2025
Africa	682	1583
North Africa	373	498
Europe	512	542
World Total	5421	8474

a. What is the fraction of the world's population living in Africa in 1994? And in 2025?

In 1994 _____   In 2025 _____

b. Is this fraction increasing or decreasing from 1994 to 2025?   _____

c. What is the fraction of the world's population living in Europe in 1994? And in 2025?

In 1994 _____   In 2025 _____

d. Is this fraction increasing or decreasing from 1994 to 2025?   _____

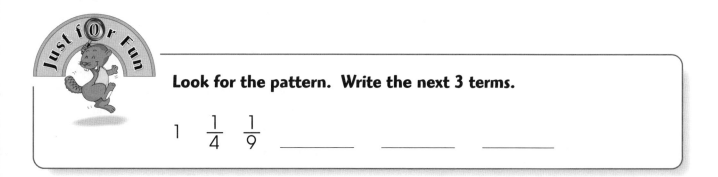

Look for the pattern. Write the next 3 terms.

1    $\dfrac{1}{4}$ $\dfrac{1}{9}$ _____   _____   _____

ISBN: 978-1-897164-15-0

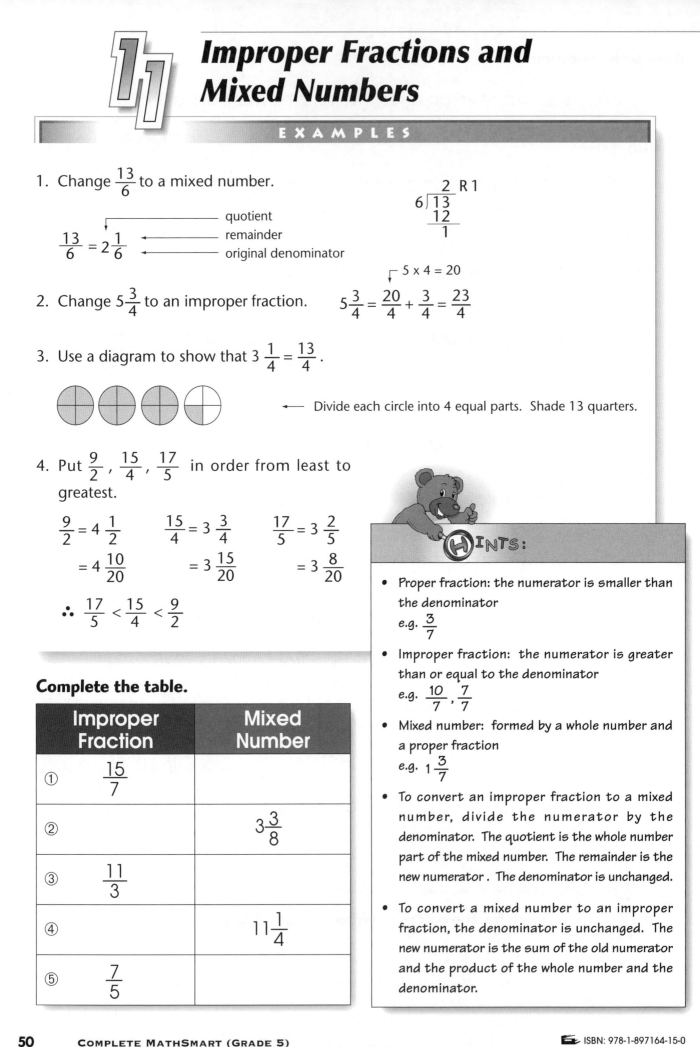

Improper Fractions and Mixed Numbers

1. Change $\frac{13}{6}$ to a mixed number.

$$\frac{13}{6} = 2\frac{1}{6}$$

quotient
remainder
original denominator

$$6\overline{)13} \quad \begin{array}{r} 2 \ \text{R} 1 \\ \hline 13 \\ 12 \\ \hline 1 \end{array}$$

2. Change $5\frac{3}{4}$ to an improper fraction.

$5 \times 4 = 20$

$$5\frac{3}{4} = \frac{20}{4} + \frac{3}{4} = \frac{23}{4}$$

3. Use a diagram to show that $3\frac{1}{4} = \frac{13}{4}$.

← Divide each circle into 4 equal parts. Shade 13 quarters.

4. Put $\frac{9}{2}$, $\frac{15}{4}$, $\frac{17}{5}$ in order from least to greatest.

$$\frac{9}{2} = 4\frac{1}{2} \qquad \frac{15}{4} = 3\frac{3}{4} \qquad \frac{17}{5} = 3\frac{2}{5}$$
$$= 4\frac{10}{20} \qquad \quad = 3\frac{15}{20} \qquad \quad = 3\frac{8}{20}$$

$$\therefore \ \frac{17}{5} < \frac{15}{4} < \frac{9}{2}$$

HINTS:

- Proper fraction: the numerator is smaller than the denominator
  e.g. $\frac{3}{7}$

- Improper fraction: the numerator is greater than or equal to the denominator
  e.g. $\frac{10}{7}$, $\frac{7}{7}$

- Mixed number: formed by a whole number and a proper fraction
  e.g. $1\frac{3}{7}$

- To convert an improper fraction to a mixed number, divide the numerator by the denominator. The quotient is the whole number part of the mixed number. The remainder is the new numerator. The denominator is unchanged.

- To convert a mixed number to an improper fraction, the denominator is unchanged. The new numerator is the sum of the old numerator and the product of the whole number and the denominator.

Complete the table.

	Improper Fraction	Mixed Number
①	$\frac{15}{7}$	
②		$3\frac{3}{8}$
③	$\frac{11}{3}$	
④		$11\frac{1}{4}$
⑤	$\frac{7}{5}$	

ISBN: 978-1-897164-15-0

Write the fractions or mixed numbers on the right screens.

$$3\frac{3}{10} \quad \frac{9}{9} \quad \frac{4}{7} \quad \frac{5}{20} \quad \frac{25}{20} \quad \frac{7}{9} \quad 3\frac{1}{2} \quad 1\frac{5}{20} \quad \frac{15}{8} \quad \frac{11}{12} \quad \frac{16}{7} \quad 1\frac{2}{5}$$

⑥ Proper Fraction

_____ _____

_____ _____

⑦ Improper Fraction

_____ _____

_____ _____

⑧ Mixed Number

_____ _____

_____ _____

Write the mixed numbers represented by each group of the following diagrams. Then convert each to an improper fraction.

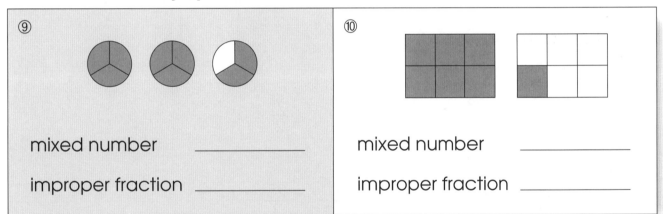

⑨

mixed number _____

improper fraction _____

⑩

mixed number _____

improper fraction _____

Place the improper fractions on the number line below.

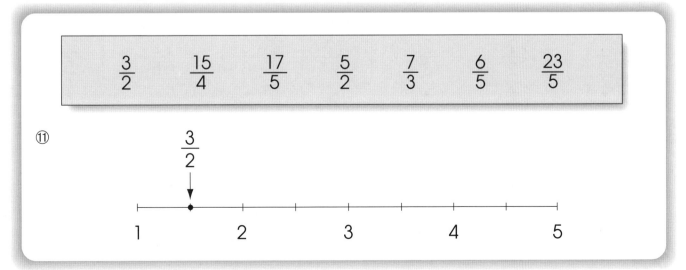

$$\frac{3}{2} \quad \frac{15}{4} \quad \frac{17}{5} \quad \frac{5}{2} \quad \frac{7}{3} \quad \frac{6}{5} \quad \frac{23}{5}$$

⑪

$\frac{3}{2}$

1   2   3   4   5

ISBN: 978-1-897164-15-0

Write an improper fraction to represent each number on the number line below.

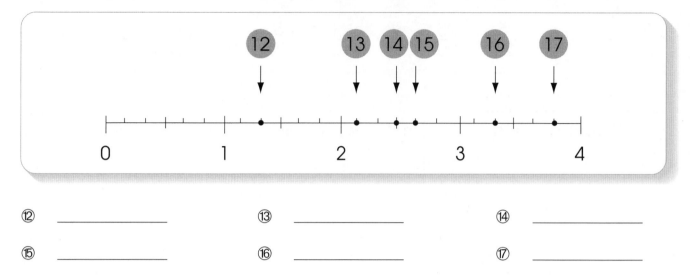

⑫ _____

⑬ _____

⑭ _____

⑮ _____

⑯ _____

⑰ _____

Order the fractions from greatest to least using > .

⑱ $\dfrac{5}{3}$ $\dfrac{7}{2}$ $\dfrac{9}{4}$ $\dfrac{7}{3}$ $\dfrac{15}{4}$ _____

⑲ $\dfrac{17}{2}$ $\dfrac{17}{5}$ $\dfrac{17}{6}$ $\dfrac{17}{3}$ $\dfrac{17}{4}$ _____

Circle the right numbers in each group.

⑳ The numbers between 3 and 4

$\dfrac{22}{3}$ $\dfrac{15}{7}$ $\dfrac{23}{6}$ $\dfrac{19}{6}$ $\dfrac{17}{4}$ $\dfrac{7}{2}$

㉑ The numbers between 8 and 9

$\dfrac{27}{4}$ $\dfrac{60}{7}$ $\dfrac{49}{6}$ $\dfrac{15}{2}$ $\dfrac{37}{5}$ $\dfrac{25}{3}$

Match the fractions and the mixed numbers.

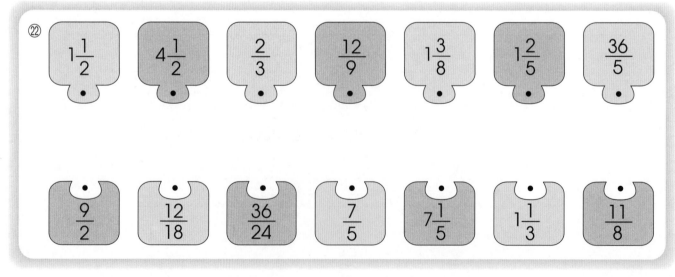

ISBN: 978-1-897164-15-0

Answer the questions. Show your work. Drawing diagrams may be helpful.

㉓ 5 friends each drink $\frac{1}{2}$ L of juice. How much juice do they drink?

Write your answer

    a.   as a mixed number.   _____ L

    b.   as an improper fraction.   _____ L

㉔ Joanne has $2\frac{1}{4}$ dollars in her pocket. The coins are all quarters. How many quarters does she have?

_____ quarters

㉕ Each worker paves $\frac{1}{5}$ of a driveway per day. How many driveways do 8 workers pave per day?

_____ driveways

㉖ A group of students eat $4\frac{1}{2}$ pizzas among them. If they eat $\frac{1}{2}$ pizza each, how many students are there?

_____ students

㉗ Candy says that $\frac{15}{4}$ is greater than $\frac{13}{3}$ since 15 > 13 and 4 > 3. Is this statement true or false? Explain.

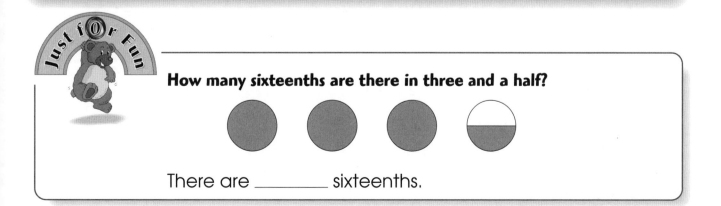

How many sixteenths are there in three and a half?

There are _____ sixteenths.

ISBN: 978-1-897164-15-0

Adding Fractions with the Same Denominator

1. $\dfrac{1}{4} + \dfrac{3}{4} = \dfrac{1+3}{4} = \dfrac{4}{4} = \dfrac{4 \div 4}{4 \div 4} = 1$

add the numerators;
keep the denominator

reduce to lowest terms

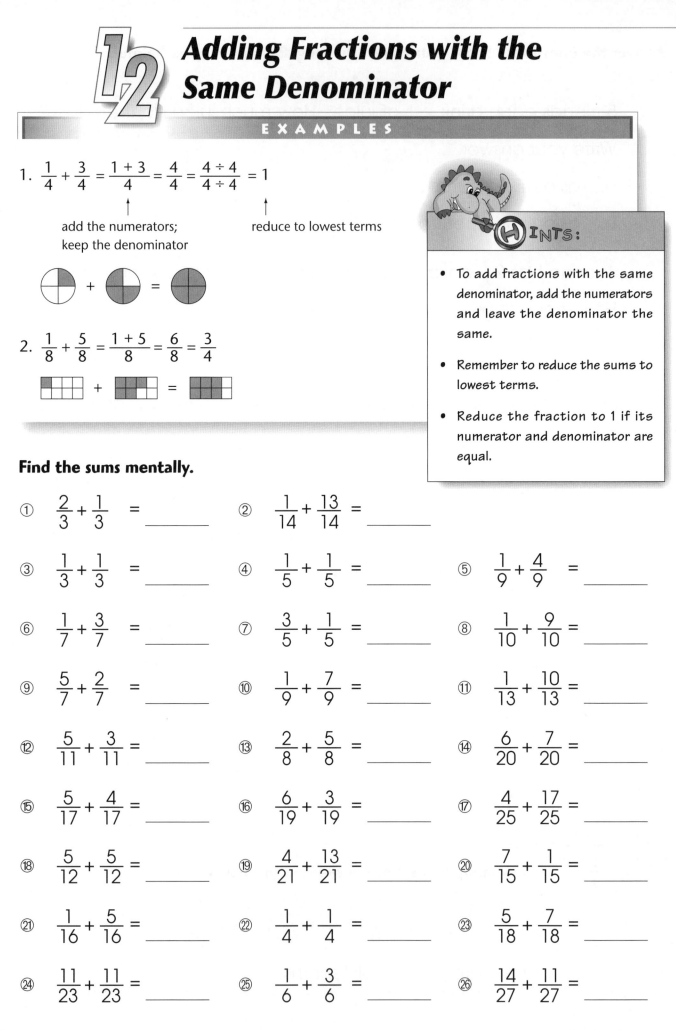

HINTS:

- To add fractions with the same denominator, add the numerators and leave the denominator the same.

- Remember to reduce the sums to lowest terms.

- Reduce the fraction to 1 if its numerator and denominator are equal.

2. $\dfrac{1}{8} + \dfrac{5}{8} = \dfrac{1+5}{8} = \dfrac{6}{8} = \dfrac{3}{4}$

Find the sums mentally.

① $\dfrac{2}{3} + \dfrac{1}{3} =$ _____

② $\dfrac{1}{14} + \dfrac{13}{14} =$ _____

③ $\dfrac{1}{3} + \dfrac{1}{3} =$ _____

④ $\dfrac{1}{5} + \dfrac{1}{5} =$ _____

⑤ $\dfrac{1}{9} + \dfrac{4}{9} =$ _____

⑥ $\dfrac{1}{7} + \dfrac{3}{7} =$ _____

⑦ $\dfrac{3}{5} + \dfrac{1}{5} =$ _____

⑧ $\dfrac{1}{10} + \dfrac{9}{10} =$ _____

⑨ $\dfrac{5}{7} + \dfrac{2}{7} =$ _____

⑩ $\dfrac{1}{9} + \dfrac{7}{9} =$ _____

⑪ $\dfrac{1}{13} + \dfrac{10}{13} =$ _____

⑫ $\dfrac{5}{11} + \dfrac{3}{11} =$ _____

⑬ $\dfrac{2}{8} + \dfrac{5}{8} =$ _____

⑭ $\dfrac{6}{20} + \dfrac{7}{20} =$ _____

⑮ $\dfrac{5}{17} + \dfrac{4}{17} =$ _____

⑯ $\dfrac{6}{19} + \dfrac{3}{19} =$ _____

⑰ $\dfrac{4}{25} + \dfrac{17}{25} =$ _____

⑱ $\dfrac{5}{12} + \dfrac{5}{12} =$ _____

⑲ $\dfrac{4}{21} + \dfrac{13}{21} =$ _____

⑳ $\dfrac{7}{15} + \dfrac{1}{15} =$ _____

㉑ $\dfrac{1}{16} + \dfrac{5}{16} =$ _____

㉒ $\dfrac{1}{4} + \dfrac{1}{4} =$ _____

㉓ $\dfrac{5}{18} + \dfrac{7}{18} =$ _____

㉔ $\dfrac{11}{23} + \dfrac{11}{23} =$ _____

㉕ $\dfrac{1}{6} + \dfrac{3}{6} =$ _____

㉖ $\dfrac{14}{27} + \dfrac{11}{27} =$ _____

ISBN: 978-1-897164-15-0

Add and reduce the answers to lowest terms. Show your work.

27. $\dfrac{6}{20} + \dfrac{7}{20}$ = _____

28. $\dfrac{4}{15} + \dfrac{8}{15}$ = _____

29. $\dfrac{2}{9} + \dfrac{1}{9}$ = _____

30. $\dfrac{11}{14} + \dfrac{1}{14}$ = _____

31. $\dfrac{5}{8} + \dfrac{1}{8}$ = _____

32. $\dfrac{3}{10} + \dfrac{3}{10}$ = _____

33. $\dfrac{3}{16} + \dfrac{5}{16}$ = _____

34. $\dfrac{1}{12} + \dfrac{5}{12}$ = _____

35. $\dfrac{1}{20} + \dfrac{3}{20}$ = _____

36. $\dfrac{1}{6} + \dfrac{1}{6}$ = _____

37. $\dfrac{3}{7} + \dfrac{1}{7}$ = _____

38. $\dfrac{1}{18} + \dfrac{2}{18}$ = _____

39. $\dfrac{1}{24} + \dfrac{5}{24}$ = _____

40. $\dfrac{5}{32} + \dfrac{3}{32}$ = _____

41. $\dfrac{2}{7} + \dfrac{3}{7} + \dfrac{2}{7}$ = _____

42. $\dfrac{2}{11} + \dfrac{2}{11} + \dfrac{3}{11} + \dfrac{4}{11}$ = _____

Complete each equation with a diagram. Then write each addition sentence using fractions. Give the sums in lowest terms.

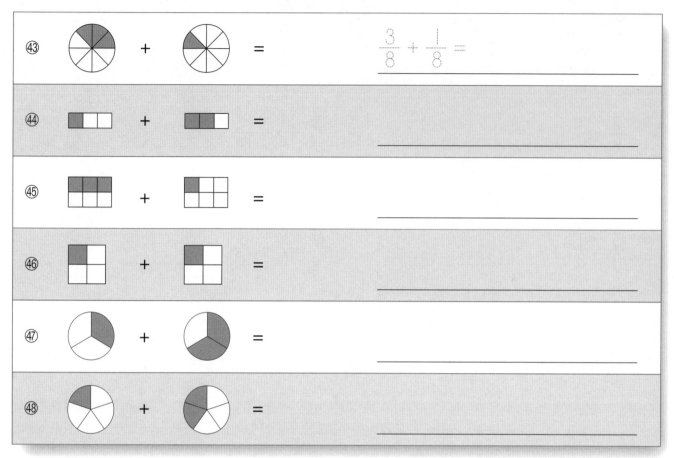

43
$$\frac{3}{8} + \frac{1}{8} = $$

44

45

46

47

48

Fill in the boxes.

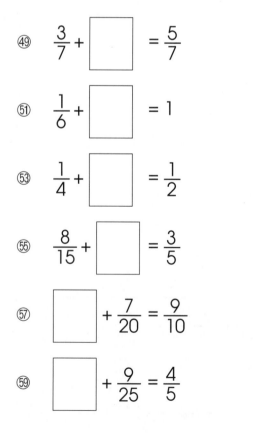

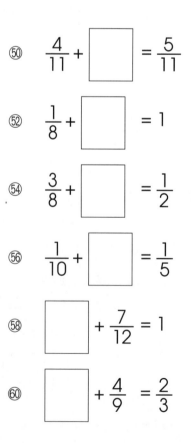

49 $\dfrac{3}{7} + \boxed{} = \dfrac{5}{7}$

50 $\dfrac{4}{11} + \boxed{} = \dfrac{5}{11}$

51 $\dfrac{1}{6} + \boxed{} = 1$

52 $\dfrac{1}{8} + \boxed{} = 1$

53 $\dfrac{1}{4} + \boxed{} = \dfrac{1}{2}$

54 $\dfrac{3}{8} + \boxed{} = \dfrac{1}{2}$

55 $\dfrac{8}{15} + \boxed{} = \dfrac{3}{5}$

56 $\dfrac{1}{10} + \boxed{} = \dfrac{1}{5}$

57 $\boxed{} + \dfrac{7}{20} = \dfrac{9}{10}$

58 $\boxed{} + \dfrac{7}{12} = 1$

59 $\boxed{} + \dfrac{9}{25} = \dfrac{4}{5}$

60 $\boxed{} + \dfrac{4}{9} = \dfrac{2}{3}$

ISBN: 978-1-897164-15-0

Answer the questions. Show your work.

61. Suzie has 3 dogs. They each eat $\frac{1}{4}$ of a tin of dog food each day. How much food do they eat among them each day?

   They eat _____ tin of dog food.

62. Bob, Carrie and Dan go out for pizza. They order 1 pizza. Bob and Carrie each eat $\frac{2}{6}$ of a pizza and Dan eats $\frac{1}{6}$ of a pizza.

   a. How many pizzas do they eat among them?

   b. Is there any pizza left?

63. Janet needs 2 pieces of ribbon, one of $\frac{5}{8}$ m and the other of $\frac{1}{8}$ m.

   a. How much ribbon does she need altogether?

   b. If she buys 1 m of ribbon, will she have enough?

64. Brenda spends $\frac{3}{10}$ of her weekly allowance on Monday and $\frac{1}{10}$ of her allowance on Tuesday.

   a. What fraction of her allowance has she spent?

   b. What fraction of her allowance does she have left?

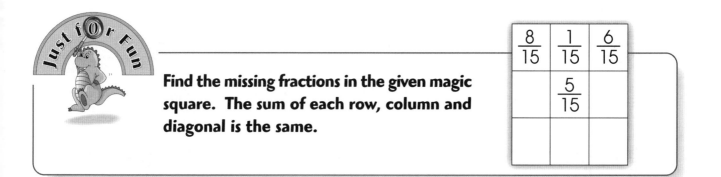

Find the missing fractions in the given magic square. The sum of each row, column and diagonal is the same.

$\frac{8}{15}$	$\frac{1}{15}$	$\frac{6}{15}$
	$\frac{5}{15}$	

Adding Improper Fractions and Mixed Numbers

1. $\dfrac{13}{7} + \dfrac{1}{7} = \dfrac{13 + 1}{7}$ ← add the numerators; keep the denominator

              $= \dfrac{14}{7}$

              $= 2$ ← reduce to lowest terms

2. $1\dfrac{1}{4} + 2\dfrac{1}{4} = \dfrac{5}{4} + \dfrac{9}{4}$ ← change mixed number to improper fraction

                $= \dfrac{14}{4}$

                $= 3\dfrac{1}{2}$ ← change back to mixed number

3. $1\dfrac{1}{4} + 2\dfrac{1}{4} = 1 + \dfrac{1}{4} + 2 + \dfrac{1}{4}$ ← split the mixed numbers into whole numbers and fractions

                $= 3 + \dfrac{1 + 1}{4}$ ← add the whole numbers and fractions separately

                $= 3\dfrac{2}{4}$

                $= 3\dfrac{1}{2}$ ← reduce to lowest terms

HINTS:

- Adding mixed numbers:
  change the mixed numbers to improper fractions and add the fractions;
  or
  add the whole numbers and fractions separately.
- Remember to reduce the sums to lowest terms.
- If the sum is an improper fraction, change back to a mixed number.

Find the sums mentally. All the answers are whole numbers.

① $1\dfrac{1}{2} + \dfrac{1}{2} = $ _____

② $2\dfrac{1}{3} + \dfrac{2}{3} = $ _____

③ $4\dfrac{1}{4} + \dfrac{3}{4} = $ _____   ④ $\dfrac{8}{3} + \dfrac{1}{3} = $ _____   ⑤ $\dfrac{11}{2} + \dfrac{3}{2} = $ _____

⑥ $\dfrac{11}{5} + \dfrac{4}{5} = $ _____   ⑦ $5\dfrac{3}{5} + \dfrac{2}{5} = $ _____   ⑧ $\dfrac{17}{3} + \dfrac{4}{3} = $ _____

⑨ $\dfrac{2}{9} + 2\dfrac{7}{9} = $ _____   ⑩ $\dfrac{11}{6} + \dfrac{1}{6} = $ _____   ⑪ $1\dfrac{2}{7} + \dfrac{5}{7} = $ _____

⑫ $\dfrac{5}{8} + 2\dfrac{3}{8} = $ _____   ⑬ $\dfrac{3}{10} + 3\dfrac{7}{10} = $ _____   ⑭ $\dfrac{13}{11} + \dfrac{9}{11} = $ _____

Find the sums. Show your work. Write the answers in lowest terms as mixed numbers.

⑮ $2\frac{1}{8} + \frac{1}{8}$ = _____

⑯ $4\frac{2}{5} + 2\frac{1}{5}$ = _____

⑰ $3\frac{1}{5} + \frac{1}{5}$ = _____

⑱ $5\frac{1}{4} + \frac{1}{4}$ = _____

⑲ $\frac{11}{5} + \frac{6}{5}$ = _____

⑳ $1\frac{3}{4} + 1\frac{3}{4}$ = _____

㉑ $\frac{3}{8} + \frac{9}{8}$ = _____

㉒ $2\frac{2}{3} + 1\frac{2}{3}$ = _____

㉓ $\frac{3}{10} + \frac{13}{10}$ = _____

㉔ $2\frac{7}{16} + \frac{7}{16}$ = _____

㉕ $2\frac{7}{8} + \frac{3}{8}$ = _____

㉖ $\frac{3}{10} + \frac{17}{10}$ = _____

㉗ $1\frac{3}{8} + 3\frac{3}{8}$ = _____

㉘ $\frac{13}{6} + \frac{1}{6}$ = _____

㉙ $4\frac{1}{5} + 3\frac{2}{5} + 1\frac{4}{5}$ = _____

㉚ $\frac{5}{6} + 1\frac{1}{6} + 4$ = _____

Fill in the boxes.

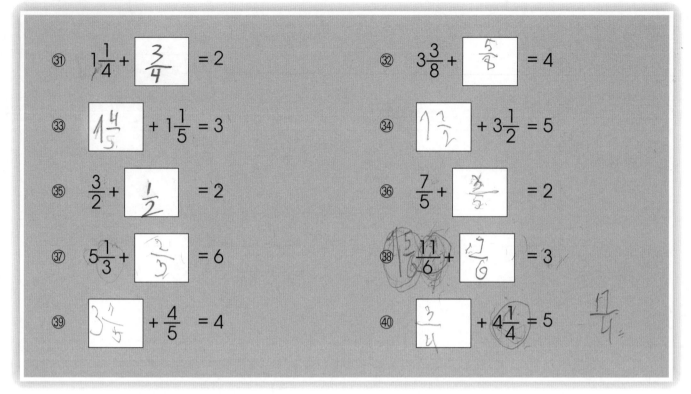

③1 $1\frac{1}{4} + \boxed{\frac{3}{4}} = 2$

③2 $3\frac{3}{8} + \boxed{\frac{5}{8}} = 4$

③3 $\boxed{1\frac{4}{5}} + 1\frac{1}{5} = 3$

③4 $\boxed{1\frac{2}{2}} + 3\frac{1}{2} = 5$

③5 $\frac{3}{2} + \boxed{\frac{1}{2}} = 2$

③6 $\frac{7}{5} + \boxed{\frac{3}{5}} = 2$

③7 $5\frac{1}{3} + \boxed{\frac{2}{3}} = 6$

③8 $\frac{11}{6} + \boxed{\frac{7}{6}} = 3$

③9 $\boxed{3\frac{1}{5}} + \frac{4}{5} = 4$

④0 $\boxed{\frac{3}{4}} + 4\frac{1}{4} = 5$

$\frac{17}{4} =$

Write True (T) or False (F) for each of the following statements.

④1 $\frac{2}{3} + \frac{2}{3} > 1$ ($<$)

④2 $1\frac{3}{4} + \frac{1}{2} > 2$ ($<$)

④3 $\frac{1}{3} + \frac{1}{3} > \frac{5}{6}$ ($>$)

④4 $2\frac{1}{2} < 2\frac{4}{7}$ ($>$)

④5 $1\frac{3}{8} + \frac{3}{4} > 2$ ($<$)

④6 $1\frac{1}{3} > 1\frac{4}{11}$ ($>$)

④7 $1\frac{2}{5} = \frac{7}{5}$ ($=$)

④8 $3\frac{1}{3} > 3\frac{1}{2}$ ($<$)

Answer only the questions that have a sum greater than 3.

④9 $2\frac{2}{3} + \frac{2}{3}$ = _____

⑤0 $2\frac{1}{3} + \frac{1}{3}$ = _____

⑤1 $\frac{15}{7} + \frac{5}{7}$ = _____

⑤2 $1\frac{5}{8} + 1\frac{7}{8}$ = _____

⑤3 $\frac{9}{4} + \frac{5}{4}$ = _____

⑤4 $\frac{4}{5} + \frac{12}{5}$ = _____

⑤5 $\frac{5}{6} + 1\frac{5}{6}$ = _____

⑤6 $1\frac{7}{9} + 1\frac{7}{9}$ = _____

ISBN: 978-1-897164-15-0

Answer the questions. Show your work.

57. Ann has 3 cats. Shadow eats $1\frac{1}{4}$ cans of food per week. Rocky eats $2\frac{1}{4}$ cans and Peppy eats $1\frac{3}{4}$ cans. How many cans of food do they eat among them per week?

58. Shares in Riverview International were sold for $45\frac{3}{8}$ ¢ per share. They increase in value by $2\frac{1}{8}$ ¢. What is the new selling price?

59. Janet is sewing 2 dresses. One needs $3\frac{1}{8}$ m of fabric and the other needs $4\frac{3}{4}$ m.

   a. How much fabric must she buy?

   b. Would 8 m be enough?

60. Peggy keeps a record of her weekly TV watching in the chart below.

Day	Sun.	Mon.	Tue.	Wed.	Thu.	Fri.	Sat.
Time (hours)	$1\frac{1}{4}$	$1\frac{1}{4}$	$\frac{3}{4}$	$1\frac{1}{4}$	2	$1\frac{3}{4}$	$2\frac{3}{4}$

How much TV did she watch during the week?

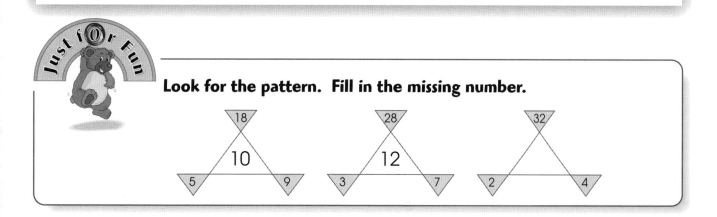

Just for Fun

Look for the pattern. Fill in the missing number.

14 Subtracting Fractions with the Same Denominator

1. $\dfrac{3}{8} - \dfrac{1}{8} = \dfrac{3-1}{8}$ ⟵ subtract the numerators; keep the denominator

$= \dfrac{2}{8}$

$= \dfrac{1}{4}$ ⟵ reduce to lowest terms

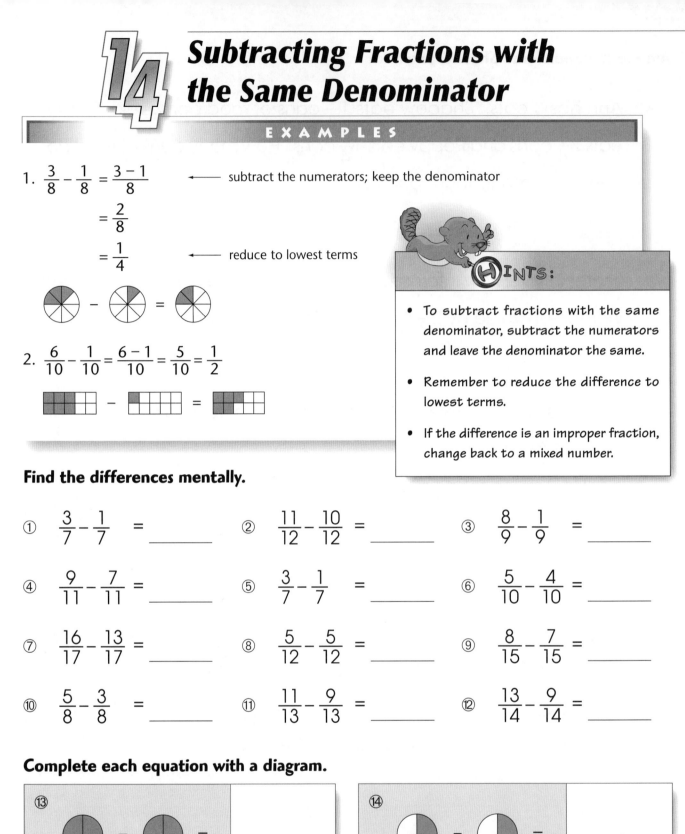

HINTS:

- To subtract fractions with the same denominator, subtract the numerators and leave the denominator the same.

- Remember to reduce the difference to lowest terms.

- If the difference is an improper fraction, change back to a mixed number.

2. $\dfrac{6}{10} - \dfrac{1}{10} = \dfrac{6-1}{10} = \dfrac{5}{10} = \dfrac{1}{2}$

Find the differences mentally.

① $\dfrac{3}{7} - \dfrac{1}{7} = $ _____

② $\dfrac{11}{12} - \dfrac{10}{12} = $ _____

③ $\dfrac{8}{9} - \dfrac{1}{9} = $ _____

④ $\dfrac{9}{11} - \dfrac{7}{11} = $ _____

⑤ $\dfrac{3}{7} - \dfrac{1}{7} = $ _____

⑥ $\dfrac{5}{10} - \dfrac{4}{10} = $ _____

⑦ $\dfrac{16}{17} - \dfrac{13}{17} = $ _____

⑧ $\dfrac{5}{12} - \dfrac{5}{12} = $ _____

⑨ $\dfrac{8}{15} - \dfrac{7}{15} = $ _____

⑩ $\dfrac{5}{8} - \dfrac{3}{8} = $ _____

⑪ $\dfrac{11}{13} - \dfrac{9}{13} = $ _____

⑫ $\dfrac{13}{14} - \dfrac{9}{14} = $ _____

Complete each equation with a diagram.

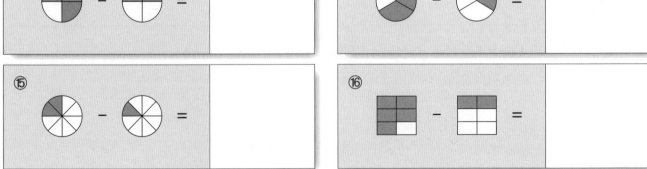

 ISBN: 978-1-897164-15-0

Subtract and reduce the answers to lowest terms. Show your work.

⑰ $\dfrac{9}{10} - \dfrac{4}{10} =$ _____

⑱ $\dfrac{5}{8} - \dfrac{1}{8} =$ _____

⑲ $\dfrac{4}{9} - \dfrac{1}{9} =$ _____

⑳ $\dfrac{7}{12} - \dfrac{4}{12} =$ _____

㉑ $\dfrac{5}{6} - \dfrac{1}{6} =$ _____

㉒ $\dfrac{13}{16} - \dfrac{1}{16} =$ _____

㉓ $\dfrac{3}{4} - \dfrac{1}{4} =$ _____

㉔ $\dfrac{10}{14} - \dfrac{2}{14} =$ _____

㉕ $\dfrac{7}{9} - \dfrac{1}{9} =$ _____

㉖ $\dfrac{3}{8} - \dfrac{1}{8} =$ _____

㉗ $\dfrac{17}{20} - \dfrac{2}{20} =$ _____

㉘ $\dfrac{42}{50} - \dfrac{12}{50} =$ _____

㉙ $\dfrac{16}{24} - \dfrac{8}{24} =$ _____

㉚ $\dfrac{13}{25} - \dfrac{3}{25} =$ _____

㉛ $\dfrac{19}{26} - \dfrac{6}{26} =$ _____

㉜ $\dfrac{6}{12} - \dfrac{1}{12} - \dfrac{2}{12} =$ _____

ISBN: 978-1-897164-15-0

Fill in the missing number in each box.

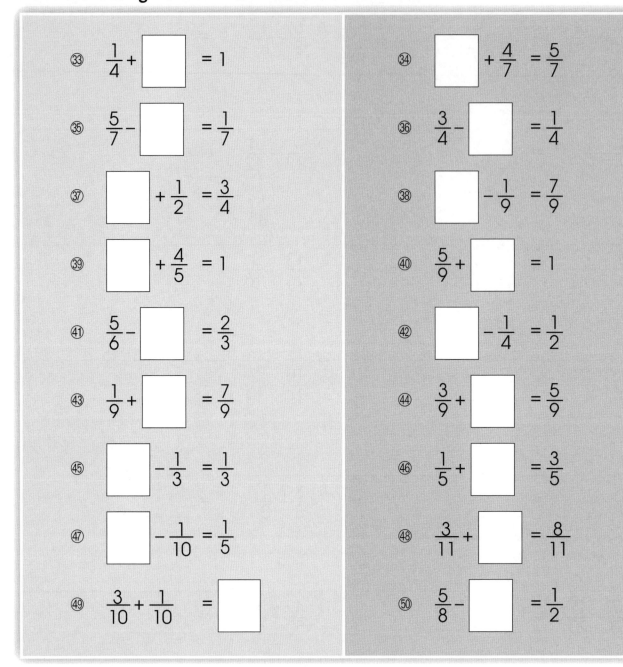

33. $\dfrac{1}{4} + \boxed{} = 1$

34. $\boxed{} + \dfrac{4}{7} = \dfrac{5}{7}$

35. $\dfrac{5}{7} - \boxed{} = \dfrac{1}{7}$

36. $\dfrac{3}{4} - \boxed{} = \dfrac{1}{4}$

37. $\boxed{} + \dfrac{1}{2} = \dfrac{3}{4}$

38. $\boxed{} - \dfrac{1}{9} = \dfrac{7}{9}$

39. $\boxed{} + \dfrac{4}{5} = 1$

40. $\dfrac{5}{9} + \boxed{} = 1$

41. $\dfrac{5}{6} - \boxed{} = \dfrac{2}{3}$

42. $\boxed{} - \dfrac{1}{4} = \dfrac{1}{2}$

43. $\dfrac{1}{9} + \boxed{} = \dfrac{7}{9}$

44. $\dfrac{3}{9} + \boxed{} = \dfrac{5}{9}$

45. $\boxed{} - \dfrac{1}{3} = \dfrac{1}{3}$

46. $\dfrac{1}{5} + \boxed{} = \dfrac{3}{5}$

47. $\boxed{} - \dfrac{1}{10} = \dfrac{1}{5}$

48. $\dfrac{3}{11} + \boxed{} = \dfrac{8}{11}$

49. $\dfrac{3}{10} + \dfrac{1}{10} = \boxed{}$

50. $\dfrac{5}{8} - \boxed{} = \dfrac{1}{2}$

Find the answers.

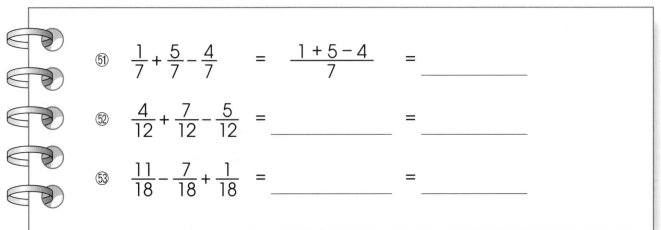

51. $\dfrac{1}{7} + \dfrac{5}{7} - \dfrac{4}{7} \quad = \quad \dfrac{1 + 5 - 4}{7} \quad = \quad \underline{\hspace{2cm}}$

52. $\dfrac{4}{12} + \dfrac{7}{12} - \dfrac{5}{12} \quad = \quad \underline{\hspace{2cm}} \quad = \quad \underline{\hspace{2cm}}$

53. $\dfrac{11}{18} - \dfrac{7}{18} + \dfrac{1}{18} \quad = \quad \underline{\hspace{2cm}} \quad = \quad \underline{\hspace{2cm}}$

 ISBN: 978-1-897164-15-0

Answer the questions. Show your work.

54. Ron read $\frac{5}{8}$ of his book on Monday and $\frac{3}{8}$ on Tuesday. How much more did he read on Monday than on Tuesday?

He read _____ more of his book on Monday.

55. Ben takes $\frac{3}{4}$ hour to do his Math homework but Carla only takes $\frac{1}{4}$ hour. How much longer does Ben take?

56. Carol takes $\frac{5}{6}$ hour to walk to school. Dave takes $\frac{1}{6}$ hour for the same walk. How much less time does Dave take?

57. Paula takes 40 minutes to wash her car.

a. What fraction of the job will she have done after 10 minutes?

b. What fraction of the job still remains?

58. Bob buys 10 plants for his garden. 2 are violet and 4 are red.

a. What fraction of the plants are violet? What fraction are red?

b. What fraction of the plants are neither red nor violet?

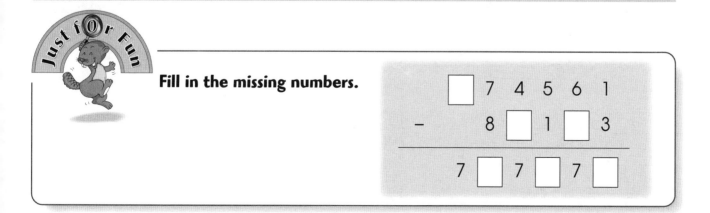

Fill in the missing numbers.

$$
\begin{array}{r}
\boxed{}\ 7\ 4\ 5\ 6\ 1 \\
-\quad 8\ \boxed{}\ 1\ \boxed{}\ 3 \\
\hline
7\ \boxed{}\ 7\ \boxed{}\ 7\ \boxed{}
\end{array}
$$

ISBN: 978-1-897164-15-0

15 Subtracting Improper Fractions and Mixed Numbers

EXAMPLES

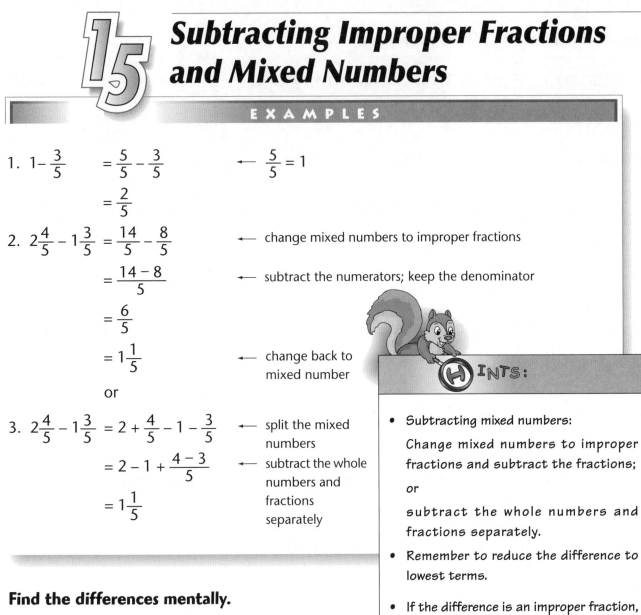

1. $1 - \dfrac{3}{5} = \dfrac{5}{5} - \dfrac{3}{5}$ ← $\dfrac{5}{5} = 1$

      $= \dfrac{2}{5}$

2. $2\dfrac{4}{5} - 1\dfrac{3}{5} = \dfrac{14}{5} - \dfrac{8}{5}$ ← change mixed numbers to improper fractions

            $= \dfrac{14 - 8}{5}$ ← subtract the numerators; keep the denominator

            $= \dfrac{6}{5}$

            $= 1\dfrac{1}{5}$ ← change back to mixed number

            or

3. $2\dfrac{4}{5} - 1\dfrac{3}{5} = 2 + \dfrac{4}{5} - 1 - \dfrac{3}{5}$ ← split the mixed numbers

            $= 2 - 1 + \dfrac{4 - 3}{5}$ ← subtract the whole numbers and fractions separately

            $= 1\dfrac{1}{5}$

HINTS:

- Subtracting mixed numbers:

  Change mixed numbers to improper fractions and subtract the fractions; or

  subtract the whole numbers and fractions separately.

- Remember to reduce the difference to lowest terms.

- If the difference is an improper fraction, change back to a mixed number.

Find the differences mentally.

① $2\dfrac{4}{7} - \dfrac{3}{7} = \underline{\hspace{3em}}$

② $2\dfrac{3}{5} - \dfrac{1}{5} = \underline{\hspace{3em}}$ ③ $\dfrac{11}{9} - \dfrac{4}{9} = \underline{\hspace{3em}}$ ④ $1\dfrac{7}{8} - 1\dfrac{6}{8} = \underline{\hspace{3em}}$

⑤ $\dfrac{21}{4} - \dfrac{18}{4} = \underline{\hspace{3em}}$ ⑥ $5\dfrac{3}{4} - 5 = \underline{\hspace{3em}}$ ⑦ $\dfrac{3}{2} - \dfrac{3}{2} = \underline{\hspace{3em}}$

⑧ $12\dfrac{3}{9} - 12\dfrac{1}{9} = \underline{\hspace{3em}}$ ⑨ $5\dfrac{1}{3} - 2\dfrac{1}{3} = \underline{\hspace{3em}}$ ⑩ $1\dfrac{4}{9} - 1\dfrac{3}{9} = \underline{\hspace{3em}}$

⑪ $8\dfrac{7}{13} - 8\dfrac{4}{13} = \underline{\hspace{3em}}$ ⑫ $\dfrac{13}{10} - \dfrac{3}{10} = \underline{\hspace{3em}}$ ⑬ $10\dfrac{7}{8} - 10 = \underline{\hspace{3em}}$

⑭ $\dfrac{10}{3} - \dfrac{8}{3} = \underline{\hspace{3em}}$ ⑮ $3\dfrac{5}{6} - 3\dfrac{1}{6} = \underline{\hspace{3em}}$ ⑯ $9\dfrac{7}{8} - 4\dfrac{7}{8} = \underline{\hspace{3em}}$

ISBN: 978-1-897164-15-0

Find the differences. Show your work. Write the answers in lowest terms.

⑰ $1\dfrac{1}{2} - \dfrac{3}{2} =$ _____

⑱ $2\dfrac{3}{4} - \dfrac{1}{4} =$ _____

⑲ $\dfrac{6}{5} - \dfrac{1}{5} =$ _____

⑳ $\dfrac{9}{4} - \dfrac{3}{4} =$ _____

㉑ $5\dfrac{1}{4} - 4\dfrac{3}{4} =$ _____

㉒ $3\dfrac{1}{8} - 2\dfrac{7}{8} =$ _____

㉓ $\dfrac{11}{4} - \dfrac{3}{4} =$ _____

㉔ $\dfrac{12}{10} - \dfrac{8}{10} =$ _____

㉕ $2\dfrac{1}{6} - 1\dfrac{5}{6} =$ _____

㉖ $\dfrac{20}{9} - \dfrac{11}{9} =$ _____

㉗ $2\dfrac{3}{8} - \dfrac{9}{8} =$ _____

㉘ $1\dfrac{1}{11} - \dfrac{12}{11} =$ _____

㉙ $\dfrac{21}{10} - 1\dfrac{1}{10} =$ _____

㉚ $\dfrac{21}{3} - 5\dfrac{1}{3} =$ _____

㉛ $5\dfrac{3}{4} - 2\dfrac{1}{4} - \dfrac{2}{4} =$ _____

㉜ $9 - 6\dfrac{1}{5} - 1\dfrac{3}{5} =$ _____

ISBN: 978-1-897164-15-0

Fill in the missing number in each box.

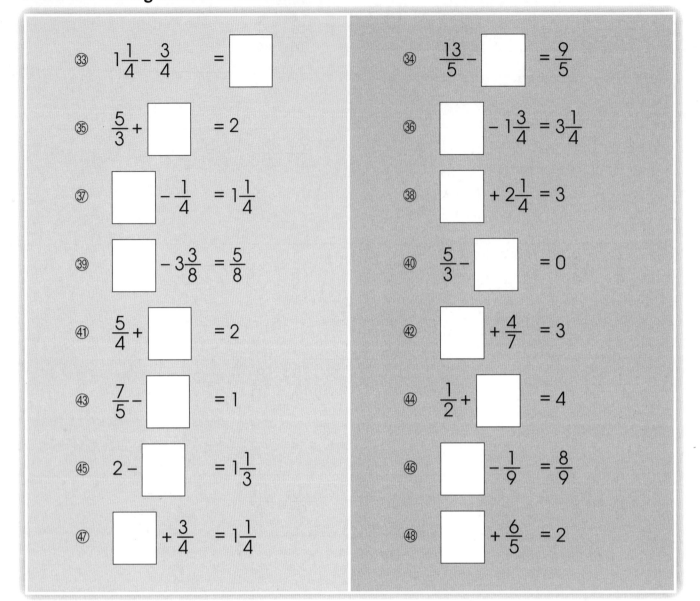

㉝ $1\frac{1}{4} - \frac{3}{4} = \square$

㉞ $\frac{13}{5} - \square = \frac{9}{5}$

㉟ $\frac{5}{3} + \square = 2$

㊱ $\square - 1\frac{3}{4} = 3\frac{1}{4}$

㊲ $\square - \frac{1}{4} = 1\frac{1}{4}$

㊳ $\square + 2\frac{1}{4} = 3$

㊴ $\square - 3\frac{3}{8} = \frac{5}{8}$

㊵ $\frac{5}{3} - \square = 0$

㊶ $\frac{5}{4} + \square = 2$

㊷ $\square + \frac{4}{7} = 3$

㊸ $\frac{7}{5} - \square = 1$

㊹ $\frac{1}{2} + \square = 4$

㊺ $2 - \square = 1\frac{1}{3}$

㊻ $\square - \frac{1}{9} = \frac{8}{9}$

㊼ $\square + \frac{3}{4} = 1\frac{1}{4}$

㊽ $\square + \frac{6}{5} = 2$

Find the answers.

㊾ $3\frac{4}{6} + 4\frac{1}{6} - 2\frac{2}{6}$ = ____________________ = __________

㊿ $9 - 3\frac{1}{8} + 1\frac{2}{8}$ = ____________________ = __________

(51) $4\frac{1}{6} - 3\frac{3}{6} + 1\frac{4}{6}$ = ____________________ = __________

(52) $3\frac{2}{7} + 2\frac{4}{7} - 1\frac{5}{7}$ = ____________________ = __________

ISBN: 978-1-897164-15-0

Answer the questions. Show your work. Write the fractions in lowest terms.

㊾ On Monday, Jonathan watched TV for $2\frac{3}{4}$ hours and Pat watched TV for $3\frac{1}{4}$ hours. How much longer did Pat spend watching TV?

㊿ On Monday, Ron ran $8\frac{3}{8}$ km and on Wednesday he ran $6\frac{5}{8}$ km. How much farther did he run on Monday?

⑤⑤ ABC shares sell for $3\frac{1}{5}$ dollars each and BFI share sell for $2\frac{4}{5}$ dollars each. What is the difference between the share prices?

⑤⑥ The perimeter of the triangle is 1 m. What is the length of the third side?

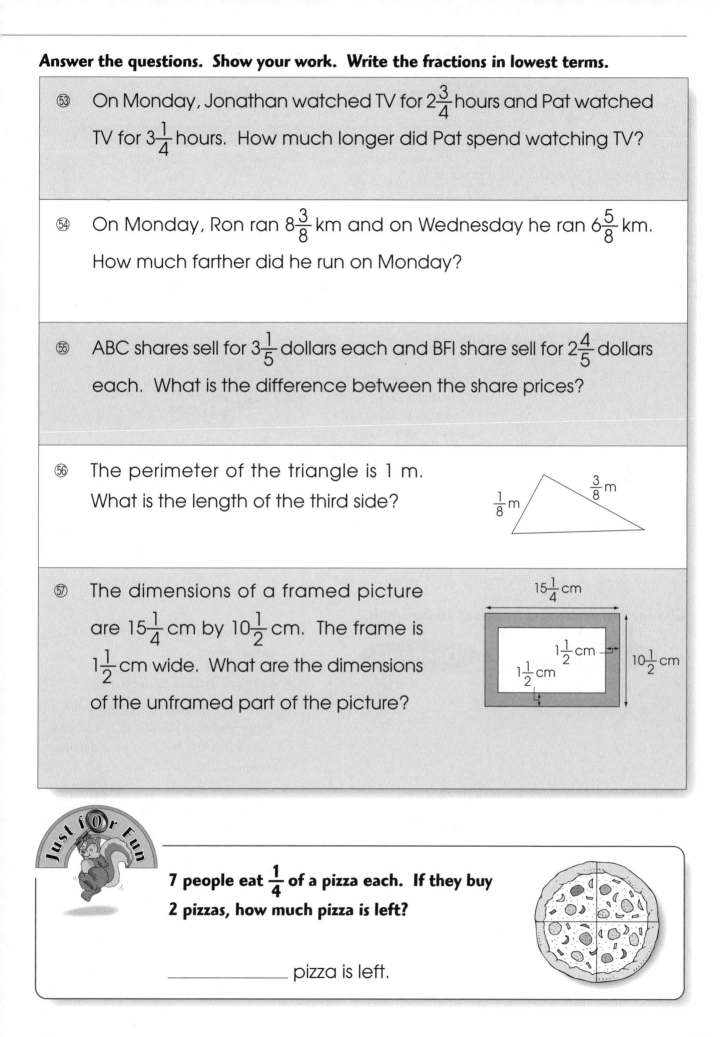

⑤⑦ The dimensions of a framed picture are $15\frac{1}{4}$ cm by $10\frac{1}{2}$ cm. The frame is $1\frac{1}{2}$ cm wide. What are the dimensions of the unframed part of the picture?

Just for Fun

7 people eat $\frac{1}{4}$ of a pizza each. If they buy 2 pizzas, how much pizza is left?

_____ pizza is left.

ISBN: 978-1-897164-15-0

Relating Decimals and Fractions

EXAMPLES

1. Convert 0.7 and 0.55 to fractions.

$0.7 = \dfrac{7}{10}$ ← put 1 zero in the denominator since 0.7 has 1 decimal place

$0.55 = \dfrac{55}{100} = \dfrac{11}{20}$ ← reduce the fraction to lowest terms

put 2 zeros in the denominator since 0.55 has 2 decimal places

2. Convert $\dfrac{1}{4}$ and $2\dfrac{1}{5}$ to decimals.

$\dfrac{1}{4} = 0.25$

$$\begin{array}{r} 0.25 \\ 4\overline{)1.0} \\ 8 \\ \hline 20 \\ 20 \end{array}$$

← divide numerator by denominator and continue dividing until the remainder is zero

$2\dfrac{1}{5} = 2 + \dfrac{1}{5} = 2 + 0.2 = 2.2$

change the fraction part to decimal

$$\begin{array}{r} 0.2 \\ 5\overline{)1\ 0} \\ 1\ 0 \end{array}$$

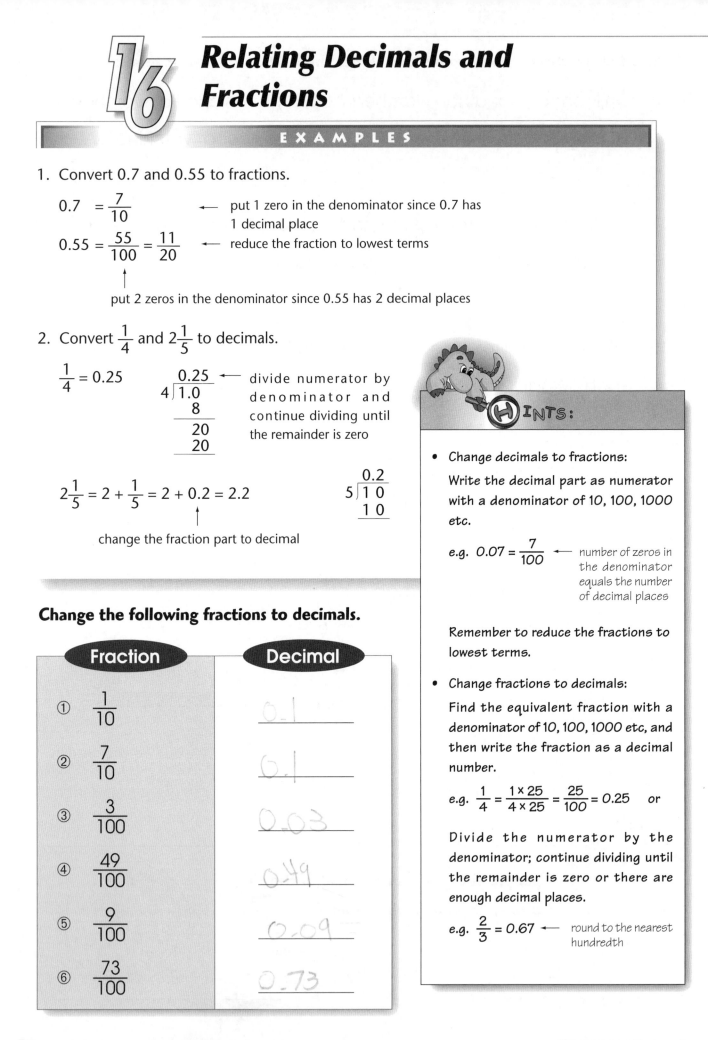

HINTS:

- Change decimals to fractions:

  Write the decimal part as numerator with a denominator of 10, 100, 1000 etc.

  e.g. $0.07 = \dfrac{7}{100}$ ← number of zeros in the denominator equals the number of decimal places

  Remember to reduce the fractions to lowest terms.

- Change fractions to decimals:

  Find the equivalent fraction with a denominator of 10, 100, 1000 etc, and then write the fraction as a decimal number.

  e.g. $\dfrac{1}{4} = \dfrac{1 \times 25}{4 \times 25} = \dfrac{25}{100} = 0.25$ or

  Divide the numerator by the denominator; continue dividing until the remainder is zero or there are enough decimal places.

  e.g. $\dfrac{2}{3} = 0.67$ ← round to the nearest hundredth

Change the following fractions to decimals.

Fraction	Decimal
① $\dfrac{1}{10}$	0.1
② $\dfrac{7}{10}$	0.1
③ $\dfrac{3}{100}$	0.03
④ $\dfrac{49}{100}$	0.49
⑤ $\dfrac{9}{100}$	0.09
⑥ $\dfrac{73}{100}$	0.73

ISBN: 978-1-897164-15-0

Change the following decimals to fractions.

Decimal	Fraction		Decimal	Fraction
⑦ 0.3	_____		⑧ 0.7	_____
⑨ 0.9	_____		⑩ 0.01	_____
⑪ 0.09	_____		⑫ 0.07	_____
⑬ 0.31	_____		⑭ 0.19	_____
⑮ 0.47	_____		⑯ 0.03	_____

Use division to convert each of the following fractions to decimals.

Fraction	Decimal		Fraction	Decimal
⑰ $\dfrac{1}{2}$	_____		⑱ $\dfrac{1}{5}$	_____
⑲ $\dfrac{3}{4}$	_____		⑳ $\dfrac{3}{5}$	_____
㉑ $\dfrac{1}{8}$	_____		㉒ $\dfrac{5}{8}$	_____
㉓ $\dfrac{3}{8}$	_____		㉔ $\dfrac{4}{5}$	_____

Convert the following fractions to decimals. Round the answers to the nearest hundredth if necessary.

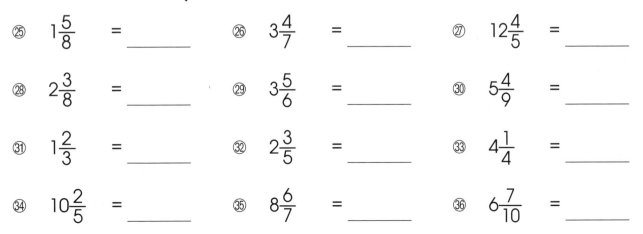

㉕ $1\dfrac{5}{8}$ = _____ ㉖ $3\dfrac{4}{7}$ = _____ ㉗ $12\dfrac{4}{5}$ = _____

㉘ $2\dfrac{3}{8}$ = _____ ㉙ $3\dfrac{5}{6}$ = _____ ㉚ $5\dfrac{4}{9}$ = _____

㉛ $1\dfrac{2}{3}$ = _____ ㉜ $2\dfrac{3}{5}$ = _____ ㉝ $4\dfrac{1}{4}$ = _____

㉞ $10\dfrac{2}{5}$ = _____ ㉟ $8\dfrac{6}{7}$ = _____ ㊱ $6\dfrac{7}{10}$ = _____

Change the decimals to fractions. Give your answers in lowest terms.

(37) $0.65 = \frac{65}{100} =$ ______ (38) $0.75 =$ ______ $=$ ______

(39) $0.05 =$ ______ $=$ ______ (40) $0.12 =$ ______ $=$ ______

(41) $0.45 =$ ______ $=$ ______ (42) $0.36 =$ ______ $=$ ______

(43) $1.45 =$ ______ $=$ ______ (44) $6.55 =$ ______ $=$ ______

(45) $2.8 =$ ______ $=$ ______ (46) $2.25 =$ ______ $=$ ______

How many cents are there in each of the following fractions of a dollar?

(47) $\$\frac{1}{4} =$ ______ ¢ (48) $\$\frac{3}{4} =$ ______ ¢

(49) $\$\frac{2}{5} =$ ______ ¢ (50) $\$\frac{3}{5} =$ ______ ¢

(51) $\$\frac{7}{10} =$ ______ ¢ (52) $\$\frac{9}{10} =$ ______ ¢

Circle the larger number in each pair.

(53) 0.65 $\frac{1}{2}$ (54) $\frac{4}{5}$ 0.9 (55) 1.3 $1\frac{2}{5}$

(56) $\frac{2}{3}$ 0.62 (57) 4.26 $4\frac{1}{4}$ (58) 0.57 $\frac{8}{15}$

(59) 3.69 $3\frac{3}{5}$ (60) 8.38 $8\frac{1}{3}$ (61) $6\frac{3}{8}$ 6.37

Arrange the following numbers in order from least to greatest.

(62) $1\frac{7}{8}$ 1.54 $1\frac{8}{9}$ ______ < ______ < ______

(63) 2.68 $2\frac{3}{5}$ $2\frac{4}{7}$ ______ < ______ < ______

(64) $5\frac{9}{10}$ $5\frac{4}{5}$ 5.83 ______ < ______ < ______

ISBN: 978-1-897164-15-0

Complete the table. Then list the fractions in order from least to greatest.

Fraction	$\frac{1}{8}$	$\frac{1}{4}$	$\frac{3}{4}$	$\frac{3}{8}$	$\frac{7}{8}$	$\frac{1}{5}$	$\frac{7}{10}$
⑥⑤ Decimal							

⑥⑥ _____ < _____ < _____ < _____ < _____ < _____ < _____

Answer the questions.

⑥⑦ Canada produces about 0.24 of the world's supply of nickel ore. Express this as a fraction in lowest terms. _____

⑥⑧ Paul climbs 100 steps up a 160-step tower.

    a. What fraction of the tower has he climbed? _____

    b. Express your answer as a decimal. _____

⑥⑨ $\frac{2}{5}$ of the cost of a litre of gas is tax.

    a. Express this fraction as a decimal. _____

    b. If gas costs 75¢ a litre, how much is the tax? _____

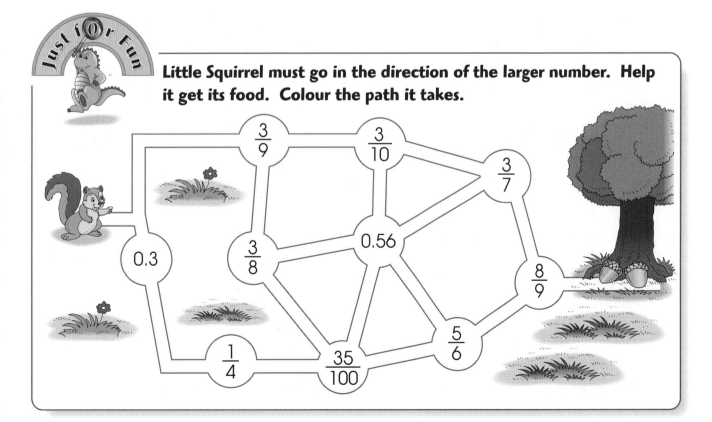

Just for Fun

Little Squirrel must go in the direction of the larger number. Help it get its food. Colour the path it takes.

Circle the letter which represents the correct answer in each problem.

① A fraction equivalent to $\frac{3}{4}$ is

   A. $\frac{5}{6}$ B. $\frac{6}{8}$ C. $\frac{35}{45}$ D. $\frac{9}{16}$

② The fraction $\frac{36}{92}$ expressed in lowest terms is

   A. $\frac{1}{2}$ B. $\frac{18}{46}$ C. $\frac{9}{23}$ D. $\frac{2}{5}$

③ The fraction $\frac{1}{8}$ expressed as a decimal is

   A. 0.12   B. 0.2   C. 0.1   D. 0.125

④ The decimal 0.95 expressed as a fraction in lowest terms is

   A. $\frac{19}{20}$ B. $\frac{9}{10}$ C. $\frac{9.5}{10}$ D. $\frac{9}{100}$

⑤ The mixed number $3\frac{1}{3}$ expressed as an improper fraction is

   A. $\frac{1}{2}$ B. $\frac{10}{3}$ C. $\frac{31}{3}$ D. $\frac{10}{9}$

⑥ The improper fraction $\frac{27}{7}$ expressed as a mixed number is

   A. $3\frac{1}{7}$ B. $27\frac{1}{7}$ C. $4\frac{6}{7}$ D. $3\frac{6}{7}$

⑦ The sum of $\frac{3}{11}$ and $\frac{7}{11}$ is

   A. $\frac{10}{11}$ B. $\frac{10}{22}$ C. $\frac{21}{121}$ D. $\frac{21}{11}$

⑧ The difference between $\frac{7}{9}$ and $\frac{2}{9}$ is

   A. $\frac{1}{7}$ B. 5   C. $\frac{5}{9}$ D. $\frac{14}{81}$

⑨ The improper fraction $\frac{24}{5}$ expressed as a decimal is

   A. 2.8   B. 4.8   C. 24.2   D. 5.2

Represent each diagram as a fraction in lowest terms and also as a decimal.

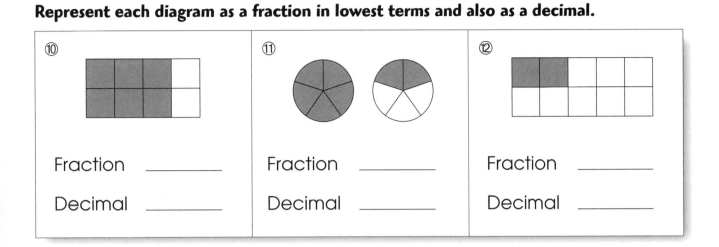

⑩

Fraction _____

Decimal _____

⑪

Fraction _____

Decimal _____

⑫

Fraction _____

Decimal _____

Write the numbers labelled A - E on the number line below as fractions and decimals.

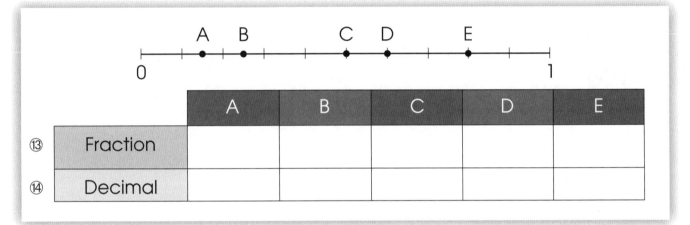

		A	B	C	D	E
⑬	Fraction					
⑭	Decimal					

Change the fractions to mixed numbers. Place the fractions on the number line below.

⑮ $\dfrac{15}{4}$ = _____

⑯ $\dfrac{3}{2}$ = _____

⑰ $\dfrac{17}{5}$ = _____

⑱ $\dfrac{19}{9}$ = _____

⑲ $\dfrac{4}{3}$ = _____

⑳ $\dfrac{7}{2}$ = _____

㉑ $\dfrac{14}{3}$ = _____

㉒ $\dfrac{25}{6}$ = _____

㉓ $\dfrac{35}{8}$ = _____

㉔ $\dfrac{7}{4}$ = _____

㉕ $\dfrac{13}{5}$ = _____

㉖ $\dfrac{24}{5}$ = _____

㉗

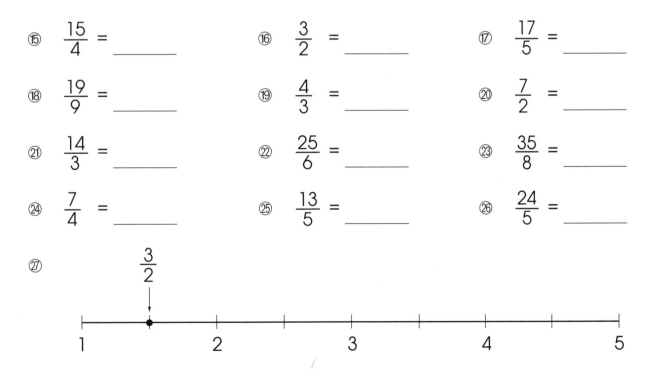

ISBN: 978-1-897164-15-0

Add or subtract. Write your answers in lowest terms.

㉘ $\dfrac{10}{3} - \dfrac{10}{3}$ = _____

㉙ $\dfrac{9}{2} - \dfrac{5}{2}$ = _____

㉚ $7\dfrac{1}{4} - 3\dfrac{1}{4}$ = _____

㉛ $6\dfrac{3}{8} - 5\dfrac{1}{8}$ = _____

㉜ $\dfrac{16}{5} + \dfrac{6}{5}$ = _____

㉝ $5\dfrac{1}{4} + 3\dfrac{3}{4}$ = _____

㉞ $5\dfrac{1}{4} - 4\dfrac{3}{4}$ = _____

㉟ $3\dfrac{1}{5} - 2\dfrac{3}{5}$ = _____

The chart below shows the minimum hourly wage in a number of Canadian provinces. Read the chart and answer the questions. Write the number sentences where necessary.

Province	B.C.	Alberta	Manitoba	Ontario	Quebec	PEI	Nova Scotia
Wage ($)	7.60	5.90	6.00	6.85	6.90	5.40	5.60

㊱ What is the difference between the highest and lowest wages?

_____ = _____

㊲ How much would a student working for 5 hours at minimum wage earn in

　　a. Ontario? _____ = _____

　　b. B.C.? _____ = _____

㊳ What is the difference between the two amounts in ㊲ ?

_____ = _____

㊴ Write the minimum wage in Quebec as

　　a. a mixed number.　　　　　_____

　　b. an improper fraction.　　　_____

㊵ Brenda lives in Alberta and earns $ $\dfrac{3}{4}$ per hour more than the minimum wage. How much does she earn per hour?

_____ = _____

ISBN: 978-1-897164-15-0

Solve the problems. Show your work.

㊶　In 1969, Canada's population was 21.3 million and in 1994, it was 29.2 million.

　　a.　Express each of these numbers as a mixed number in lowest terms.

　　b.　What was the increase in Canada's population between 1969 and 1994? Express your answer as a decimal and also as a mixed number.

　　c.　If this trend continues, what will the population of Canada be in 2019?

㊷　Dan is training for a Marathon race. His monthly goal is 100 km. He ran 35 km during the first week of the month.

　　a.　What fraction of his monthly goal has he run? Express your answer as a proper fraction in lowest terms and as a decimal.

　　b.　What distance does he still have to run during the month to achieve his goal?

　　c.　What fraction of the total distance does he still have to run? Express your answer as a fraction and as a decimal.

　　d.　What is the difference between the fraction of the total distance run in the first week and the fraction run during the rest of the month?

ISBN: 978-1-897164-15-0

43 Mr King drinks an average of $2\frac{1}{4}$ cups of tea each day. Mrs King drinks an average of $3\frac{3}{4}$ cups per day.

    a.   How many cups of tea do they drink between them each day?

    b.   What is the difference between the amounts they drink per day?

    c.   Change the amount Mr King drinks to a decimal. How much tea will Mr King drink per week?

    d.   Change the amount Mrs King drinks to a decimal. How much tea will Mrs King drink per week?

44 Peter watches TV for $8\frac{1}{5}$ hours per week. David watches $9\frac{3}{5}$ hours and Ruth watches $7\frac{1}{5}$ hours.

    a.   How much TV do they watch among them in a week?

    b.   How much longer does David watch TV than Peter?

    c.   How much longer does David watch TV than Ruth?

    d.   Ruth's mother says that Ruth must cut down watching TV by $1\frac{3}{5}$ hours. How much TV can she watch now?

Overview

In Section I, fraction and decimal skills were practised. In this section, these skills are expanded to include comparing fractions, reducing fractions to lowest terms, and finding equivalent fractions.

Students also practise solving simple equations, analysing line graphs and finding and constructing angles within 2-D shapes. The properties of 3-D figures and the concept of number patterns are included.

In the Measurement units, students learn how to find the area of 2-D shapes. They also practise calculating the volume of rectangular prisms and the capacity of containers.

In the Geometry units, students carry out transformations of points as well as shapes. Time applications include the calculation of the duration of an event. Money applications involve finding change and calculating sale prices.

Review

Find the answers.

①
```
  2908
+ 1374
```

②
```
   324
x    6
```

③
```
  6843
-  123
```

④
```
5 ) 375
```

⑤
```
  3856
-  298
```

⑥
```
  1296
+ 2345
```

⑦ 868 ÷ 4 = _____

⑧ 412 x 7 = _____

⑨ 1000 x 8 = _____

⑩ 9 x 100 = _____

Quick Tip

To multiply a number by 10, 100, ..., just add 1, 2, ... zeros to the number.

Fill in the missing numbers in the patterns.

⑪ 10, 20, 30, _____ , _____ , _____ , _____ , _____ , _____ , _____

⑫ 3, 6, 9, _____ , _____ , _____ , _____ , _____ , _____ , _____

⑬ 9, 18, 27, _____ , _____ , _____ , _____ , _____ , _____ , _____

⑭ 7, 14, 21, _____ , _____ , _____ , _____ , _____ , _____ , _____

⑮ 15, 30, 45, _____ , _____ , _____ , _____ , _____ , _____ , _____

Use the patterns above to find the products.

⑯ 6 x 7 = _____

⑰ 8 x 3 = _____

⑱ 5 x 10 = _____

⑲ 9 x 6 = _____

⑳ 7 x 8 = _____

㉑ 8 x 9 = _____

㉒ 7 x 9 = _____

㉓ 8 x 10 = _____

㉔ 8 x 15 = _____

㉕ 15 x 6 = _____

Quick Tip

Even if the order of multiplication has changed, the product is still the same,

e.g. 3 x 9 = 9 x 3 = 27

ISBN: 978-1-897164-15-0

Find the answers.

㉖ 7 x 8 = 56

56 ÷ 8 = ______

㉗ 6 x 5 = 30

30 ÷ 6 = ______

㉘ 72 ÷ 9 = 8

8 x 9 = ______

㉙ 98 + 2 = 100

100 – 2 = ______

㉚ 24 – 16 = 8

8 + 16 = ______

㉛ 123 ÷ 3 = 41

41 x 3 = ______

㉜ 56 + 48 = 104

104 – 56 = ______

㉝ 83 – 38 = 45

83 – 45 = ______

㉞ 112 ÷ 8 = 14

112 ÷ 14 = ______

Fill in the missing numbers.

㉟ 2 + ______ = 10

㊱ 25 – ______ = 21

㊲ 17 + ______ = 25

㊳ 21 – ______ = 15

㊴ ______ – 7 = 8

㊵ ______ + 7 = 20

㊶ 123 – ______ = 119

㊷ ______ + 120 = 150

㊸ ______ – 8 = 12

㊹ ______ + 130 = 149

㊺ ______ + 25 = 41

㊻ ______ – 110 = 28

Add or subtract.

㊼ 2.9 + 3.1 = ______

㊽ 5.9 – 1.7 = ______

㊾ 3.8 + 2.7 = ______

㊿ 9.2 – 5.6 = ______

(51) 16.1 – 4.5 = ______

(52) 23.6 + 8.9 = ______

(53) 37.4 – 12.6 = ______

(54) 11.4 + 45.7 = ______

(55) 230 + 51.7 = ______

(56) 182 – 23.9 = ______

(57) 7.4 + 26 = ______

(58) 41 – 9.8 = ______

(59) 87 – 34.9 = ______

(60) 31.6 + 57.5 = ______

ISBN: 978-1-897164-15-0

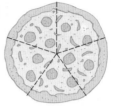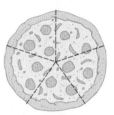

The children are eating pizzas. See how much each child eats and solve the problems.

Paul eats $\frac{3}{5}$ of a pizza. Stan eats $\frac{2}{5}$ of a pizza. Steve eats $\frac{4}{5}$ of a pizza. Sue eats $\frac{1}{5}$ of a pizza.

⑥ Who eats the most pizza? _____

⑥ Who eats the least pizza? _____

⑥ If they have 2 pizzas, will there be any pizza left over? _____

⑥ Put the children in order from the child who eats the most pizza to the one who eats the least.

_____ , _____ , _____ , _____

Complete the chart below.

Fraction	⑥⑤	⑥⑥	$\frac{1}{4}$	$\frac{2}{5}$	$\frac{3}{10}$	$\frac{37}{100}$
Decimal	0.9	0.04	⑥⑦	⑥⑧	⑥⑨	⑦⓪

Write the decimals to the nearest hundredth at which the javelins land.

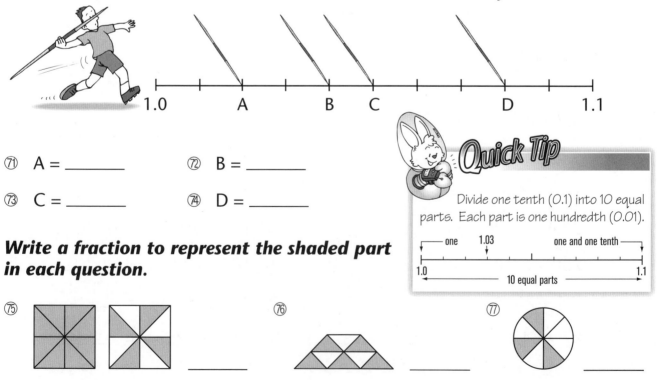

⑦ A = _____ ⑦ B = _____

⑦ C = _____ ⑦ D = _____

Quick Tip

Divide one tenth (0.1) into 10 equal parts. Each part is one hundredth (0.01).

Write a fraction to represent the shaded part in each question.

⑦⑤ ⑦⑥ ⑦⑦

Solve the problems.

⑦⑧ Paul buys a 70¢ chocolate bar. He pays $1.00. How much change does he get?

$ _____

⑦⑨ Pat pays a toonie for a $1.50 sandwich. How much change does he get?

_____ ¢

⑧⓪ Sarah has $32.75 in her piggy bank. How much does she have if her mom gives her $15.50 more?

$ _____

⑧① A pair of jeans costs $52.50. Peggy has only $45.75. How much more does she need to pay for the jeans?

$ _____

⑧② Sam bought a $1.85 hamburger and a $1.90 milkshake for his lunch. How much did his lunch cost?

$ _____

What transformation is used to get each image? Write translation, reflection or rotation.

⑧③ A → B   _____

⑧④ A → C   _____

⑧⑤ A → D   _____

⑧⑥ B → C   _____

Find the perimeter and area of each shape.

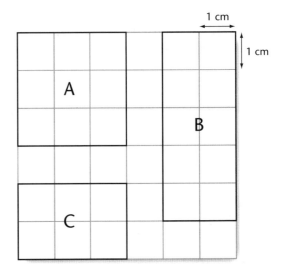

⑧⑦ A   perimeter = _____ cm

area = _____ cm^2

⑧⑧ B   perimeter = _____ cm

area = _____ cm^2

⑧⑨ C   perimeter = _____ cm

area = _____ cm^2

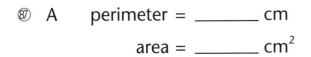

1 Operations with Whole Numbers

Find the sums or differences.

①
```
    3098
    1230
 +  4362
```

②
```
    3408
    1290
 +  2671
```

③
```
    2000
 -  1098
```

④
```
    5298
 -  1084
```

⑤
```
    4287
 -  1999
```

⑥
```
    4753
 -  2398
```

Find the products.

Example

```
    34
 x  56
```

1st
6 x 34 →

```
    34
 x  56
    204
```

2nd
50 x 34 →

```
    34
 x  56
    204
   1700
```

3rd
add the products →

```
    34
 x  56
    204
   1700
   1904
```

34 x 56 = 1904

⑦
```
    54
 x  27
```

⑧
```
    38
 x  49
```

⑨
```
    17
 x  65
```

Find the quotients and check your answers by multiplication and addition.

⑩ 9 ⟌ 6678

Check

_____ x 9 = _____

⑪ 6 ⟌ 559

Check

⑫ 7 ⟌ 4914

Check

ISBN: 978-1-897164-15-0

What is the message? Do the division and match the letters with the remainders.

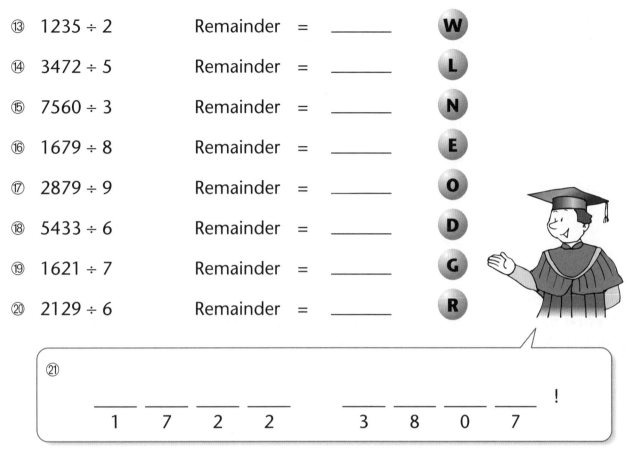

⑬ 1235 ÷ 2   Remainder = _____   **W**

⑭ 3472 ÷ 5   Remainder = _____   **L**

⑮ 7560 ÷ 3   Remainder = _____   **N**

⑯ 1679 ÷ 8   Remainder = _____   **E**

⑰ 2879 ÷ 9   Remainder = _____   **O**

⑱ 5433 ÷ 6   Remainder = _____   **D**

⑲ 1621 ÷ 7   Remainder = _____   **G**

⑳ 2129 ÷ 6   Remainder = _____   **R**

㉑

____ ____ ____ ____   ____ ____ ____ ____ !
  1   7   2   2   3   8   0   7

Do the calculations mentally. Put a check mark ✔ in the box if the answer is correct; otherwise, write the correct answer in the box.

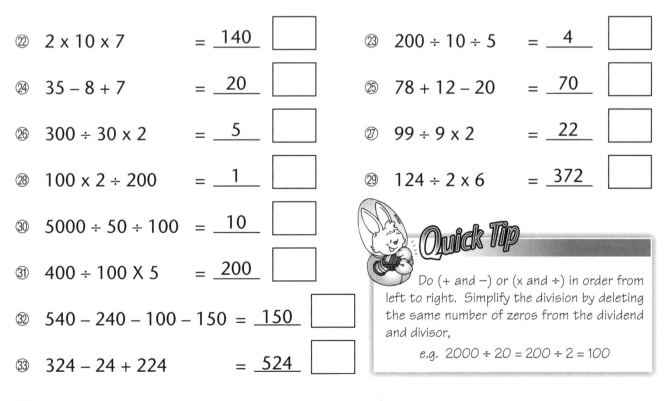

㉒ 2 x 10 x 7   = __140__ ☐   ㉓ 200 ÷ 10 ÷ 5   = __4__ ☐

㉔ 35 − 8 + 7   = __20__ ☐   ㉕ 78 + 12 − 20   = __70__ ☐

㉖ 300 ÷ 30 x 2   = __5__ ☐   ㉗ 99 ÷ 9 x 2   = __22__ ☐

㉘ 100 x 2 ÷ 200   = __1__ ☐   ㉙ 124 ÷ 2 x 6   = __372__ ☐

㉚ 5000 ÷ 50 ÷ 100   = __10__ ☐

㉛ 400 ÷ 100 X 5   = __200__ ☐

Quick Tip

Do (+ and −) or (x and ÷) in order from left to right. Simplify the division by deleting the same number of zeros from the dividend and divisor,

e.g. 2000 ÷ 20 = 200 ÷ 2 = 100

㉜ 540 − 240 − 100 − 150 = __150__ ☐

㉝ 324 − 24 + 224   = __524__ ☐

ISBN: 978-1-897164-15-0

Write the answers in numerals.

㉞ Mandy has one thousand three hundred four beads. Jane has two thousand seven hundred twenty-one beads. How many beads do Jane and Mandy have in all? _____ beads

㉟ How many more beads does Jane have than Mandy? _____ beads

㊱ Mandy has 324 green beads. How many of Mandy's beads are not green? _____ beads

㊲ Jane has 456 green beads. How many of Jane's beads are not green? _____ beads

㊳ How many green beads do Jane and Mandy have in all? _____ beads

Calculate and shade the answers in the number puzzle horizontally or vertically. Shade each digit only once. The sum of all the remaining 1-digit numbers is the number of sheets of stickers Sarah has bought.

㊴ 239 – 158 = _____   ㊵ 1234 – 999 = _____

㊶ 58 x 21 = _____   ㊷ 2345 + 999 = _____

㊸ 1080 ÷ 9 = _____   ㊹ 15 x 14 = _____

㊺ 3456 + 1398 = _____   ㊻ 1981 – 1973 = _____

㊼ 17 x 11 = _____   ㊽ 203 ÷ 7 = _____

㊾ 576 ÷ 8 = _____

㊿

2	3	5	1	8	7
5	1	2	1	8	4
7	2	3	1	1	8
2	9	8	2	2	5
0	7	1	0	1	4
3	3	4	4	0	8

51 Sum = _____

52 Sarah has bought _____ sheets of stickers.

   ISBN: 978-1-897164-15-0

Brad and Pat go swimming. Solve the problems and show your work.

53 Brad takes 90 seconds to swim one length of the pool. How long does he take to swim 12 lengths?

He takes _____ seconds to swim 12 lengths.

54 Pat takes 75 seconds to swim one length. How long does he take to swim 15 lengths?

55 Brad swims 12 lengths and Pat swims 15 lengths. What is the difference between their times?

56 During the first 7 days of August, 1848 swimmers used the pool. What was the average number of swimmers per day?

MIND BOGGLER

Who swims farther? You may use a calculator.

Refer to questions 53 and 54. How many lengths of the pool can Brad and Pat each swim in 1 hour?

Brad can swim _____ lengths. Pat can swim _____ lengths.

Quick Tip

1 hour = 60 minutes
1 minute = 60 seconds

2 Fractions

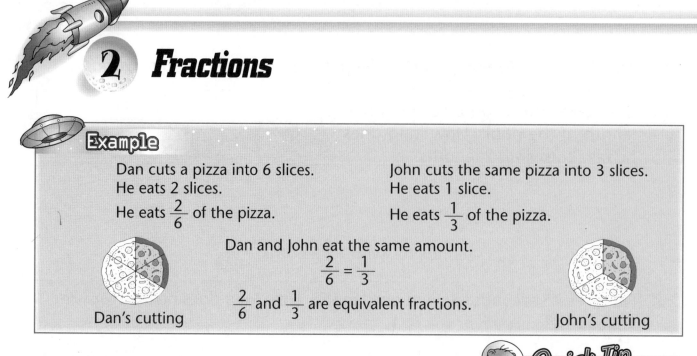

Complete the equivalent fractions by filling in the missing numerators or denominators.

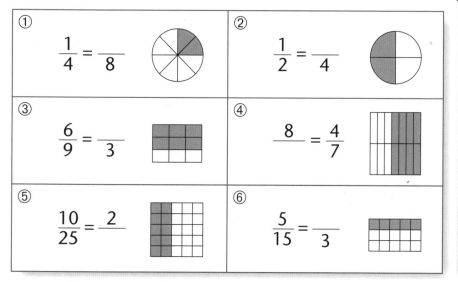

① $\frac{1}{4} = \frac{}{8}$

② $\frac{1}{2} = \frac{}{4}$

③ $\frac{6}{9} = \frac{}{3}$

④ $\frac{8}{} = \frac{4}{7}$

⑤ $\frac{10}{25} = \frac{2}{}$

⑥ $\frac{5}{15} = \frac{}{3}$

Quick Tip

$\overset{\times 2}{\frac{1}{3} = \frac{2}{6}}$ $\overset{\div 2}{\frac{2}{6} = \frac{1}{3}}$

$\frac{1}{3}$ and $\frac{2}{6}$ are equivalent fractions.

Multiply or divide both the numerator and denominator by the same number to get an equivalent fraction.

$\frac{1}{3}$ is in lowest terms since the only number that can divide both the denominator and the numerator is 1.

Match each fraction with its lowest terms. Write the letter in the circle.

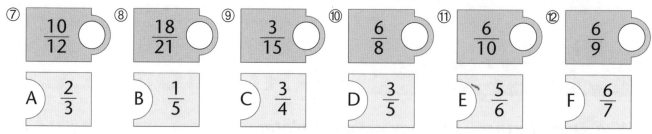

⑦ $\frac{10}{12}$ ⑧ $\frac{18}{21}$ ⑨ $\frac{3}{15}$ ⑩ $\frac{6}{8}$ ⑪ $\frac{6}{10}$ ⑫ $\frac{6}{9}$

A) $\frac{2}{3}$ B) $\frac{1}{5}$ C) $\frac{3}{4}$ D) $\frac{3}{5}$ E) $\frac{5}{6}$ F) $\frac{6}{7}$

Colour the diagrams to show the fractions. Circle the larger fractions.

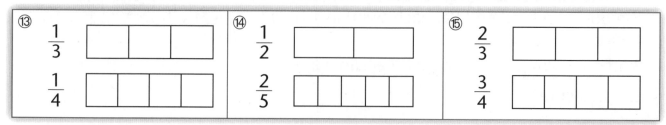

⑬ $\frac{1}{3}$ $\frac{1}{4}$

⑭ $\frac{1}{2}$ $\frac{2}{5}$

⑮ $\frac{2}{3}$ $\frac{3}{4}$

ISBN: 978-1-897164-15-0

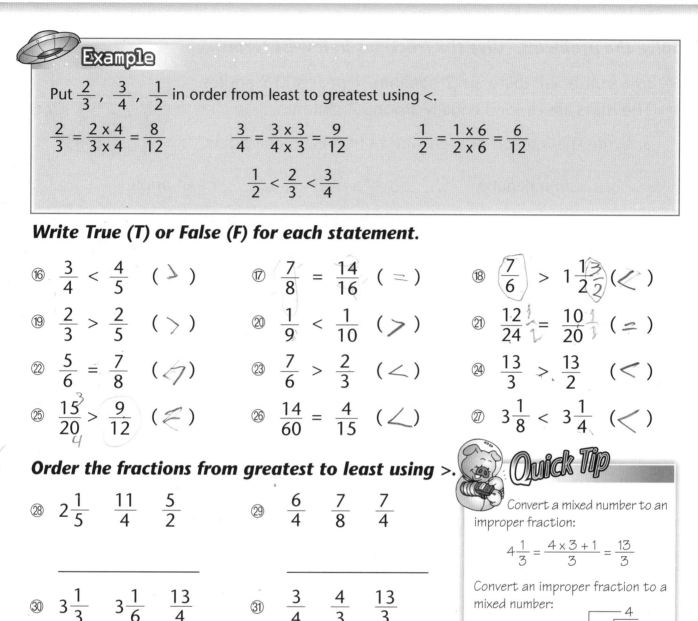

Example

Put $\frac{2}{3}$, $\frac{3}{4}$, $\frac{1}{2}$ in order from least to greatest using <.

$$\frac{2}{3} = \frac{2 \times 4}{3 \times 4} = \frac{8}{12} \qquad \frac{3}{4} = \frac{3 \times 3}{4 \times 3} = \frac{9}{12} \qquad \frac{1}{2} = \frac{1 \times 6}{2 \times 6} = \frac{6}{12}$$

$$\frac{1}{2} < \frac{2}{3} < \frac{3}{4}$$

Write True (T) or False (F) for each statement.

16. $\frac{3}{4} < \frac{4}{5}$ (⋗)

17. $\frac{7}{8} = \frac{14}{16}$ (=)

18. $\frac{7}{6} > 1\frac{1}{2}$ (<)

19. $\frac{2}{3} > \frac{2}{5}$ (>)

20. $\frac{1}{9} < \frac{1}{10}$ (>)

21. $\frac{12}{24} = \frac{10}{20}$ (=)

22. $\frac{5}{6} = \frac{7}{8}$ (⋗)

23. $\frac{7}{6} > \frac{2}{3}$ (<)

24. $\frac{13}{3} > \frac{13}{2}$ (<)

25. $\frac{15}{20} > \frac{9}{12}$ (⋖)

26. $\frac{14}{60} = \frac{4}{15}$ (<)

27. $3\frac{1}{8} < 3\frac{1}{4}$ (<)

Order the fractions from greatest to least using >.

28. $2\frac{1}{5}$ $\frac{11}{4}$ $\frac{5}{2}$

_____

29. $\frac{6}{4}$ $\frac{7}{8}$ $\frac{7}{4}$

_____

30. $3\frac{1}{3}$ $3\frac{1}{6}$ $\frac{13}{4}$

_____

31. $\frac{3}{4}$ $\frac{4}{3}$ $\frac{13}{3}$

_____

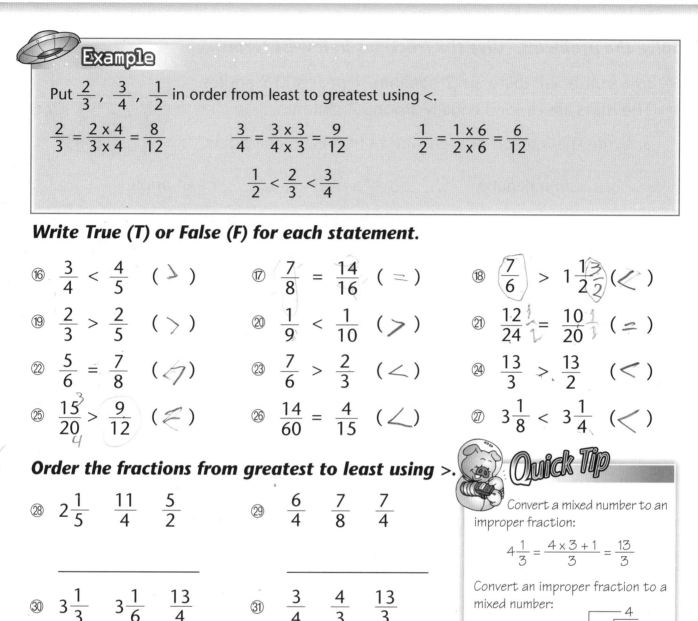

Quick Tip

Convert a mixed number to an improper fraction:

$$4\frac{1}{3} = \frac{4 \times 3 + 1}{3} = \frac{13}{3}$$

Convert an improper fraction to a mixed number:

$$\frac{13}{3} = 4\frac{1}{3}$$

$$3\overline{)13} \quad \frac{12}{1}$$

Write each fraction in lowest terms and as a decimal.

Examples

$\frac{1}{10} = 0.1$ $\qquad$ $\frac{5}{10} = 0.5$ $\qquad$ $\frac{1}{100} = 0.01$ $\qquad$ $\frac{21}{10} = 2\frac{1}{10} = 2.1$

		$\frac{6}{10}$	$\frac{85}{100}$	$\frac{54}{100}$	$\frac{36}{100}$	$\frac{75}{100}$	$\frac{38}{10}$	$\frac{15}{10}$
32.	Fraction in lowest terms							
33.	Decimal							

Solve the problems. Give the fractions in lowest terms.

㉞ In a fruit bowl, there are 2 bananas, 1 pear and 3 apples. The fruits are divided equally among 4 children.

  a. Write the fraction of each kind of fruit each child gets.

  _____ of a banana   _____ of a pear   _____ of an apple

  b. Write the fractions in order from least to greatest using <.

  _____

㉟ On Halloween, Dan collects 9 chocolate bars.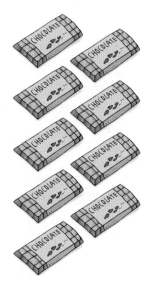

  a. If he divides the chocolate bars equally between himself and his brother, each gets _____ bars.

  b. If he divides them equally among 6 children, each gets _____ bars.

  c. If he divides them equally among 4 children, each gets _____ bars.

㊱ In Mrs. Ling's class, there are 30 students.

  a. $\frac{2}{5}$ of the students are girls. There are _____ girls in the class.

  b. On Friday $\frac{1}{6}$ of the students are away. _____ students are not in the class on Friday.

  c. 9 children go home for lunch. What fraction of the children stay at school for lunch?

  _____

  d. Can Mrs. Ling divide the class into 4 equal groups? Explain.

  _____

  _____

Divide 30 students into 5 groups. Each group has 6 students.

$\frac{1}{5}$ of 30 is 6.

ISBN: 978-1-897164-15-0

There are 12 children at Ali's party. Help Ali solve the problems.

37. The children will play in the garden for $\frac{1}{2}$ hour, watch a video for $\frac{3}{5}$ hour, and have snacks for $\frac{3}{4}$ hour.

    a. Which activity will take the longest time? _____

    b. Which activity will take the least time? _____

38. 3 pizzas are divided equally among 12 children. How much pizza does each child get? Give your answer in two equivalent fractions.

    _____ of a pizza
    _____ of a pizza

39. There are 4 bottles of pop. How much pop can each child have?

    _____ bottle

40. The birthday cake is divided into 16 equal slices. If each child eats 1 slice, what fraction of the cake is left over?

    _____ of the cake

41. Ali receives some storybooks for his birthday. He puts them on the bookshelf. Now there are 100 books in all on the shelf. If only 18 of the books belong to Ali, write a decimal to represent the fraction of books that belong to him.

    _____ of the books

42. Ali gets 10 gifts. 3 of the gifts are books and 5 are board games. Write a decimal to represent each kind of gift.

    a. Books _____

    b. Board games _____

    c. Neither books nor board games _____

MIND BOGGLER

Who has more books?

$\frac{3}{5}$ of 40 books are mine.

Kevin

0.35 of 100 books are mine.

Jane

_____ has more books.

ISBN: 978-1-897164-15-0

3 Decimals

Add or subtract the decimals.

①
```
    5.43
  + 2.08
```

②
```
    7.84
  + 1.16
```

③
```
    3.09
  + 0.97
```

④
```
    8.97
  - 1.45
```

⑤
```
    5.69
  - 2.81
```

⑥
```
    6.23
  - 3.85
```

⑦ 12.23 + 8.98 = _____

⑧ 23.45 – 2.93 = _____

⑨ 82.36 – 35.47 = _____

⑩ 21.98 + 27.09 = _____

⑪ 38.46 + 0.91 = _____

⑫ 42.38 – 0.92 = _____

⑬ 55.55 – 16.87 = _____

⑭ 41.63 – 7.9 = _____

Complete each of the following statements by filling in the fractions with denominators of 10 or 100.

Example

ones — tenths — hundredths

2.96 = 2 ones + 9 tenths + 6 hundredths

= 2 + 0.9 + 0.06

9 tenths $= \dfrac{9}{10} = 0.9$

6 hundredths $= \dfrac{6}{100} = 0.06$

96 hundredths $= \dfrac{96}{100} = 0.96$

⑮ 0.07 = _____

⑯ 0.49 $= \dfrac{4}{10} +$ _____ = _____

⑰ 0.7 $= \dfrac{}{100} = \dfrac{}{10}$

⑱ 0.79 = _____ $+ \dfrac{9}{100} =$ _____

⑲ 0.6 + 0.05 = _____

⑳ 0.3 + 0.04 = _____

㉑ 123.45 = 100 + 20 + 3 + _____ + _____

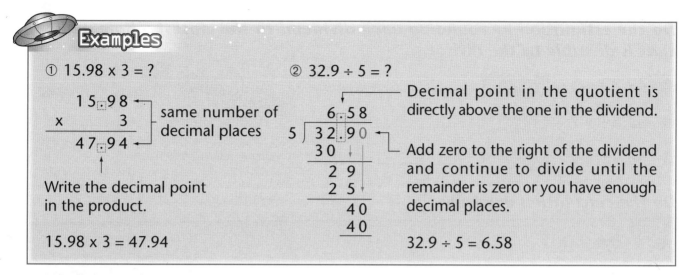

Examples

① 15.98 x 3 = ?

```
      15.98  ┐
   x      3  ├ same number of
   ─────────  │ decimal places
      47.94  ┘
         ↑
```

Write the decimal point in the product.

15.98 x 3 = 47.94

② 32.9 ÷ 5 = ?

Decimal point in the quotient is directly above the one in the dividend.

```
        6.58
   5 ) 32.90
        30 ↓
         2 9
         2 5
           40
           40
```

Add zero to the right of the dividend and continue to divide until the remainder is zero or you have enough decimal places.

32.9 ÷ 5 = 6.58

Find the products.

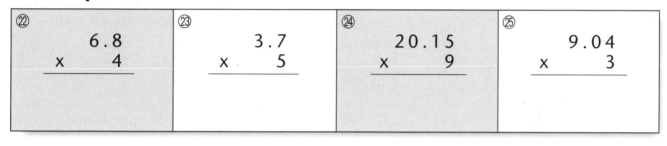

㉒	㉓	㉔	㉕
6.8 x 4	3.7 x 5	20.15 x 9	9.04 x 3

㉖ 17.41 x 7 = _____

㉗ 0.93 x 6 = _____

㉘ 24.09 x 8 = _____

㉙ 18.75 x 2 = _____

Estimate and check ✔ the correct products. Cross ✘ the incorrect ones.

㉚ 5.07 x 2 = 10.14 ◯

㉛ 15.18 x 5 = 65.90 ◯

㉜ 0.93 x 7 = 65.1 ◯

㉝ 21.8 x 8 = 11.44 ◯

㉞ 6.98 x 6 = 41.88 ◯

㉟ 2.34 x 9 = 210.6 ◯

Find the quotients.

㊱	㊲	㊳
7) 51.1	4) 25.16	5) 19.9

㊴ 73.86 ÷ 6 = _____

㊵ 70.8 ÷ 8 = _____

㊶ 13.5 ÷ 2 = _____

Do the estimation by rounding each dividend to the closest whole number that is divisible by the divisor.

㊷ 49.82 ÷ 5 **Estimate** : ________ = _____

㊸ 53.84 ÷ 7 **Estimate** : ________ = _____

㊹ 46.23 ÷ 9 **Estimate** : ________ = _____

Quick Tip

Estimate the quotient of 32.9 ÷ 5.
Round 32.9 to 35 (the closest whole number divisible by 5).

35 ÷ 5 = 7

The quotient of 32.9 ÷ 5 is about 7.

Do the calculation mentally.

Examples

① 38.47 x 10 = 384.7

38.47 x 100 = 3847.0

When multiplied by 10 or 100, move the decimal point 1 or 2 places to the right.

② 38.4 ÷ 10 = 3.84

38.4 ÷ 100 = 0.384

When divided by 10 or 100, move the decimal point 1 or 2 places to the left.

③ 1.6 x 30
= 1.6 x 3 x 10
= 4.8 x 10
= 48

㊺ 9.83 x 100 = ________

㊻ 12.93 x 10 = ________

㊼ 45.2 ÷ 10 = ________

㊽ 12.84 ÷ 10 = ________

㊾ 91.23 x 10 = ________

㊿ 16.3 ÷ 100 = ________

(51) 0.8 x 100 = ________

(52) 0.8 ÷ 10 = ________

(53) 1.2 ÷ 10 = ________

(54) 0.3 x 40 = ________

(55) 2.4 x 30 = ________

(56) 100 x 9.91 = ________

(57) 2.4 x 20 = ________

(58) 3.17 x 20 = ________

(59) 1.2 x 400 = ________

(60) 5.5 x 40 = ________

(61) 3.09 x 50 = ________

(62) 0.54 x 800 = ________

In each problem, put a decimal point in the right place of the shaded number to get the given answer. Add zeros if necessary.

(63) 5 6 8 x 10 = 56.8

(64) 3 8 ÷ 10 = 0.38

(65) 2 1 x 100 = 210

(66) 1 2 3 x 10 = 123

(67) 7 2 x 10 = 7.2

(68) 5 2 0 ÷ 100 = 0.52

ISBN: 978-1-897164-15-0

Kim and Karen go shopping. Help them solve the problems. Show your work.

---

⑥⑨ Kim pays for a blouse with a $100 bill. How much change does she get?

$ 29.95

_____ = _____

She gets $ _____ change.

---

⑦⓪ Kim also pays for a pair of sandals with three $20 bills. How much change does she get?

$ 52.99

---

⑦① How much does Kim pay altogether for the blouse and sandals?

---

⑦② Karen buys 3 computer games. How much does she pay altogether?

GAME

$ 12.75

---

⑦③ How much does each pair of socks cost?

10 pairs for $ 32.60

---

⑦④ They each order the same lunch. How much do they pay altogether?

$ 6.93

---

⑦⑤ Each sweater costs $42.50. Karen buys 4 sweaters. How much does she pay?

ABC

Buy 3 Get 1 Free

---

⑦⑥ They share the cost of a teddy bear for Jane. How much does each one pay?

$ 78.50

MIND BOGGLER

Kim and Karen buy a gift for Darren. Kim pays $10 more than Karen. How much does each pay?

Kim pays $ _____ and Karen pays $ _____ .

$ 46.40

ISBN: 978-1-897164-15-0

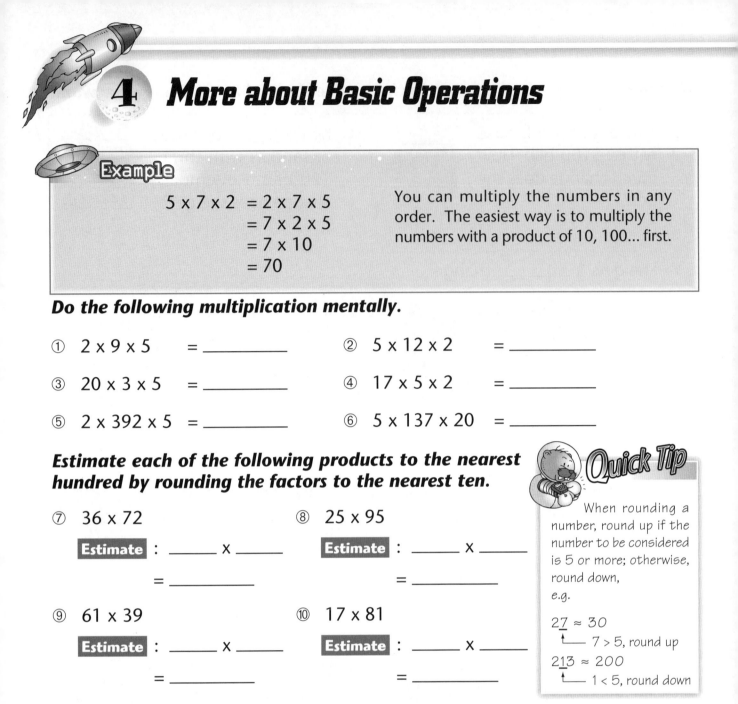

4 More about Basic Operations

Example

$5 \times 7 \times 2 = 2 \times 7 \times 5$
$= 7 \times 2 \times 5$
$= 7 \times 10$
$= 70$

You can multiply the numbers in any order. The easiest way is to multiply the numbers with a product of 10, 100... first.

Do the following multiplication mentally.

① $2 \times 9 \times 5$ = _____

② $5 \times 12 \times 2$ = _____

③ $20 \times 3 \times 5$ = _____

④ $17 \times 5 \times 2$ = _____

⑤ $2 \times 392 \times 5$ = _____

⑥ $5 \times 137 \times 20$ = _____

Estimate each of the following products to the nearest hundred by rounding the factors to the nearest ten.

Quick Tip

When rounding a number, round up if the number to be considered is 5 or more; otherwise, round down,
e.g.

$2\underline{7} \approx 30$
└── 7 > 5, round up
$2\underline{1}3 \approx 200$
└── 1 < 5, round down

⑦ 36×72

Estimate : _____ x _____

= _____

⑧ 25×95

Estimate : _____ x _____

= _____

⑨ 61×39

Estimate : _____ x _____

= _____

⑩ 17×81

Estimate : _____ x _____

= _____

Estimate the answers by rounding the numbers, except the 1-digit numbers, to the nearest hundred.

⑪ $529 + 398 - 199$ **Estimate** : $\underline{500 + 400 - 200}$ = _____

⑫ $781 - 239 + 99$ **Estimate** : _____ = _____

⑬ $1523 - 398 - 721$ **Estimate** : _____ = _____

⑭ $301 - 99 + 215 + 39$ **Estimate** : _____ = _____

⑮ $2594 \div 2$ **Estimate** : _____ = _____

⑯ $3025 \div 6$ **Estimate** : _____ = _____

⑰ $1234 \div 4$ **Estimate** : _____ = _____

ISBN: 978-1-897164-15-0

Solve the following multi-step problems. Show your work.

⑱ There are 4 rows of 6 desks and 2 rows of 5 desks in a classroom. How many desks are there in all?

Quick Tip

To evaluate a number sentence with mixed operations, remember to do multiplication and division first; then do addition and subtraction.

There are _____ desks in all.

⑲ In a concert hall, there are 50 rows with 35 seats in each row. All the seats are filled and 32 people have to stand at the back. How many people are there in all?

⑳ 69 students go on a field trip. 45 of them go by bus. The others go by van with 6 passengers in each van. How many vans are needed?

㉑ There are 78 guests at Mrs. Wong's party. In the dining room, there are 5 oval tables with 8 seats each and 7 round tables with 6 seats each. How many empty seats are there?

㉒ Anna can swim 9 lengths of a pool in 5 minutes. How many lengths can she swim in 30 minutes?

㉓ If the pool is 25 m long, how many metres does Anna swim in 30 minutes?

A medium-sized car uses 9 L of gas for 100 km of town driving and 7 L of gas for highway driving. Solve the problems by completing the tables.

㉔ How far can this car travel in town on 45 L of gas?

Distance travelled (km)	100	
Gas used (L)	9	45

It can travel _____ km.

㉕ How many L of gas are needed to travel 50 km in town?

Distance travelled (km)	100	50
Gas used (L)		

_____ L of gas are needed.

㉖ How many L of gas are needed for a 600-km highway journey?

Distance travelled (km)	100	600
Gas used (L)		

_____ L of gas are needed.

㉗ Gas costs 70¢ per litre. How much will a 600-km highway journey cost?

Gas used (L)	1	
Cost ($)		

It will cost $ _____ .

㉘ A new "Envirocar" uses only 4 L of gas for 100 km on the highway. How much can be saved on a 600-km journey as compared with a medium-sized car?

	Distance travelled (km)	Gas used (L)	Cost ($)
Envirocar	100	4	
Envirocar	600		
Medium-sized car	600		

Amount saved: _____ = _____

㉙ The medium-sized car and the Envirocar start from Acton and complete a round trip as the diagram shows. Find the gas cost of each car.

Bellfield
400 km
300 km
600 km
Acton
Drummond

	Distance travelled (km)	Gas used (L)	Cost ($)
Medium-sized car			
Envirocar			

ISBN: 978-1-897164-15-0

Pete, Paul and Sue are collecting baseball cards.
A pack of 20 cards costs $1.79. Estimate and
solve the two-step problems.

③⓪ Pete has 320 cards. Estimate the
total cost of the cards to the
nearest whole number. _____

③① Paul's cards cost him $17.90 in
all. How many cards does he
have? _____

Quick Tip

To estimate, round the cost
for a pack of cards to the nearest
dollar first.

③② Sue has $10 to spend on cards.
How many packs can she buy? _____

③③ How much change does Sue get? _____

③④ How much more money must Sue save until she
can buy another pack? _____

③⑤ Mr. Wu takes Pete, Paul and Sue to a baseball game by train. Baseball tickets
cost $35 each. The train fare is $9 for an adult and $6 for a child. Estimate first
and then find the exact amount that Mr. Wu has to pay in all.

Estimate: _____ Exact amount: _____

③⑥ How much change does Mr. Wu get from two
$100 bills? _____

③⑦ Each bag of popcorn costs $4. What is the maximum
number of bags of popcorn that Mr. Wu can buy
with the change? _____

MIND BOGGLER

How many handshakes?

5 friends meet at the baseball game.
They each shake hands once with
their friends. How many handshakes
are there in all?

There are _____ handshakes in all.

ISBN: 978-1-897164-15-0

5 Units of Measure

Use a ruler and a piece of string to find the circumference and diameter of each of the following circles in cm to the nearest tenth.

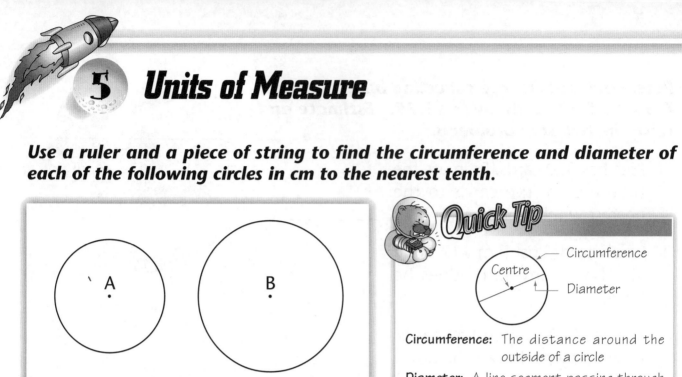

Circle	A	B
① Circumference (cm)		
② Diameter (cm)		

Quick Tip

Circumference

Centre

Diameter

Circumference: The distance around the outside of a circle

Diameter: A line segment passing through the centre of a circle

The length of the string = The circumference of the circle

Find these objects at home and measure their circumferences to the nearest cm using a string and a ruler.

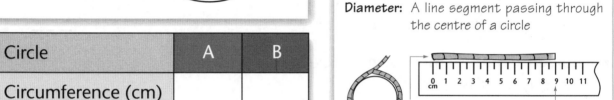

③　　　　　④　　　　　⑤　　　　　⑥

_____ cm　　_____ cm　　_____ cm　　_____ cm

If the lamp post is 4 m tall, estimate the height of the other objects in the picture in metres.

⑦ Height of the fence　　= _____

⑧ Height of the tree　　 = _____

⑨ Height of the building = _____

Ground

ISBN: 978-1-897164-15-0

Complete the table.

	Date	Date in SI notation
⑩	November 29, 1943	
⑪	February 5, 2001	
⑫		2002 09 24
⑬		2003 03 20

Quick Tip

In SI (International System) notation, August 20, 2001 is written as

2001 08 20

Calculate the number of days between the following dates.

⑭ From 2002 03 21 to 2002 05 01   _____ days

⑮ From 2002 12 20 to 2003 01 27   _____ days

Write the times or draw the clock hands to show the given times to the nearest minute.

⑯ _____

⑰ _____

⑱ 11:35

⑲ 2:28

Calculate the time intervals.

Examples

① From 7:30:20 a.m. to 9:00 a.m.

$$
\begin{array}{r}
9:00 \rightarrow 8:59:60 \\
(1\ h = 60\ min) \quad - \ 7:30:20 \\
(1\ min = 60\ s) \quad \hline
1:29:40
\end{array}
$$

The time interval is 1 h 29 min 40 s.

② From 7:30 a.m. to 2:15 p.m.

$$
\begin{array}{r}
12:00\ noon \rightarrow 11:60 \\
- \ 7:30 \\
\hline
4:30
\end{array}
$$

$$
\begin{array}{r}
4:30 \text{ (in the morning)} \\
+ \ 2:15 \text{ (in the afternoon)} \\
\hline
6:45
\end{array}
$$

The time interval is 6 h 45 min.

⑳ 9:12:05 a.m.   to   9:46:23 a.m.   _____

㉑ 3:07:26 p.m.   to   3:12:09 p.m.   _____

㉒ 8:15:34 a.m.   to   11:23:12 a.m.   _____

㉓ 6:30:00 a.m.   to   7:55:00 p.m.   _____

㉔ 11:10:20 a.m.   to   12:13:10 p.m.   _____

Use the diagram to solve the problems. Show your work.

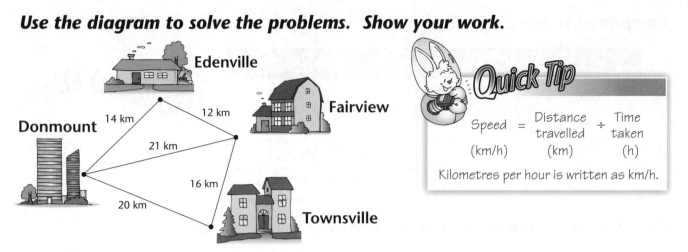

㉕ It takes Sam 1 hour to cycle from Edenville to Fairview. What is his speed?

His speed is _____ km/h.

㉖ Sarah takes 2 hours to cycle from Donmount to Fairview passing through Edenville. What is her average speed?

㉗ Tim and Paul start to cycle from Donmount to Fairview at the same time. Tim cycles via Edenville at a speed of 13 km/h and Paul via Townville at a speed of 12 km/h. Who arrives at Fairview first? How much earlier does he arrive?

㉘ a. A car travels at 40 km/h. Complete the table to show how far it can travel in the given times.

Time (h)	1	$\frac{1}{2}$	$\frac{1}{4}$	$\frac{3}{4}$	$1\frac{1}{2}$
Distance travelled (km)	40				

b. How long does it take to drive from Donmount to Townville directly? _____

c. How long does it take to drive back and forth 5 times between Fairview and Edenville? _____

ISBN: 978-1-897164-15-0

The distance around the track at Donville school is 250 m. Solve the problems.

250 m

㉙ Ron is training for the school track meet. He runs around the track 8 times.

Quick Tip

1 km = 1000 m
1 cm = 10 mm
1 m = 10 dm = 100 cm

a. How many metres has he run? _____

b. How many kilometres has he run? _____

㉚ Sarah records Ron's time. Write the times and calculate how long Ron's run takes.

a. Starting time _____

b. Finishing time _____

c. Time taken in minutes _____

d. Time taken in hours _____

Start   **Finish**

㉛ If Ron continued at the same speed, how many km could he run in half an hour? _____

㉜ At what speed in km/h does Ron run? _____

㉝ Janice can jog around the same track 4 times in 10 minutes. Write how far she can cover

a. in 10 minutes (in metres). _____

b. in 60 minutes (in metres). _____

c. in 10 minutes (in kilometres). _____

d. in 60 minutes (in kilometres). _____

㉞ What is Janice's speed in km/h? _____

MIND BOGGLER

How many times within 24 hours would the two hands of a clock overlap?

Two clock hands would overlap _____ times within 24 hours.

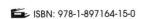

Use a ruler to measure the perimeter of each shape to the nearest cm.

① 3cm 3cm 3cm

___12___ cm

② 5cm 3cm 4cm

___12___ cm

Quick Tip

The perimeter of a shape is the distance around the outside of the shape.

③

___10___ cm

④

___13___ cm

⑤

___10___ cm

Find the perimeters (P) of the following shapes.

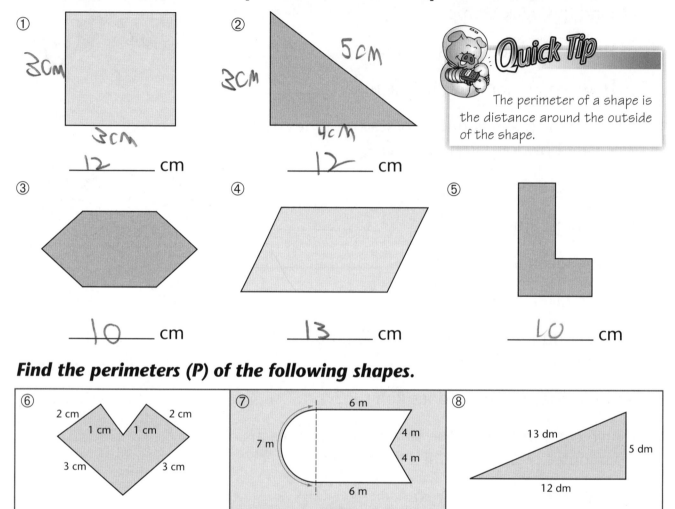

⑥ 2 cm, 1 cm, 1 cm, 2 cm, 3 cm, 3 cm

P = ___12 Cm___

⑦ 6 m, 4 m, 7 m, 4 m, 6 m

P = ___27 M___

⑧ 13 dm, 5 dm, 12 dm

P = ___30 dm___

⑨ 4 dm, 2 dm, 4 dm, 5 dm, 5 dm

P = ___20 dM___

⑩ 8 cm, 5 cm, 5 cm, 14 cm

P = ___32 cM___

⑪ 4.5 m, 4.5 m, 4.5 m, 4.5 m

P = ___18 m___

⑫ 6 mm, 12 mm, 3 mm, 12 mm, 6 mm

P = ___39 MM___

ISBN: 978-1-897164-15-0

Count the squares to estimate the areas of the following irregular shapes to the nearest cm².

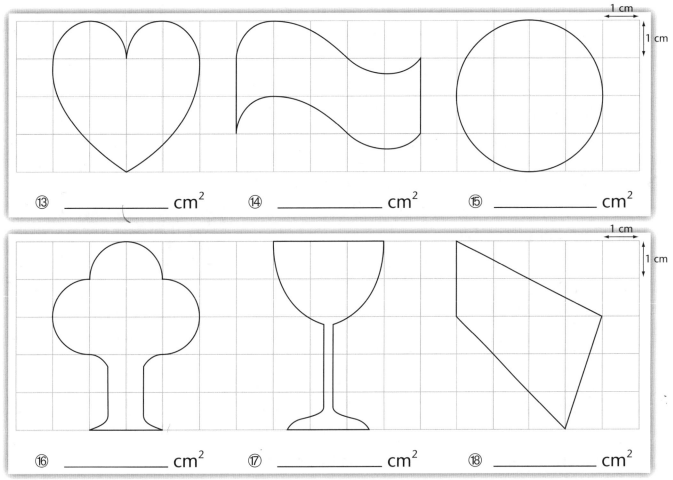

1 cm

1 cm

⑬ _____ cm²   ⑭ _____ cm²   ⑮ _____ cm²

1 cm

1 cm

⑯ _____ cm²   ⑰ _____ cm²   ⑱ _____ cm²

Calculate the perimeters (P) and areas (A) of the following shapes.

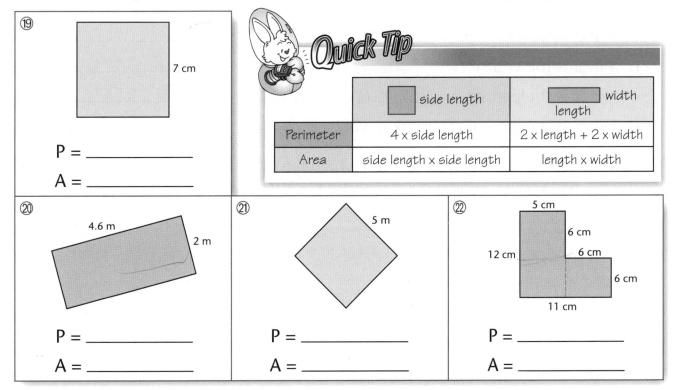

⑲

7 cm

P = _____

A = _____

Quick Tip

	side length	length × width
Perimeter	4 × side length	2 × length + 2 × width
Area	side length × side length	length × width

⑳

4.6 m

2 m

P = _____

A = _____

㉑

5 m

P = _____

A = _____

㉒

5 cm

6 cm

12 cm

6 cm

6 cm

11 cm

P = _____

A = _____

ISBN: 978-1-897164-15-0

Solve the problems.

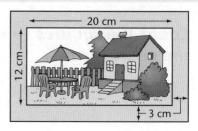

㉓ The dimensions of a picture are 20 cm by 12 cm. The picture is mounted on a frame which is 3 cm wide.

a. What are the dimensions of the framed picture? _____

b. What is the perimeter of the framed picture? _____

c. What is the area of the framed picture? _____

㉔ A small TV screen measures 30 cm by 20 cm. A large TV screen measures 60 cm by 40 cm.

a. Complete the table.

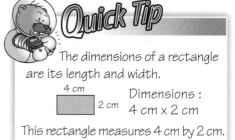

	Perimeter	Area
Small screen		
Large screen		

b. About how many times is the perimeter of the large screen larger than that of the small screen? _____

c. About how many times is the area of the large screen larger than that of the small screen? _____

㉕ Measure the length and width of this book to the nearest cm.

a. What is the length? _____

b. What is the width? _____

c. What is the perimeter of the book cover? _____

d. What is the area of the book cover? _____

㉖ Draw 2 different rectangles A and B which have the same area of 12 cm^2. Then draw a rectangle C which has the same perimeter as A. Label your drawings.

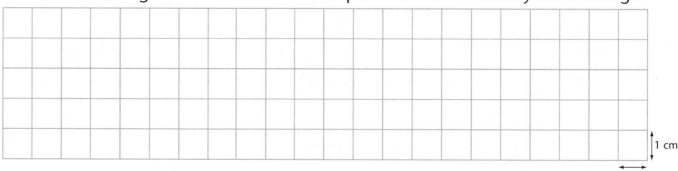

2C

ISBN: 978-1-897164-15-0

Katie is going to refurbish her bedroom. Look at the diagram and solve the problems.

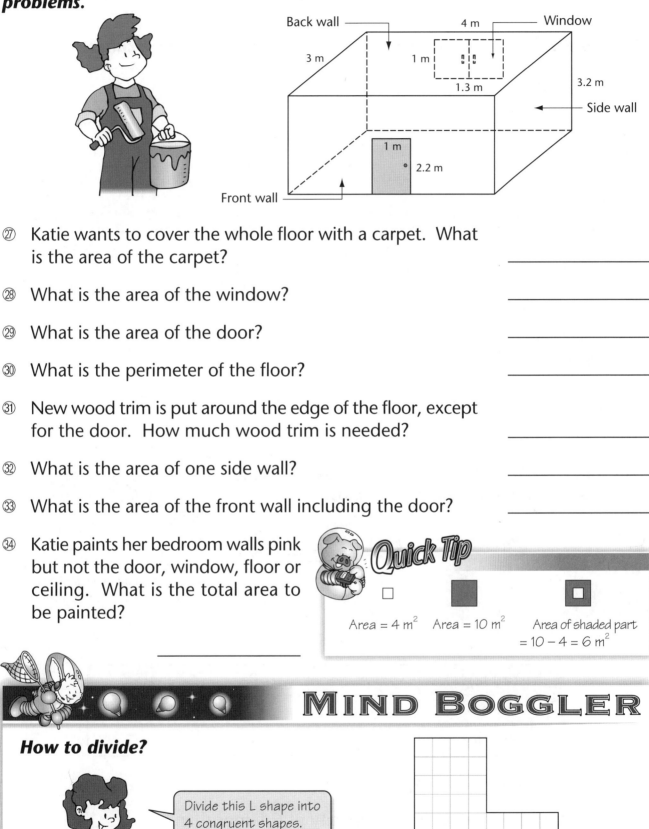

㉗ Katie wants to cover the whole floor with a carpet. What is the area of the carpet? _____

㉘ What is the area of the window? _____

㉙ What is the area of the door? _____

㉚ What is the perimeter of the floor? _____

㉛ New wood trim is put around the edge of the floor, except for the door. How much wood trim is needed? _____

㉜ What is the area of one side wall? _____

㉝ What is the area of the front wall including the door? _____

㉞ Katie paints her bedroom walls pink but not the door, window, floor or ceiling. What is the total area to be painted?

_____

Quick Tip

☐ Area = 4 m^2 ■ Area = 10 m^2 ▣ Area of shaded part = 10 − 4 = 6 m^2

MIND BOGGLER

How to divide?

Divide this L shape into 4 congruent shapes.

ISBN: 978-1-897164-15-0

7 Volume, Capacity and Mass

Find the volume of each tower built by Sam with centimetre cubes.

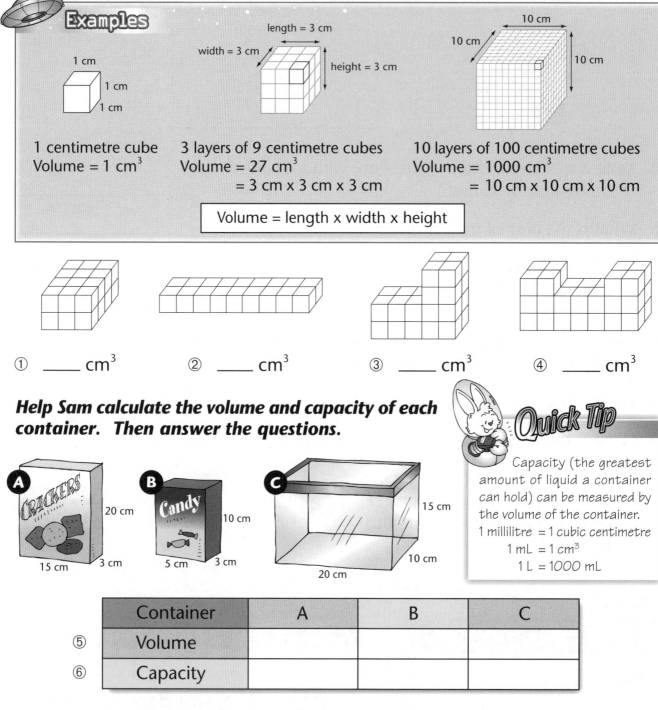

Examples

1 centimetre cube
Volume = 1 cm^3

3 layers of 9 centimetre cubes
Volume = 27 cm^3
= 3 cm x 3 cm x 3 cm

10 layers of 100 centimetre cubes
Volume = 1000 cm^3
= 10 cm x 10 cm x 10 cm

Volume = length x width x height

① _____ cm^3 ② _____ cm^3 ③ _____ cm^3 ④ _____ cm^3

Help Sam calculate the volume and capacity of each container. Then answer the questions.

Quick Tip

Capacity (the greatest amount of liquid a container can hold) can be measured by the volume of the container.
1 millilitre = 1 cubic centimetre
1 mL = 1 cm^3
1 L = 1000 mL

Container	A	B	C
⑤ Volume			
⑥ Capacity			

⑦ How many litres of water can C hold?   _____

⑧ About how many times is the capacity of C larger than
that of B?   _____

⑨ Lucy fills up B with water and pours it into A. How many
times does she need to fill up B in order to fill up A?

ISBN: 978-1-897164-15-0

Solve the problems.

⑩ A communal mailbox contains 6 identical mailboxes. What are the dimensions of each mailbox?

_____

⑪ What is the volume of each mailbox?

_____

⑫ What is the volume of the truck's container?

_____

⑬ Estimate the number of boxes, each measuring 0.5 m x 1 m x 1 m, that could be transported in this container.

_____

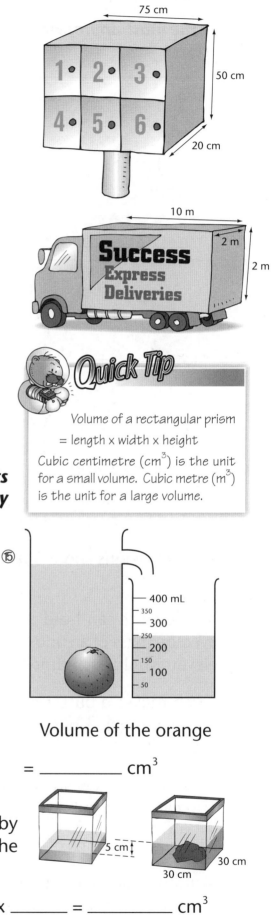

Quick Tip

Volume of a rectangular prism
= length x width x height

Cubic centimetre (cm^3) is the unit for a small volume. Cubic metre (m^3) is the unit for a large volume.

Find the volume of each of the irregular objects by measuring the amount of liquid displaced by the object.

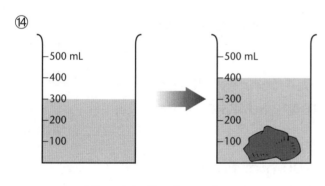

⑭

Amount of liquid displaced = _____ mL

Volume of the stone = _____ cm^3

⑮

Volume of the orange

= _____ cm^3

⑯ A fish tank has a square base measuring 30 cm by 30 cm. When Sam puts a stone into the tank, the water level rises by 5 cm.

Volume of water displaced = _____ x _____ x _____ = _____ cm^3

Volume of the stone = _____ cm^3

Write the most appropriate standard units to measure the mass of the following objects.

Quick Tip

Mass can be measured in milligram (mg), gram (g), kilogram (kg) or tonne (t).

1 t = 1000 kg
1 kg = 1000 g
1 g = 1000 mg

⑰ _____

⑱ _____

⑲ _____

⑳ _____

㉑ _____

Answer the questions.

㉒ Baby Jack weighed 3.2 kg at birth and gained 100 g per week. How much did he weigh at 12 weeks? _____ kg

㉓ A nickel weighs about 5 g. How many nickels would weigh 1 kg? _____ nickels

㉔ An elevator can hold a maximum of 1.4 tonnes. If the average mass of an adult is 70 kg, how many adults can the elevator hold each time? _____ adults

㉕ Sarah makes a butter cake by mixing 400 g of flour with 250 g of sugar. How much flour would she need for 1 kg of sugar? _____ kg

㉖ A carton of milk weighs about 2.5 kg. How many kg would 100 cartons of milk weigh? _____ kg

㉗ How many cartons of milk would weigh 1 t? _____ cartons

㉘ A timber-yard sold 100 kg of logs for $5.00. How much can the yard get from selling 30 t of logs? $ _____

㉙ How much can the yard get from selling 30 000 g of logs? $ _____

   ISBN: 978-1-897164-15-0

Sam is holding a birthday party. Help him solve the problems.

③⓪ Find the volume of 3 gift boxes Sam received.

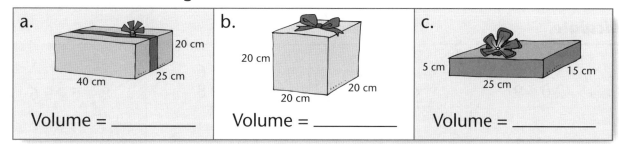

a.

20 cm
40 cm   25 cm

Volume = _____

b.

20 cm
20 cm
20 cm

Volume = _____

c.

5 cm
25 cm   15 cm

Volume = _____

③①

12 cm
12 cm   4 cm
Happy Birthday

The dimensions of Sam's birthday cake are 12 cm x 12 cm x 4 cm. What is the volume of the cake?

_____

③② The cake is cut into 16 equal slices. What are the dimensions of each slice?

_____

③③ What is the volume of each slice?

_____

③④ The whole cake has a mass of 640 g. What is the mass of each slice?

_____

③⑤ How many slices of cake would have a total mass of

a. 1 kg? _____   b. 1 t? _____

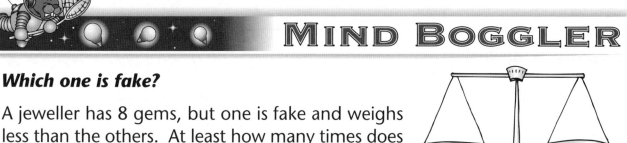

50 cm
40 cm
2 cm

③⑥ The children play the game "Bobbing for apples". 8 apples are dropped into the fish tank, and the water rises by 2 cm.

a. What is the total volume of the 8 apples?

_____

b. What is the average volume of each apple?

_____

MIND BOGGLER

Which one is fake?

A jeweller has 8 gems, but one is fake and weighs less than the others. At least how many times does the jeweller need to weigh the gems with a balance in order to find out the fake one?

He needs to weigh at least _____ times.

ISBN: 978-1-897164-15-0

Calculate.

①
```
    5984
  + 2079
  _____

  − 3475
  _____
```

②
```
      53
  x   69
  _____
```

③
```
      76
  x   98
  _____
```

④
```
  8 ) 6296
```

Write the missing numbers in the equivalent fractions.

⑤ $\dfrac{15}{25} = \dfrac{}{5}$

⑥ $\dfrac{4}{9} = \dfrac{24}{}$

⑦ $\dfrac{28}{44} = \dfrac{7}{}$

Write the fractions as decimals.

⑧ $\dfrac{57}{100} = $ _____

⑨ $\dfrac{7}{10} + \dfrac{9}{100} = $ _____

⑩ $\dfrac{19}{50} = $ _____

Compare each pair of fractions. Put > or < in the circles.

⑪ $\dfrac{2}{3} \bigcirc \dfrac{5}{9}$

⑫ $\dfrac{3}{4} \bigcirc \dfrac{4}{5}$

⑬ $\dfrac{3}{8} \bigcirc \dfrac{1}{2}$

Find the answers.

⑭
```
    5.98
  + 7.23
  _____
```

⑮
```
    7.16
  − 2.97
  _____
```

⑯
```
    6.23
  x      8
  _____
```

⑰
```
  8 ) 6.32
```

Calculate mentally.

⑱ 15.93 x 100 = _____

⑲ 6.08 ÷ 10 = _____

⑳ 7.8 x 2 x 50 = _____

㉑ 3 x 5 x 20 = _____

㉒ 50 x 17 x 2 = _____

㉓ 32 x 4 x 25 = _____

㉔ 10 x 40 x 3 = _____

㉕ 4 x 27 x 25 = _____

㉖ 50 x 2 x 16 = _____

㉗ 4 x 15 x 20 = _____

ISBN: 978-1-897164-15-0

Count the squares on the grid to estimate the areas of the following shapes to the nearest cm².

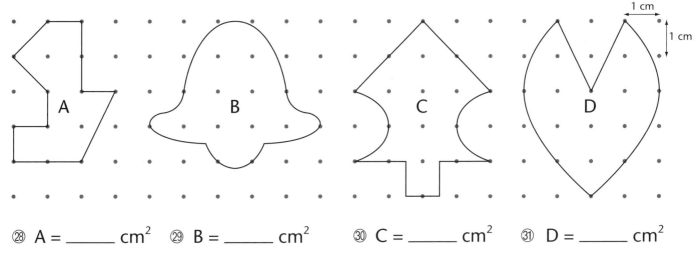

② A = _____ cm²   ② B = _____ cm²   ③ C = _____ cm²   ③ D = _____ cm²

Calculate the perimeter (P) and area (A) of each of the following shapes.

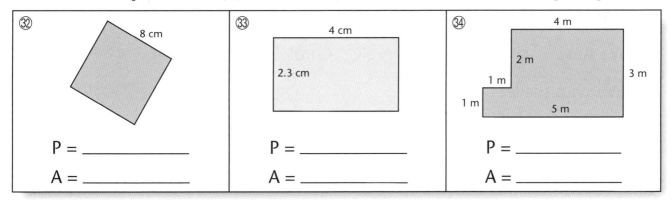

③②
P = _____
A = _____

③③
P = _____
A = _____

③④
P = _____
A = _____

Calculate the volume (V) of each of the following objects.

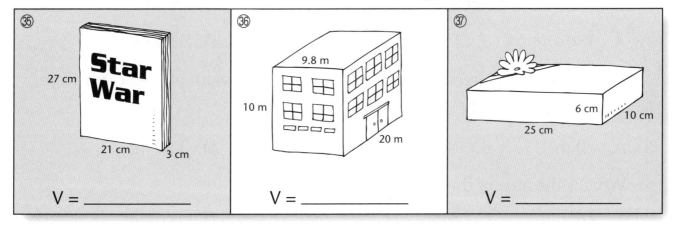

③⑤
V = _____

③⑥
V = _____

③⑦
V = _____

Find the answers.

③⑧ Fast Freddie runs 100 m in 14 seconds. If he starts at 11:58:50, at what time will he reach the finish line? _____

③⑨ John starts his 50-day diet on March 28. On which day will his diet end? _____

ISBN: 978-1-897164-15-0

Circle the letter which represents the correct answer in each problem.

40. A ball has a mass of 50 g. How many of these balls have a total mass of 1 kg?

   A. 2000   B. 200   C. 20   D. 2

41. A large truck has a mass of 10 tonnes. What is its mass in kg?

   A. 2000 kg   B. 5000 kg   C. 1000 kg   D. 10 000 kg

4 friends share 2 pizzas. Amy has $\frac{1}{3}$ of a pizza, Betty has $\frac{1}{4}$, Carol has $\frac{2}{3}$, and Dan has $\frac{7}{12}$.

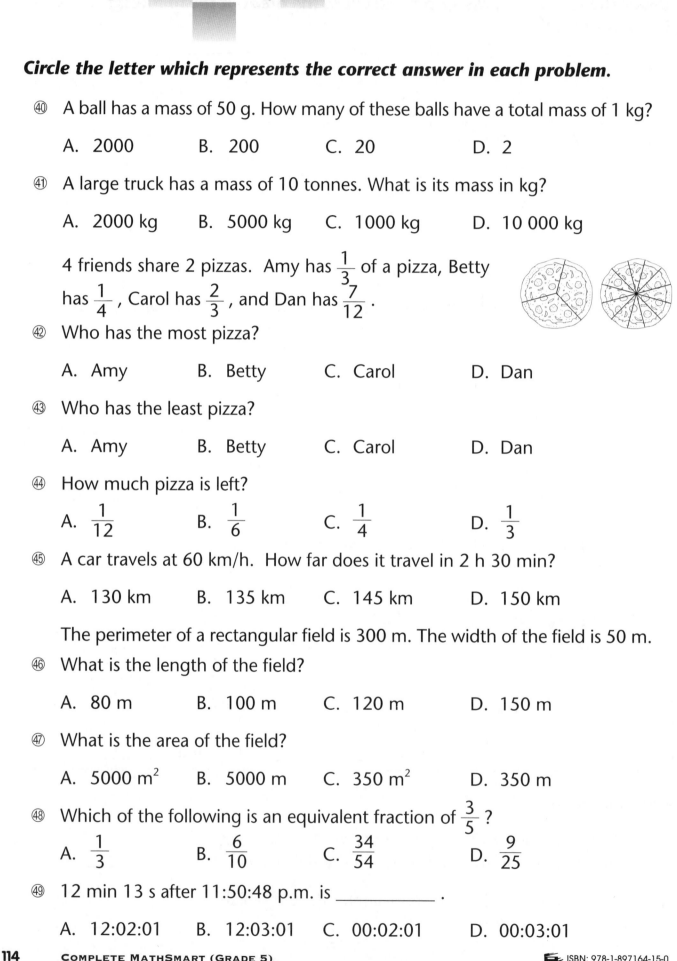

42. Who has the most pizza?

   A. Amy   B. Betty   C. Carol   D. Dan

43. Who has the least pizza?

   A. Amy   B. Betty   C. Carol   D. Dan

44. How much pizza is left?

   A. $\frac{1}{12}$ B. $\frac{1}{6}$ C. $\frac{1}{4}$ D. $\frac{1}{3}$

45. A car travels at 60 km/h. How far does it travel in 2 h 30 min?

   A. 130 km   B. 135 km   C. 145 km   D. 150 km

The perimeter of a rectangular field is 300 m. The width of the field is 50 m.

46. What is the length of the field?

   A. 80 m   B. 100 m   C. 120 m   D. 150 m

47. What is the area of the field?

   A. 5000 m²   B. 5000 m   C. 350 m²   D. 350 m

48. Which of the following is an equivalent fraction of $\frac{3}{5}$?

   A. $\frac{1}{3}$ B. $\frac{6}{10}$ C. $\frac{34}{54}$ D. $\frac{9}{25}$

49. 12 min 13 s after 11:50:48 p.m. is _____ .

   A. 12:02:01   B. 12:03:01   C. 00:02:01   D. 00:03:01

ISBN: 978-1-897164-15-0

Solve the problems. Show your work.

⑤⓪ The aquarium is filled with water to a depth of 20 cm.

a. What is the volume of the water in cm³?

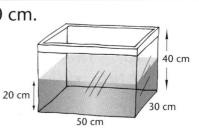

40 cm

20 cm

30 cm

50 cm

b. Some stones are put into the aquarium and the water level is now 25 cm high. What is the volume of the stones in cm³?

c. What is the capacity of the aquarium in L?

⑤① In the school hall, there are 17 rows with 18 chairs each and 3 rows with only 15 chairs each.

a. How many students can be seated in the hall ?

b. If 360 students attend an assembly in the hall, how many students have to stand?

c. There is 1 teacher for every 20 students in the hall. How many teachers are there in the hall?

d. The clock faces show the starting time and the finishing time of the assembly. How long does the assembly last?

8 Angles and 2-D Figures

Measure the size of each angle using a protractor. Then classify each angle as an acute, obtuse, right or straight angle.

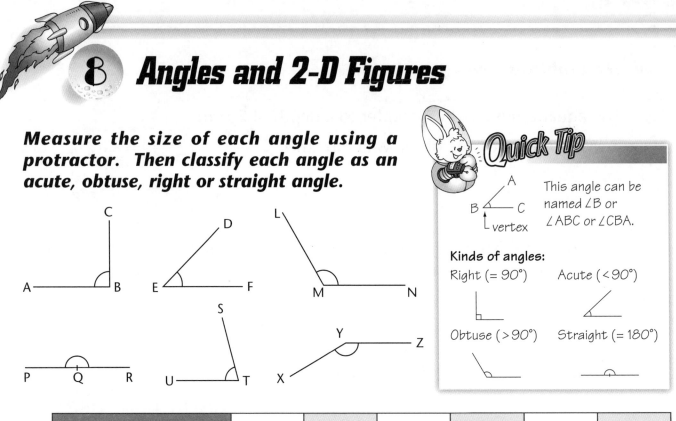

Quick Tip

This angle can be named ∠B or ∠ABC or ∠CBA.

Kinds of angles:
Right (= 90°)   Acute (< 90°)
Obtuse (> 90°)   Straight (= 180°)

Angle	∠ABC	∠DEF	∠LMN	∠PQR	∠STU	∠XYZ
① Size in degrees						
② Kind of angle						

Draw the following angles using a protractor.

③ 68°	④ 135°	⑤ 90°

Complete the triangles. Then measure the angles and lengths.

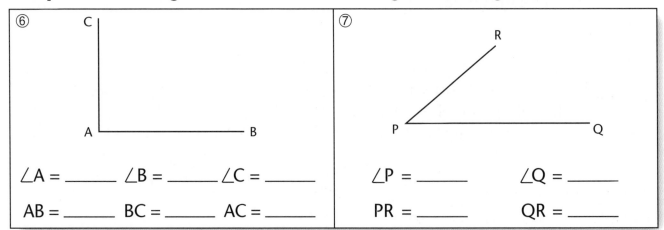

⑥
∠A = _____   ∠B = _____   ∠C = _____
AB = _____   BC = _____   AC = _____

⑦
∠P = _____   ∠Q = _____
PR = _____   QR = _____

ISBN: 978-1-897164-15-0

Classify △ABC and △PQR drawn in ⑥ and ⑦.

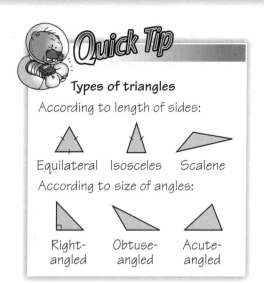

Classification according to	△ ABC	△ PQR
⑧ Length of sides		
⑨ Size of angles		

Quick Tip

Types of triangles

According to length of sides:

Equilateral   Isosceles   Scalene

According to size of angles:

Right-angled   Obtuse-angled   Acute-angled

Draw the triangles.

⑩ A right-angled isosceles triangle	⑪ An obtuse-angled scalene triangle	⑫ An acute-angled isosceles triangle

Look at the new logo designs for LR Inc. and answer the questions.

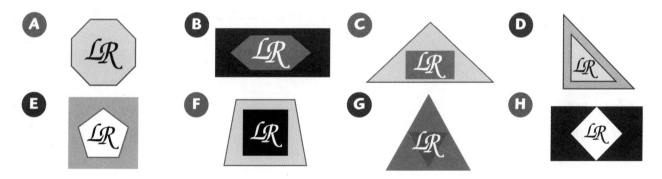

A   B   C   D

E   F   G   H

⑬ Which design is a trapezoid?   _____

⑭ Which design contains a pentagon?   _____

⑮ Which design is an octagon?   _____

⑯ Which design contains a hexagon?   _____

⑰ How many triangles are there altogether?   _____

⑱ How many rectangles are there altogether?   _____

⑲ How many quadrilaterals are there altogether?   _____

Ron has drawn some shapes. For each shape draw all the lines of symmetry and write the number of lines of symmetry in the box.

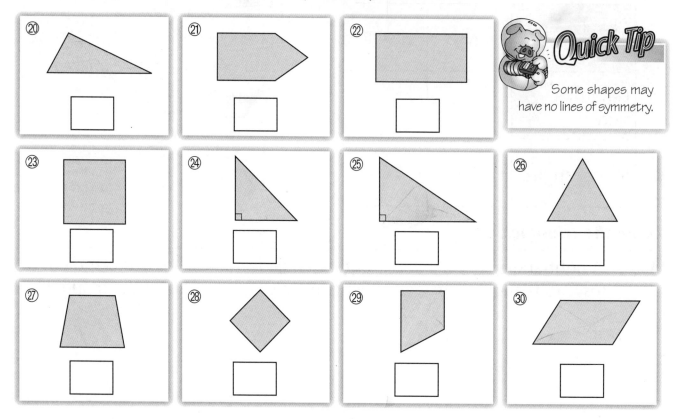

Quick Tip

Some shapes may have no lines of symmetry.

Follow the instructions to construct 2-D figures.

③① Construct a figure with only one vertical line of symmetry using at least 2 of the shapes shown above.

③② Construct 2 different right-angled triangles, both with one side measures 2 cm and the other side measures 3 cm.

Name the following 2-D figures.

③③ _____ ③④ _____ ③⑤ _____ ③⑥ _____

ISBN: 978-1-897164-15-0

For each of the figures on the left, look for its congruent and similar figures on the right. Colour the congruent figure red and the similar figure yellow.

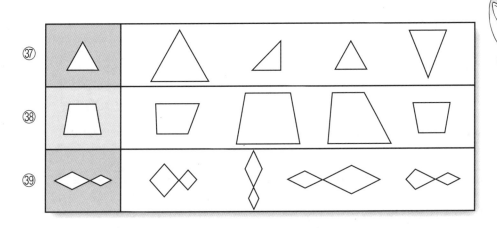

Quick Tip

Congruent figures
- figures with the same shape and size

Similar figures
- figures with the same shape but different sizes

Draw a congruent and a similar figure for each of the following shapes.

Shape	Congruent figure	Similar figure
㊵		
㊶		
㊷		

MIND BOGGLER

Think and count.

How many squares are there altogether?

There are _____ squares.

ISBN: 978-1-897164-15-0

9 3-D Figures

Look at the following 3-D figures and answer the questions.

Cube	Rectangular prism	Rectangular pyramid	Cone	Cylinder

① What is the shape of each face of a cube? _____

② How many faces does a cube have? _____

③ What is the shape of each face of a rectangular prism? _____

④ How many faces does a rectangular pyramid have?
    Write the names of its faces. _____

⑤ Which solids have a curved surface? _____

⑥ What is the shape of the base of those solids which
    have a curved surface? _____

⑦ How many vertices does a rectangular prism have? _____

⑧ How many edges does a cube have? _____

⑨ How many polyhedra are there? _____

⑩ What are they?

_____

> **Quick Tip**
> A polyhedron is a 3-D solid that has only polygonal surfaces. Polyhedra is the plural of polyhedron.

Which of the following nets make a cube? Put a check mark ✔ in the box.

⑪

A

B

C

D

E

> **Quick Tip**
> A net is a 2-D layout for a 3-D solid.

  ISBN: 978-1-897164-15-0

Look at the following pyramids. Complete the table and the statements.

⑫ Number of vertices				
⑬ Number of edges				
⑭ Number of faces				
⑮ Number of triangular faces				
⑯ Shape of base				

⑰ The number of _____ and the number of _____ are the same.

⑱ The number of _____ equals the number of sides of the base.

⑲ The number of _____ is twice the number of sides of the base.

⑳ The number of vertices is _____ more than the number of sides of the base.

Quick Tip

vertex

edge

base

triangular face

Which of the following nets make a pyramid? Put a check mark ✔ in the box.

㉑

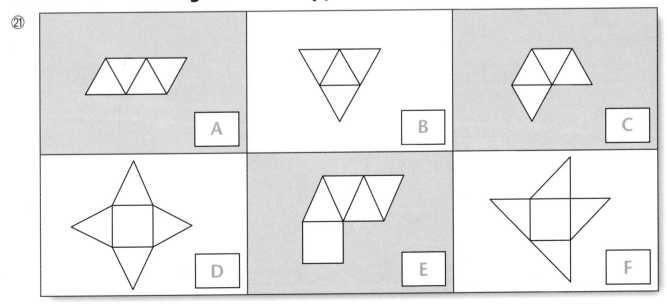

A

B

C

D

E

F

Read the clues and name the solids. The following figures may help you guess the answers.

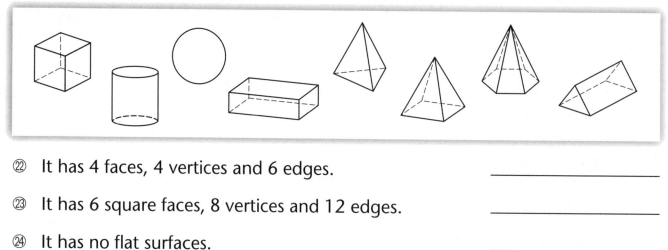

㉒ It has 4 faces, 4 vertices and 6 edges. _____

㉓ It has 6 square faces, 8 vertices and 12 edges. _____

㉔ It has no flat surfaces. _____

㉕ It has only 2 flat surfaces. _____

㉖ It has 7 faces, 7 vertices and 12 edges. _____

㉗ It has 5 faces, 6 vertices and 9 edges. _____

㉘ It has 6 rectangular faces, 8 vertices and 12 edges. _____

Write the name of the polyhedron which can be made from each net below.

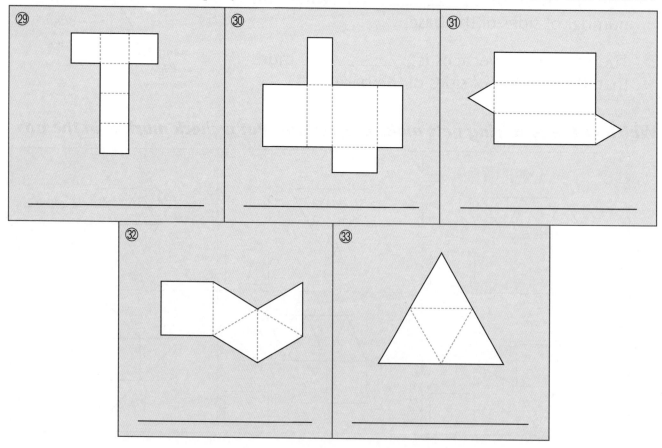

ISBN: 978-1-897164-15-0

Write the name of each solid.

Top view	▲	⊙	▪	▽	▭
Side view	▲	△	▪	▢	▬
Name of the solid	㉞	㉟	㊱	㊲	㊳

Lali uses cubes to build different structures. Draw what he sees if he looks at the structures from the top, front or side.

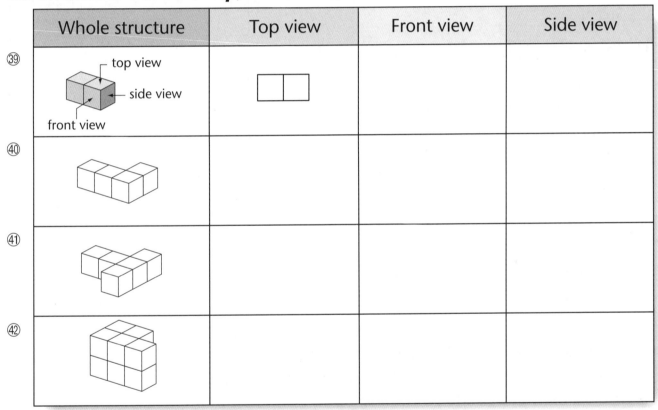

	Whole structure	Top view	Front view	Side view
㊴	top view / side view / front view	▭		
㊵				
㊶				
㊷				

MIND BOGGLER

How to do it?

I can use 3 sticks to form a triangle.

Can you use 9 sticks to form 7 triangles?

ISBN: 978-1-897164-15-0

10 Coordinates and Transformations

In Newton the avenues and streets are laid out in a grid pattern. Plot each of the following sites on the grid and label each with the representing letter and the ordered pair. Then answer the questions.

Quick Tip

The museum (M) is located at the intersection of 2nd Avenue and 5th Street. It is represented on the map by the ordered pair (2, 5).

① The hospital (H) is at 7th Avenue and 1st Street.

② The school (S) is at 4th Avenue and 8th Street.

③ The park (P) is at 6th Avenue and 8th Street.

④ The library (L) is at 5th Avenue and 3rd Street.

⑤ The food court (F) is in the mall at 6th Avenue and 2nd Street.

⑥ The doctor's office (D) is at 2nd Avenue and 1st Street.

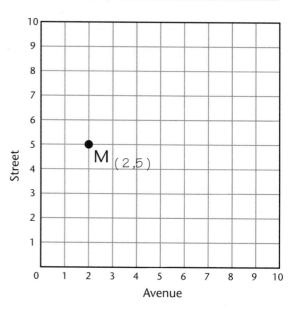

⑦ The video store (V) on 1st Street is the same distance from the library and the hospital. What is the ordered pair of the video store?

_____

⑧ The museum is the same distance from the library and the swimming pool (W). The swimming pool is the same distance from the school and the park. What is the ordered pair of the swimming pool?

_____

⑨ The library is of equal distance from two different places. What are they?

_____

⑩ What is 3 units down and 4 units right from the museum?

_____

⑪ What is 5 units up and 1 unit right from the library?

_____

⑫ Is the museum closer to the doctor's office or the school?

_____

⑬ Is the video store closer to the library or the doctor's office?

_____

ISBN: 978-1-897164-15-0

Help Tia rotate the letters of her name as instructed. Draw the images.

⑭ $\frac{1}{4}$ turn counterclockwise

⑮ $\frac{1}{4}$ turn clockwise

⑯ $\frac{1}{2}$ turn clockwise

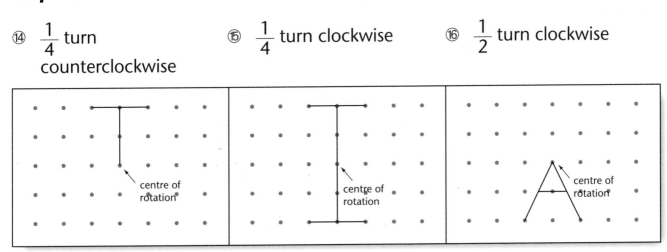

Help Harmit Ali reflect her initials in different lines of reflection. Draw the images.

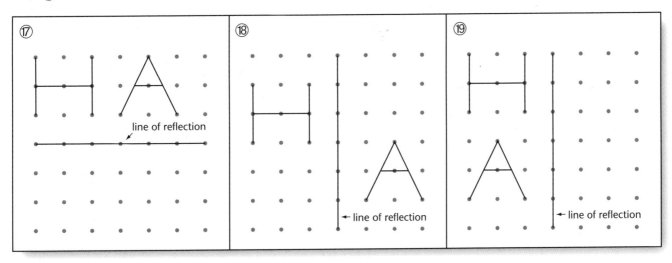

Help Indira Lal translate her initials as described. Draw the images.

⑳ 4 blocks right and 3 blocks down

㉑ 2 blocks up and 4 blocks left

㉒ 2 blocks down and 3 blocks right

Draw the transformed images as instructed and write the ordered pairs of the vertices of the images.

㉓ Translate 4 units down and 5 units left.

㉔ Make a $\frac{1}{2}$ turn clockwise about the centre of rotation.

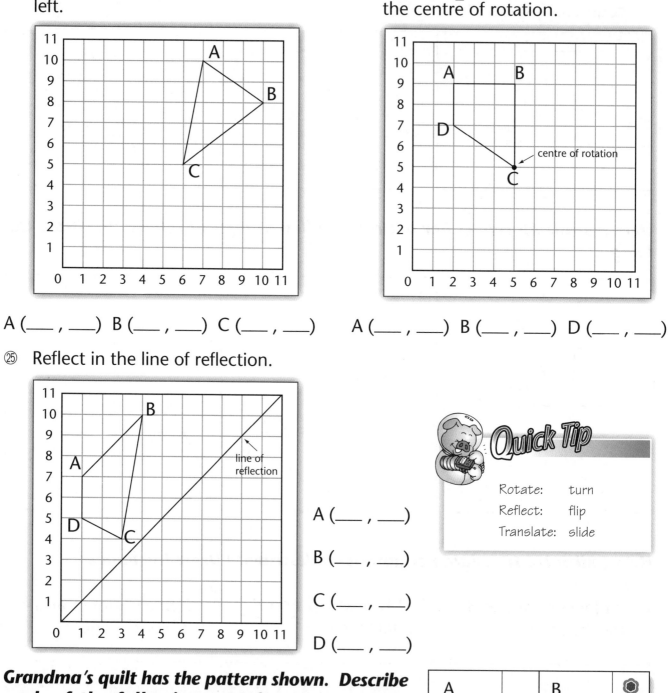

A (__ , __) B (__ , __) C (__ , __)

A (__ , __) B (__ , __) D (__ , __)

㉕ Reflect in the line of reflection.

A (__ , __)

B (__ , __)

C (__ , __)

D (__ , __)

Grandma's quilt has the pattern shown. Describe each of the following transformations using reflection, rotation or translation.

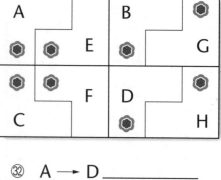

㉖ A → B _____

㉗ A → C _____

㉘ A → F _____

㉙ B → D _____

㉚ C → H _____

㉛ E → F _____

㉜ A → D _____

Grandma's pattern can tile a plane. Put a check mark ✔ in the box if the shape can form a tiling pattern.

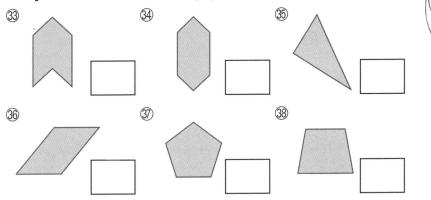

33. □
34. □
35. □
36. □
37. □
38. □

Quick Tip

The tiles in the tiling pattern cover the paper without gaps or overlapping. All the tiles in a tiling pattern are congruent. Each tile can be moved onto a nearby tile by a reflection, rotation or translation.

Look at the triangles drawn on the grid and answer the questions. Write the letters only.

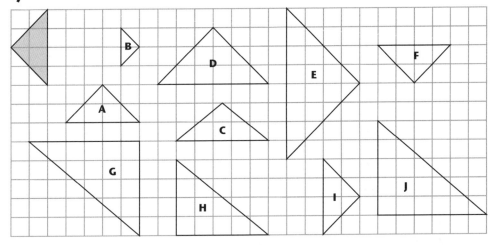

39. Which triangles are congruent to the shaded triangle? _____

40. Which triangles are similar to the shaded triangle? _____

MIND BOGGLER

Complete a parallelogram.

① On the grid provided, plot the following points.

A (4,7)   B (2,5)   C (4,4)

② Write the coordinates of the 4th point so that the four points form a parallelogram. There are 3 possible answers. Plot all the possible 4th points.

The 4th point can be _____ .

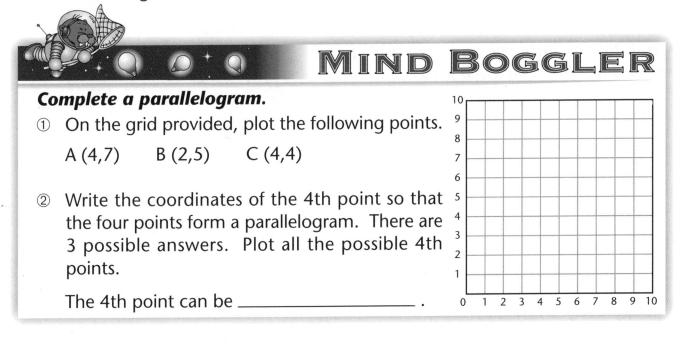

11 Patterns

Fill in the empty boxes in the following patterns.

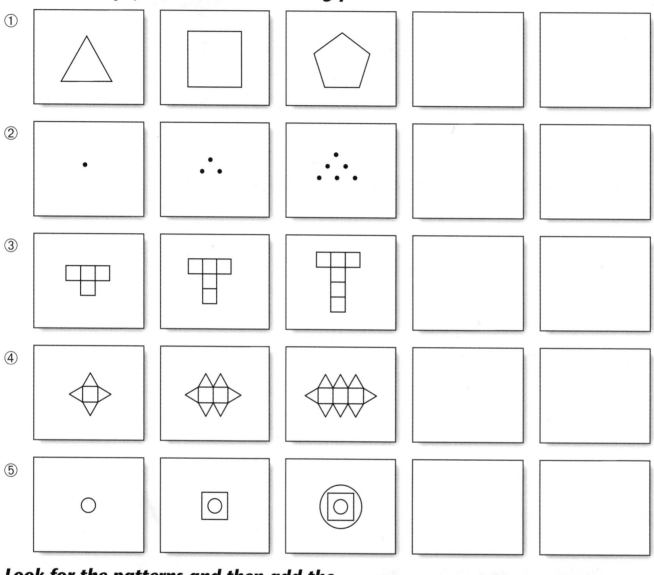

Look for the patterns and then add the next 3 numbers for each pattern.

⑥ 1, 3, 5, 7, _____ , _____ , _____

⑦ 1, 2, 4, 8, _____ , _____ , _____

⑧ 1, 3, 6, 10, _____ , _____ , _____

⑨ 12, 10, 8, 6, _____ , _____ , _____

⑩ 21, 20, 18, 15, _____ , _____ , _____

⑪ 1600, 800, 400, 200, _____ , _____ , _____

⑫ 6, 16, 116, 1116, _____ , _____ , _____

Quick Tip

Analyse the patterning rule before you extend the pattern,

e.g. 10, 20, 30, ...

Each number in this pattern is 10 more than the previous number. This number pattern with 3 more terms is :

10, 20, 30, <u>40</u>, <u>50</u>, <u>60</u>

ISBN: 978-1-897164-15-0

Describe in words the patterns of the numbers in the following number sequences.

⑬ 6, 11, 16, 21, ... _____

⑭ 5, 10, 20, 40, ... _____

⑮ 62, 55, 48, 41, ... _____

⑯ 480, 240, 120, 60, ... _____

Saiko and Suniko made up some code and so they can send secret messages to each other. Look for the letter patterns and complete the tables below to find the codes by continuing the patterns. Help them decode the messages.

⑰

A	B	D	G			
1	2	3	4	5	6	7

⑱

C	E	H	L		
8	9	10	11	12	13

⑲

F	I	M		
14	15	16	17	18

⑳

J	N	S	
19	20	21	22

㉑ If O,T,Z and U are represented by 23, 24, 25 and 26 respectively, decode this message sent by Saiko to Suniko.

11, 9, 24, 21   4, 23   24, 23   1   16, 23, 7, 15, 9   24, 23, 20, 15, 4, 10, 24

_____

㉒ Suniko sends a reply to Saiko. Decode her message.

13, 10, 15, 8, 10   16, 23, 7, 15, 9   3, 23   22, 23, 26   13, 1, 10, 24

24, 23   21, 9, 9 ?

_____

Identify changes in terms of two variables and extend the patterns. Fill in the missing numbers.

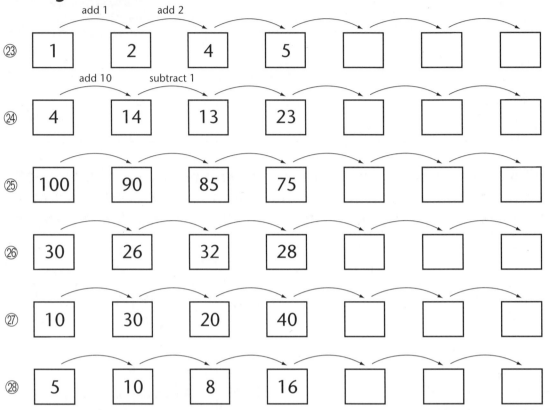

㉓
add 1	add 2					
1	2	4	5			

㉔
add 10	subtract 1					
4	14	13	23			

㉕
| 100 | 90 | 85 | 75 | | | |

㉖
| 30 | 26 | 32 | 28 | | | |

㉗
| 10 | 30 | 20 | 40 | | | |

㉘
| 5 | 10 | 8 | 16 | | | |

For each group of numbers, write the rule that you can use to obtain the 2nd number from the 1st number. Then follow the rule to write two more pairs of numbers for each group.

㉙
1st number	2	3	5		
2nd number	6	9	15		

Rule : _____

_____

㉚
1st number	12	18	24		
2nd number	6	9	12		

Rule : _____

_____

㉛
1st number	1	4	7		
2nd number	1	7	13		

Rule : _____

_____

㉜
1st number	4	6	10		
2nd number	3	4	6		

Rule : _____

_____

ISBN: 978-1-897164-15-0

Look at the pattern that grows as you add triangles with toothpicks. Draw two more diagrams, complete the table and answer the questions.

③③

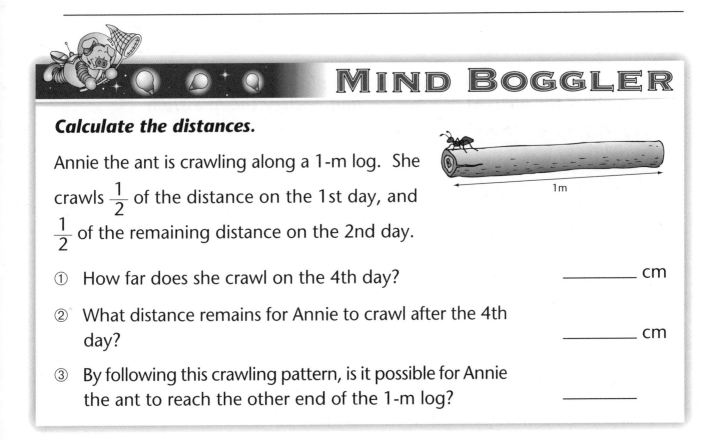

△ → ◁▷ → ◁▷◁ → [   ] → [   ]

1 triangle   2 triangles   3 triangles   4 triangles   5 triangles

③④

Number of triangles	1	2	3	4	5	6	7	8
Number of toothpicks	3	5	7					

③⑤ How many toothpicks are used to make a pattern with 10 triangles? _____ toothpicks

③⑥ How many triangles can be formed using 27 toothpicks? _____ triangles

③⑦ What is the pattern of the number of toothpicks shown in ③④?

_____

③⑧ Describe a rule that relates the number of triangles to the number of toothpicks.

_____

_____

MIND BOGGLER

Calculate the distances.

Annie the ant is crawling along a 1-m log. She crawls $\frac{1}{2}$ of the distance on the 1st day, and $\frac{1}{2}$ of the remaining distance on the 2nd day.

1m

① How far does she crawl on the 4th day? _____ cm

② What distance remains for Annie to crawl after the 4th day? _____ cm

③ By following this crawling pattern, is it possible for Annie the ant to reach the other end of the 1-m log? _____

12 Using Patterns and Simple Equations

Fabio and Sylvia put money in their piggy banks. Complete the tables to show the patterns of their savings and answer the questions.

① Fabio's savings

Day	1	2	3	4	5	6	7	8
Savings (¢)	20	30	40					

② On which day will Fabio put one dollar into his piggy bank?   Day _____

③ How much will Fabio put into the piggy bank on Day 12? $ _____

④ Sylvia's savings

Day	1	2	3	4	5	6	7	8
Savings (¢)	55	60	65					

⑤ On which day will Sylvia put one dollar into her piggy bank?   Day _____

⑥ How much will Sylvia put into the piggy bank on Day 12? $ _____

Ms. Ling's science class is growing bean plants from seeds. Complete the table to show the pattern of growing and answer the questions.

Day	3	4	5	6	7	8
⑦ Number of seeds sprouted	2	4	6			
⑧ Height of the tallest plant (cm)	0.5	1.0	1.5			

⑨ How many seeds will have sprouted by the 10th day?   _____ seeds

⑩ How long will it take till all 20 seeds have sprouted?   _____ days

⑪ When will the tallest plant reach 3.5 cm?   Day _____

⑫ What is the height of the tallest plant on Day 10?   _____ cm

ISBN: 978-1-897164-15-0

Ms. White's Grade 5 class has collected food items for the local food bank for 9 weeks. Help the children solve the problems.

⑬ Complete the table by continuing the pattern.

Week	1	2	3	4	5	6	7	8	9
Number of items collected	2	4	8	10	14				

⑭ Describe in words the pattern shown in the table.

_____

⑮ How many items has the class collected over the
9 weeks?   _____

Mrs. Wong put $250 in a special account when her son, Rob, was born. The account doubles in value every 5 years. Help them solve the problems.

⑯ Complete the table to find out how much money Rob will have when he is 20 years old.

Age	at birth	5	10	15	20
Amount ($)	250				

⑰ Rob decides to buy a used car for $1000 on his 20th birthday and invests the rest of the money in an account which doubles in value for every 6 years. Complete the table below to find out how much money Rob will have when he is 38 years old.

Age	20			
Amount ($)				

⑱ Which account is a better investment, the one which doubles every 6 years or the one which doubles every 5 years? Explain.

_____

_____

_____

The table below shows how the mass of Gerry the Gerbil increases as he gets older. Solve the problems.

⑲ Complete the table by continuing the pattern.

Age (Week)	at birth	1	2	3	4	5	6
Mass (g)	20	30	35	45	50		

⑳ Describe in words the pattern shown in the table.

_____

㉑ If this pattern continues, when will he have a mass of 90 g? _____

㉒ Pam says that as Gerry's age doubles, his mass also doubles. Is that true? Explain.

_____

Ali, Ben, Shari and Sam are training for athletic meets. Help them solve the problems.

㉓ Ali is a sprinter. He runs the same distance each day. On the 1st day, it takes him 5 min 36 s. On the 2nd day, it takes him 5 min 30 s, and on the 3rd day, it takes him 5 min 24 s. Assume that this trend continues,

   a. how long will his run take on the 5th day? _____

   b. when will his run take 5 minutes? _____

㉔ Ben is a long distance runner. He runs many times around the track. The 1st lap takes 5 min, the 2nd 5 min 20 s, and the 3rd 5 min 40 s.

   a. How long will his 6th lap take? _____

   b. Which lap will take him 7 min? _____

㉕ Shari is a long jumper. She jumps 2.5 m on Day 1, 2.55 m on Day 2, and 2.6 m on Day 3. If this trend continues,

   a. how far will she jump on Day 5? _____

   b. when will she jump 3 m? _____

㉖ Sam is a high jumper. He jumps 1.42 m in the 1st attempt, 1.43 m in the 2nd attempt, and 1.44 m in the 3rd attempt. If this trend continues,

   a. how high will he jump in the 5th attempt? _____

   b. In which attempt will he jump 1.5 m? _____

ISBN: 978-1-897164-15-0

Fill in the missing numbers in the following equations.

㉗ $17 + \underline{\hspace{1cm}} = 26$

㉘ $39 - \underline{\hspace{1cm}} = 11$

Quick Tip

Use the guess-and-test method to find the missing terms or factors in simple equations.

㉙ $2 \times \underline{\hspace{1cm}} = 20$

㉚ $50 \div \underline{\hspace{1cm}} = 25$

㉛ $93 + \underline{\hspace{1cm}} = 209$

㉜ $15 \times \underline{\hspace{1cm}} = 450$

㉝ $720 \div \underline{\hspace{1cm}} = 36$

㉞ $150 \div \underline{\hspace{1cm}} = 3$

㉟ $7 \times \underline{\hspace{1cm}} = 630$

㊱ $\underline{\hspace{1cm}} \div 2 = 17$

㊲ $502 - \underline{\hspace{1cm}} = 410$

㊳ $10 \times \underline{\hspace{1cm}} = 5$

㊴ $52 \times \underline{\hspace{1cm}} = 5.2$

㊵ $12 \times \underline{\hspace{1cm}} = 0.12$

㊶ $12 \div \underline{\hspace{1cm}} = 1.2$

㊷ $1.2 \div \underline{\hspace{1cm}} = 0.6$

㊸ $10 \times \underline{\hspace{1cm}} = 12$

㊹ $15 \times \underline{\hspace{1cm}} = 1.5$

㊺ $5.9 + \underline{\hspace{1cm}} = 7.3$

㊻ $12.7 - \underline{\hspace{1cm}} = 6.8$

㊼ $\underline{\hspace{1cm}} - 3.4 = 7.8$

㊽ $1.2 \times \underline{\hspace{1cm}} = 6.0$

㊾ $3.7 \times \underline{\hspace{1cm}} = 370$

㊿ $49 \div \underline{\hspace{1cm}} = 4.9$

� $\underline{\hspace{1cm}} \div 5 = 1.2$

㊬ $\underline{\hspace{1cm}} \div 8 = 12$

㊭ $\underline{\hspace{1cm}} \times 3 = 36$

Check ✔ the right equations.

(54) 6 more than a number y is 15.

| A | $6 - y = 15$ | | B | $6 + y = 15$ | | C | $y - 6 = 15$ |

(55) 4 less than a number b is 12.

| A | $b + 4 = 12$ | | B | $4 - b = 12$ | | C | $b - 4 = 12$ |

(56) 3 times a number p is 27.

| A | $3 \times p = 27$ | | B | $p \div 3 = 27$ | | C | $3 \div p = 27$ |

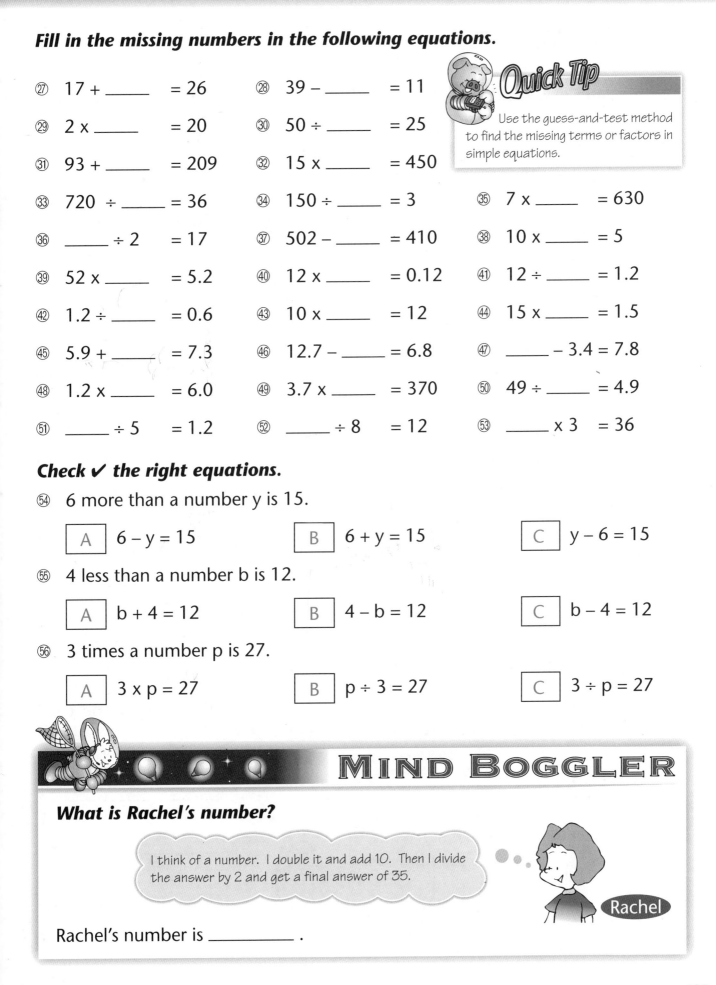

MIND BOGGLER

What is Rachel's number?

I think of a number. I double it and add 10. Then I divide the answer by 2 and get a final answer of 35.

Rachel

Rachel's number is _____ .

13 Data and Graphs

The teachers at a local school were asked what types of cars they drive. The results of the survey are shown in the pictograph below.

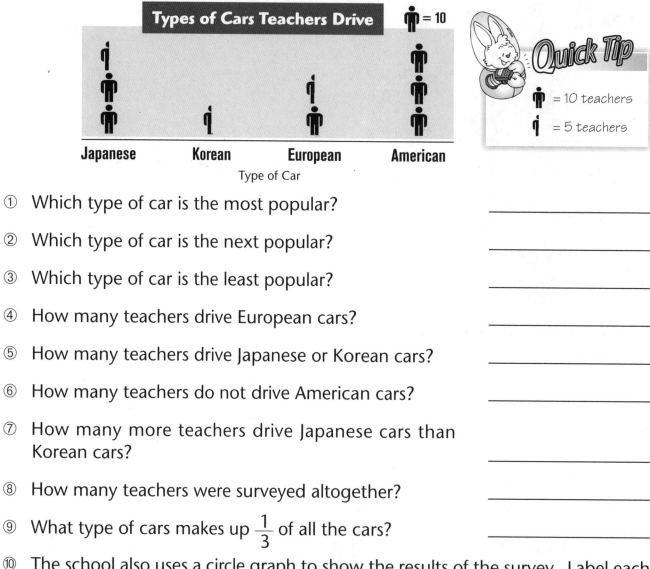

Types of Cars Teachers Drive

👤 = 10

Japanese   Korean   European   American

Type of Car

Quick Tip

👤 = 10 teachers

👤 = 5 teachers

① Which type of car is the most popular? _____

② Which type of car is the next popular? _____

③ Which type of car is the least popular? _____

④ How many teachers drive European cars? _____

⑤ How many teachers drive Japanese or Korean cars? _____

⑥ How many teachers do not drive American cars? _____

⑦ How many more teachers drive Japanese cars than Korean cars? _____

⑧ How many teachers were surveyed altogether? _____

⑨ What type of cars makes up $\frac{1}{3}$ of all the cars? _____

⑩ The school also uses a circle graph to show the results of the survey. Label each sector of the circle with the type of car represented.

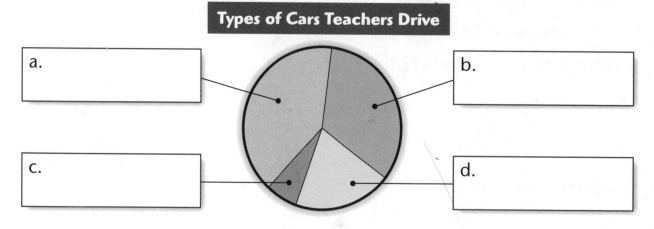

Types of Cars Teachers Drive

a.

b.

c.

d.

ISBN: 978-1-897164-15-0

A group of children surveyed among themselves their favourite ball games on TV. The results of the survey are shown in the graph below.

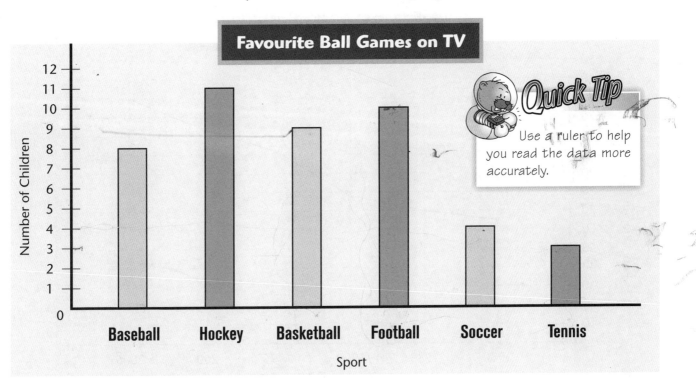

Favourite Ball Games on TV

⑪ Which is the most popular ball game? _____

⑫ Which is the least popular ball game? _____

⑬ How many children chose soccer? _____

⑭ How many children chose football or basketball? _____

⑮ How many more children chose basketball than tennis? _____

⑯ How many fewer children chose soccer than football? _____

⑰ How many types of ball games were chosen by more than 8 children? _____

⑱ How many children did not choose hockey or soccer? _____

⑲ How many children were surveyed altogether? _____

⑳ What fraction of the children surveyed chose football? _____

㉑ 2 girls chose baseball. What fraction of the children who chose baseball are girls? _____

㉒ What type of graph is used to show the results of this survey? _____

ISBN: 978-1-897164-15-0

The line graph below shows how the population of Bellfield grew between 1980 and 2005. Use the graph to answer the questions.

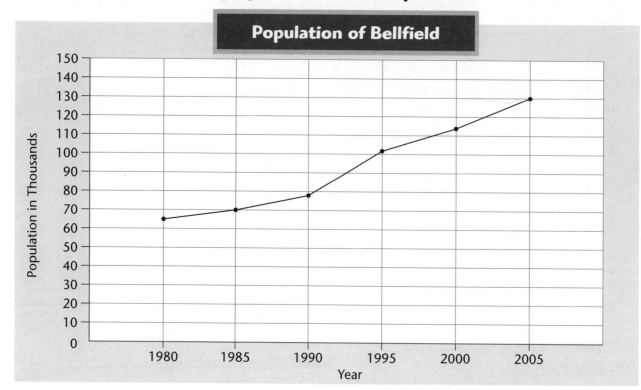

㉓ What was the population in 1980? _____

㉔ What was the population in 2005? _____

㉕ In which year did the population reach 100 000? _____

㉖ What was the increase in population between 1985 and 1990? _____

㉗ What was the increase in population between 1985 and 2005? _____

㉘ During which period did the population increase the least? _____

㉙ During which period did the population increase the most? _____

㉚ If the trend continues, what will be the population in Bellfield in 2010? Explain.

_____

_____

_____

㉛ Which is better for showing population growth, a line graph or a bar graph? Explain.

_____

 ISBN: 978-1-897164-15-0

Example

Josh wrote 9 quizzes. Here are his results (out of 10):

$$2\ 5\ 9\ 7\ 8\ 6\ 7\ 5\ 5$$

What is his mean score?

Mean: $\dfrac{2 + 5 + 9 + 7 + 8 + 6 + 7 + 5 + 5}{9} = 6$ ← Add all the results. Then divide the total by the number of quizzes to get the mean score.

What is the mode of his scores?

The mode is 5.   ← 5 occurs most among the 9 scores.

Mr. Smith conducted a survey in his Grade 5 class. Here are the results from 5 of the students. Help Mr. Smith solve the problems.

	Ali	Steve	Sam	Fabio	Sylvia
Number of pets in family	2	0	1	1	3
Number of children in family	3	2	4	2	1
Distance in km from home to school	5	8	2	7	5

㉜ Find the means. Write your answers correct to 1 decimal place.

Pets in the family _____

Children in the family _____

Distance in km from home to school _____

�33 Find the modes.

Pets in the family _____

Children in the family _____

Distance in km from home to school _____

�34 How many students have more pets than the mean?   _____ students

�35 Sam received a Labrador for his birthday. What are the mean and the mode of the number of pets in the family of these 5 students now?

Mean _____   Mode _____

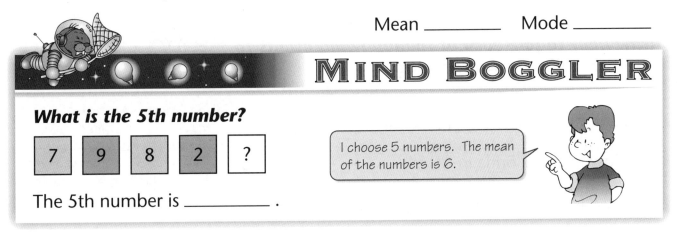

MIND BOGGLER

What is the 5th number?

7	9	8	2	?

I choose 5 numbers. The mean of the numbers is 6.

The 5th number is _____ .

14 Probability

Example

Hannah has 3 shirts – red, white and yellow, and 2 skirts – blue and grey. Her different possible outfits can be shown by using a "tree diagram".

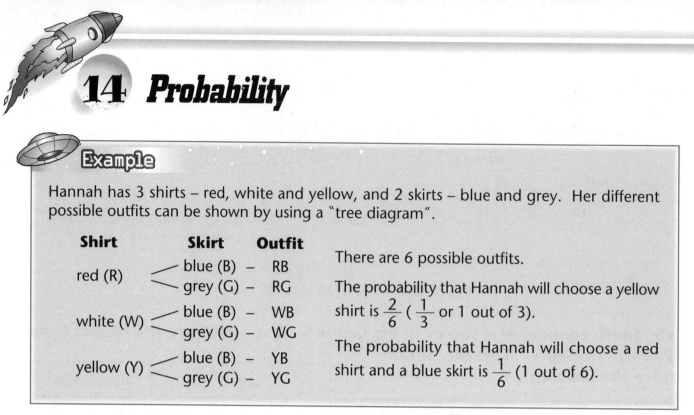

Shirt	Skirt	Outfit
red (R)	blue (B) –	RB
	grey (G) –	RG
white (W)	blue (B) –	WB
	grey (G) –	WG
yellow (Y)	blue (B) –	YB
	grey (G) –	YG

There are 6 possible outfits.

The probability that Hannah will choose a yellow shirt is $\frac{2}{6}$ ($\frac{1}{3}$ or 1 out of 3).

The probability that Hannah will choose a red shirt and a blue skirt is $\frac{1}{6}$ (1 out of 6).

Help Cindy find out the possible choices of poppy seed or sesame seed bagel that may have the filling of tuna (T), egg (E), or cheese (C).

① Complete the tree diagram to show her choices for lunch.

Bagel	Filling	Combination
Poppy seed (P)		
Sesame seed (S)		

② How many possible combinations are there for the lunch? _____

③ What is the probability that she will have a sesame seed bagel? _____

④ What is the probability that she will have tuna on her bagel? _____

⑤ What is the probability that she will have a sesame seed bagel with tuna?

_____

Draw lines to join each of the following events to the probability associated with it.

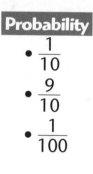

Quick Tip

Event		Probability
⑥ Snow falls in Montreal in January. •		• $\frac{1}{10}$
⑦ Snow falls in Florida in March. •		• $\frac{9}{10}$
⑧ Snow falls in Toronto in March. •		• $\frac{1}{100}$

Probability can be written as fractions with the total possible outcomes as the denominator and the number of outcomes of a particular event as the numerator. The more probable the event, the larger the fraction is.

ISBN: 978-1-897164-15-0

Stephen spins the spinner shown. Help him solve the problems.

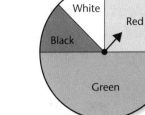

⑨ What colour is the spinner most likely to land on?

Green

⑩ Which colours is the spinner equally likely to land on?

red

⑪ What is the probability that the spinner will land on red?   _likly_

⑫ What is the probability that the spinner will land on green?   _very likly_

⑬ What is the probability that the spinner will land on green or red?

likly

⑭ If Stephen spins the spinner 100 times, how many times is it likely to land on red or green?

_60_

Sarah rolls two dice and adds the numbers that come up. Use her results to solve the problems.

⑮ Complete the table to show all the possible sums.

+	1	2	3	4	5	6
1	2	3	4	5	6	7
2	3	4	5	6	7	8
3	4	5	6	7	8	9
4	5	6	7	8	9	10
5	6	7	8	9	10	11
6	7	8	9	10	11	12

Quick Tip

Addition table

1 + 2 = 3

+	1	2	3
1		3	
2			
3	4		

3 + 1 = 4

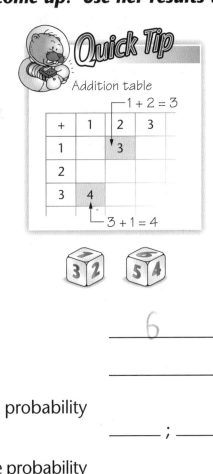

⑯ How many possible sums are there?   _6_

⑰ How many different sums are possible?   _____

⑱ Which sum is most likely to come up? What is the probability to get this sum?   ____ ; ____

⑲ Which sums are least likely to come up? What is the probability to get each sum?   ____ ; ____

⑳ Which sum is as likely to get as 9?   _____

ISBN: 978-1-897164-15-0

In Mr. Keller's Grade 5 class, there are 14 boys and 10 girls. Mr. Keller wants to choose a student to erase the blackboard. Refer to the table below and answer the questions.

Don't forget to write fractions in lowest terms in your answers.

	Boys	Girls	Total no. of children
Number of children	14	10	24
Number of children with fair hair	4	8	12
Number of children with dark hair	10	2	12
Number of children born in Canada	12	6	18
Number of children born outside Canada	2	4	6

㉑ What is the probability that a girl will be chosen? _____ $\frac{10}{24}$

㉒ Is it more probable that Mr. Keller will choose a boy or a girl? _____ boy

㉓ What is the probability that a student born in Canada will be chosen? _____

㉔ What is the probability that a girl born in Canada will be chosen? _____ $\frac{6}{24}$

㉕ What is the probability that a boy with fair hair will be chosen? _____

㉖ Is it less probable for Mr. Keller to choose a girl with fair hair than the one with dark hair? _____

㉗ Mr. Keller wants to choose a girl to erase the blackboard. What is the probability that a girl with fair hair will be chosen? _____

㉘ On Monday, 1 girl and 2 boys were absent. What was the probability that Mr. Keller would choose a girl? _____

㉙ 3 new students, 1 boy and 2 girls, are added to Mr. Keller's class. They have recently arrived in Canada. What is the probability now that a boy born outside Canada will be chosen? _____

ISBN: 978-1-897164-15-0

Riverview School is going to have its annual barbecue. The weather forecast says that there is a 1 out of 4 chance of rain on the day of the barbecue. The circle graphs below show the food, drinks and snacks prepared by the school. Refer to the graphs and answer the questions.

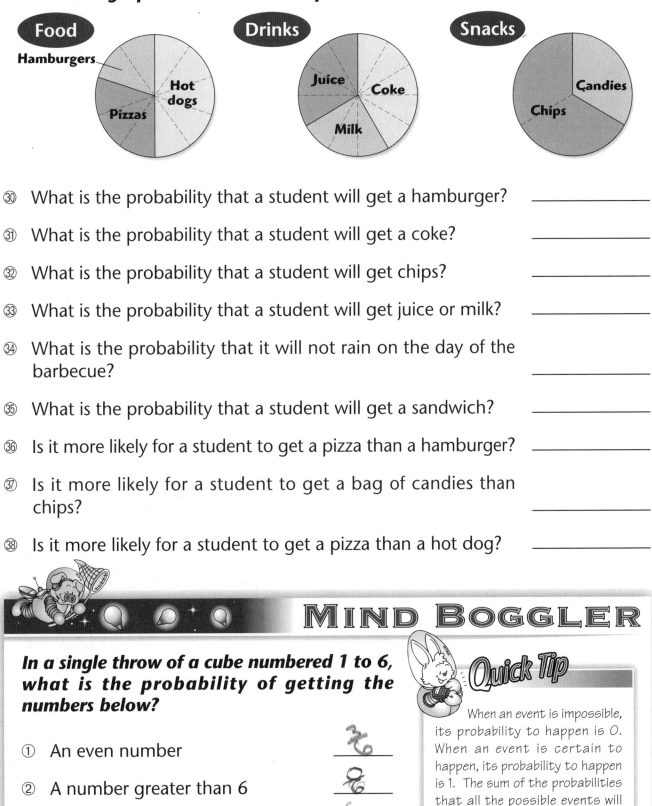

Food — Hamburgers, Hot dogs, Pizzas

Drinks — Juice, Coke, Milk

Snacks — Candies, Chips

30 What is the probability that a student will get a hamburger? _____

31 What is the probability that a student will get a coke? _____

32 What is the probability that a student will get chips? _____

33 What is the probability that a student will get juice or milk? _____

34 What is the probability that it will not rain on the day of the barbecue? _____

35 What is the probability that a student will get a sandwich? _____

36 Is it more likely for a student to get a pizza than a hamburger? _____

37 Is it more likely for a student to get a bag of candies than chips? _____

38 Is it more likely for a student to get a pizza than a hot dog? _____

MIND BOGGLER

In a single throw of a cube numbered 1 to 6, what is the probability of getting the numbers below?

① An even number $\frac{3}{6}$

② A number greater than 6 $\frac{0}{6}$

③ Any of the numbers from 1 to 6 $\frac{6}{6}$

Quick Tip

When an event is impossible, its probability to happen is 0. When an event is certain to happen, its probability to happen is 1. The sum of the probabilities that all the possible events will happen is 1.

ISBN: 978-1-897164-15-0

Final Test

Circle the letter which represents the correct answer in each problem.

① Triangle ABC is a/an ____ triangle.
   A. obtuse-angled   B. equilateral
   C. isosceles   D. right

② The shape of the stop sign is a/an ____ .
   A. quadrilateral   B. pentagon
   C. hexagon   D. octagon

③ Two triangles are similar if they
   A. have the same shape and size.
   B. have the same shape but different sizes.
   C. are both scalene triangles.
   D. are both right triangles.

④ The capital letter H has ____ lines of symmetry.
   A. 0   B. 1   C. 2   D. 3

⑤ A is a/an ____ angle.
   A. acute   B. obtuse
   C. reflex   D. right

⑥ The net on the right is for a ____ .
   A. square pyramid   B. triangular pyramid
   C. cube   D. rectangular pyramid

⑦ A solid with only 4 triangular faces is a ____ .
   A. tetrahedron   B. cone   C. pyramid   D. prism

⑧ The coordinates of point A are ____ .
   A. (0,4)   B. (3,0)
   C. (0,3)   D. (4,0)

⑨ The coordinates of the image of point A after rotating
   through a quarter turn clockwise about (0,0) are ____ .
   A. (0,4)   B. (3,0)   C. (0,3)   D. (4,0)

⑩ A bag contains 5 blue marbles and 25 green marbles. The probability of picking
   a blue marble is ____ .
   A. $\frac{1}{5}$ B. $\frac{1}{6}$ C. $\frac{1}{3}$ D. $\frac{4}{5}$

ISBN: 978-1-897164-15-0

⑪ The transformation which maps A onto B is _____ .

A. Reflection   B. Rotation

C. Translation   D. None of these

⑫ The transformation which maps A onto C is _____ .

A. Reflection   B. Rotation

C. Translation   D. None of these

⑬ The transformation which maps A onto E is _____ .

A. Reflection   B. Rotation

C. Translation   D. None of these

The tiling pattern for questions ⑪ – ⑭.

⑭ The transformation which maps B onto G is _____ .

A. Reflection   B. Rotation

C. Translation   D. None of these

⑮ The fraction of time in a day that Sam spends sleeping is _____ .

A. $\frac{1}{3}$ B. $\frac{1}{4}$

C. $\frac{1}{5}$ D. $\frac{1}{6}$

Sam's Daily Activities

⑯ Sam spends $\frac{1}{6}$ of the day _____ .

A. sleeping   B. eating   C. relaxing   D. in school

⑰ The perimeter of the square is _____ .

A. 52 cm   B. 52 cm^2

C. 169 cm   D. 169 cm^2

13 cm

13 cm

⑱ The area of the square is _____ .

A. 52 cm   B. 52 cm^2 C. 169 cm   D. 169 cm^2

⑲ The next 3 numbers in the pattern 4, 5, 7, 8, 10, ... are _____ .

A. 11, 12, 13   B. 11, 13, 14   C. 10, 11, 12   D. 10, 12, 13

⑳ The value of ☐ in 5 x ☐ = 7.05 is _____ .

A. 2.05   B. 1.5   C. 35.25   D. 1.41

㉑ The mean of 2 numbers is 12. One of the numbers is 5. The other number is _____ .

A. 7   B. 8.5   C. 19   D. 17

㉒ The value of ☐ in ☐ ÷ 100 = 5.2 is _____ .

A. 520   B. 52   C. 0.52   D. 0.052

㉓ The value of ☐ in ☐ x 0.1=1.73 is _____ .

A. 1730   B. 173   C. 17.3   D. 0.173

㉔ What is the 8th number in the pattern 1,2,3,5,8,...?

A. 23   B. 15   C. 17   D. 34

㉕ 1 slice of cold meat has a mass of 40 g. How many slices of meat have a mass of 1 kg?

A. 2.5   B. 25   C. 5   D. 50

㉖ Avi started his run around the track at 3:58:40 and finished at 4:02:15. How long was his run?

A. 3 min 35 s   B. 4 min 25 s   C. 3 min 25 s   D. 4 min 35 s

㉗ The area of the shaded parallelogram is _____ square units.

A. 5   B. 6
C. 5.5   D. 6.5

㉘ The decimal 0.85 expressed as a fraction in lowest terms is _____ .

A. $\frac{17}{20}$ B. $\frac{4}{5}$ C. $\frac{8.5}{10}$ D. $\frac{85}{100}$

㉙ The improper fraction $\frac{25}{4}$ expressed as a decimal is _____ .

A. 2.13   B. 25.25   C. 6.25   D. 4.25

㉚ According to the weather forecast for today, the probability of rain is $\frac{1}{4}$, the probability of cloud is $\frac{1}{3}$, the probability of sun is $\frac{1}{5}$, and the probability of a thunderstorm is $\frac{1}{8}$. It is most likely that it will be _____ today.

A. rainy   B. sunny   C. cloudy   D. stormy

ISBN: 978-1-897164-15-0

Answer the questions. Show all your work.

③① In a hall there are 200 people. There are 15 rows of seats and each row has 13 seats. How many people are standing if all the seats are occupied?

③② Briana buys exercise books for her school. Each book costs $1.29.
a. How many books can she get for $10?

b. How much change does she get?

③③ What is the remainder when 5982 is divided by 7? Check your answer.

③④ A rock is put into the water as shown. Calculate the approximate volume of the rock in cm^3.

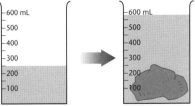

③⑤ Tim earns $10.50 per hour. He works 9 hours a day, 5 days a week.
a. How much does he earn per week?

b. Last Sunday he was paid $78.75 for 5 hours of extra work. How much was his hourly wage on Sunday?

c. How much did he earn last week?

Final Test

The table shows the population of Greensville from 1960 to 2000. Use the data to make a line graph and answer the questions.

㊱

Year	Population in Thousands
1960	60
1970	80
1980	80
1990	120
2000	140

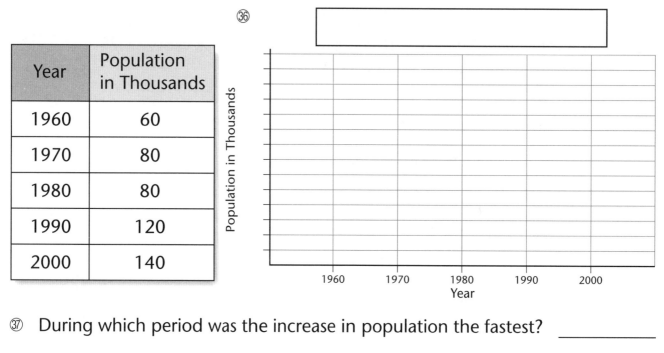

㊲ During which period was the increase in population the fastest? _____

㊳ In which year did the population reach 80 000? _____

㊴ What was the increase in population between 1960 and 2000? _____

㊵ Why is a line graph the best way to represent these data?

_____

This bar graph shows the colours of the cars in a parking lot. Use the graph to answer the questions. Write all fractions in lowest terms.

㊶ Read the graph and complete the table.

Colour	Number of Cars
Black	
White	
Green	
Blue	
Beige	
Red	

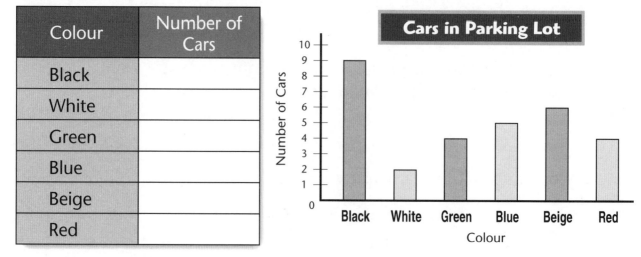

ISBN: 978-1-897164-15-0

㊷ How many cars are there in the parking lot? ________

㊸ What fraction of the cars are beige? ________

㊹ What is the probability to find a blue car in the parking lot? ________

㊺ What is the probability that a car in the parking lot is red or green? ________

㊻ What is the probability that a car in the parking lot is not black? ________

A police officer is monitoring speeding on a suburban road. He records the following speeds of 6 cars in km/h: 50, 40, 45, 50, 84, 55.

㊼ What is the mean (average) speed of these 6 cars? ________ km/h

㊽ What is the mode of these speeds? ________ km/h

㊾ What is the mean speed of the remaining 5 cars after the fastest one is stopped by the police? ________ km/h

㊿ Has the mode changed after that? ________

(51) How long does it take to travel 25 km for a car going at 50 km/h? ________ min

(52) How far can a car travel in $1\frac{1}{2}$ h at an average speed of 45 km/h? ________ km

Look at the different rates offered by an Internet service provider. Answer the questions.

Package A	:	Unlimited use	$39.99 per month
Package B	:	Up to 2 h per day	$27.99 per month
Package C	:	Up to 1 h per day	$14.99 per month

(53) Discuss how you would decide which is the best deal for you.

____

____

____

(54) The Browns use the Internet for $\frac{1}{2}$ h per day in June. Estimate how much Package C costs them per hour. ________

ISBN: 978-1-897164-15-0

Final Test

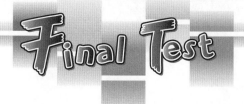

Dave and Dan each have a good collection of sports cards. The pictographs below show their collections.

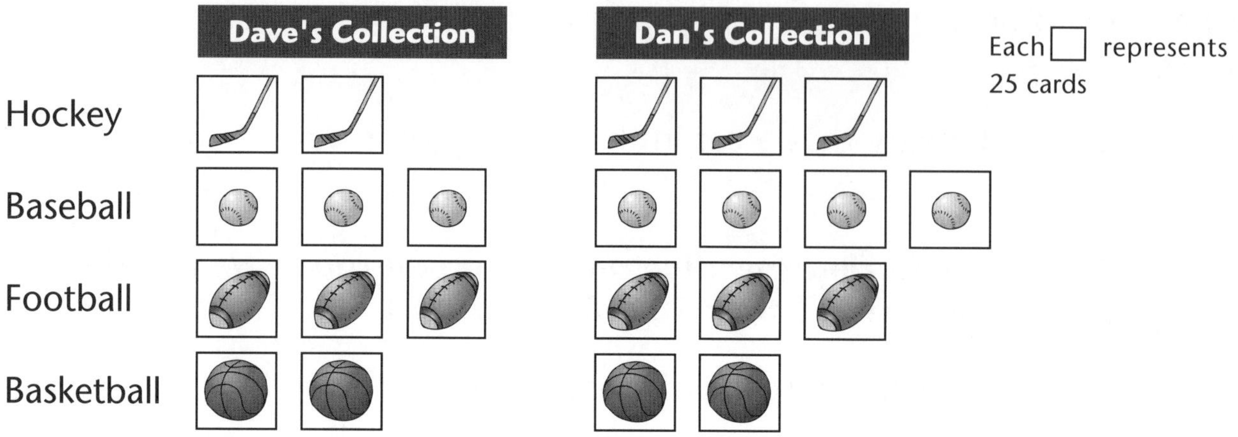

(55) How many cards has Dave collected? ________ cards

(56) How many cards has Dan collected? ________ cards

(57) What fraction of Dave's cards are hockey or baseball cards? ________

(58) What fraction of Dan's cards are basketball cards? ________

(59) How many football cards have they collected altogether? ________ cards

(60) What fraction of their combined card collection are football cards? ________

(61) How many more baseball cards has Dan collected than Dave? ________ cards

(62) If their goal is to collect 1000 cards altogether, how many more cards must they collect? ________ cards

(63) If the average cost of the cards is 5 for $1, what is the total value of their combined card collection? ________

The circle graphs below represent their card collections. Write the names of the sports to label the sectors of each circle.

(64)

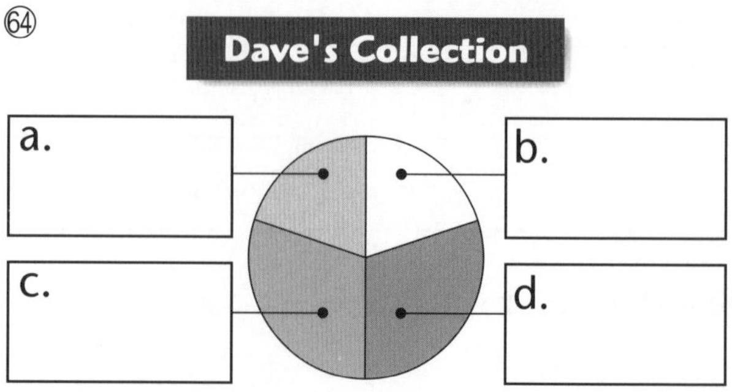

(65)

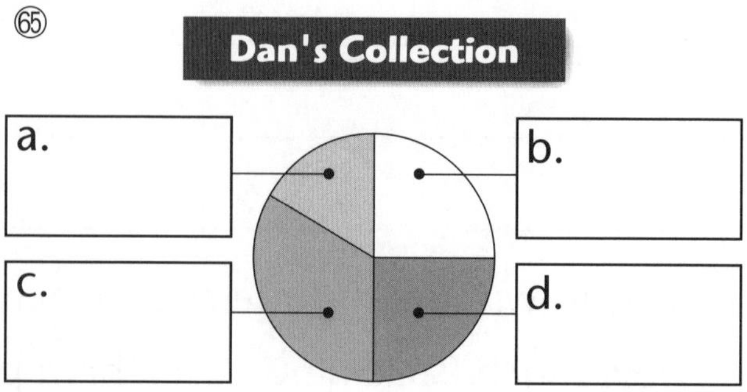

 ISBN: 978-1-897164-15-0

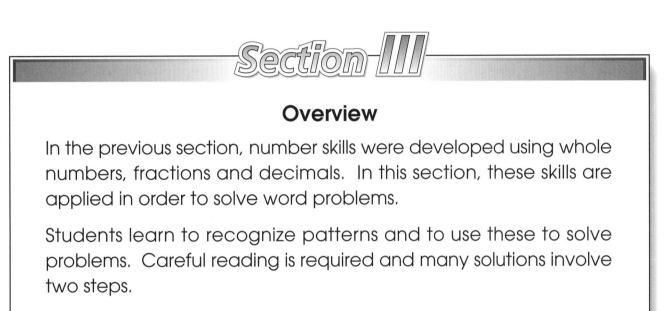

Section III

Overview

In the previous section, number skills were developed using whole numbers, fractions and decimals. In this section, these skills are applied in order to solve word problems.

Students learn to recognize patterns and to use these to solve problems. Careful reading is required and many solutions involve two steps.

Answers are written in full sentences using appropriate units.

ISBN: 978-1-897164-15-0

UNIT 1 Multiplication and Division of Whole Numbers

EXAMPLE

Gary ate 2 cookies each day per week and drank 28 glasses of milk per week. How many cookies and how much milk would he consume in 3 weeks?

Cookies Gary ate in 1 day :   2

Cookies he would eat in 3 weeks : $2 \times 7 \times 3 = 42$

Milk Gary drank in 1 week :   28

Milk he would drink in 3 weeks : $28 \times 3 = 84$

Answer : Gary would consume 42 cookies and 84 glasses of milk in 3 weeks.

Solve the problems. Show your work.

Frank's class has 28 pupils. There are 21 girls and 7 boys. Each pupil is given 3 pencils and 5 books at the beginning of the year. There are 2 extra chairs in the room.

① How many pencils are given out at the beginning of the year?

Answer : _____ pencils are given out at the beginning of the year. _____

② How many more books than pencils are given out at the beginning of the year?

Answer : _____

③ If all the chairs in the room were stacked in piles of 5 for cleaning, how many stacks would there be?

Answer : _____

④ If the girls used 2 pencils each by the end of November, how many pencils belonging to girls would there be in the classroom?

Answer : _____

⑤ For a special activity, the chairs that were being used by pupils in the classroom were to be put in rows of 7. How many rows would there be?

Answer : _____

ISBN: 978-1-897164-15-0

Donny moved into a new house with French doors. Each of these doors had 8 panes of glass. When Donny counted the doors, he found that there were 9 in all. There were also 19 windows with 2 panes of glass in each. The glass was all dirty from construction, and a cleaning company said that they would clean the windows for $5.00 each pane and the doors for $3.00 every 2 panes.

⑥ How many panes of glass are there in the doors?

Answer : _____

⑦ How many panes of glass are there in the windows?

Answer : _____

⑧ How much would it cost to clean the panes of glass in the doors?

Answer : _____

⑨ How much would it cost to clean all the glass in the house?

Answer : _____

Sally was counting her collection of old coins. She had 34 pennies, 9 nickels, 31 dimes and 19 quarters.

⑩ Sally was told that her pennies were worth 11 cents each. What was the value of Sally's pennies?

Answer : _____

⑪ Sally was told that her collection of nickels was worth 135¢. How much was each nickel worth?

Answer : _____

⑫ Her dimes were only worth 14 cents each. What was the value of her collection of dimes?

Answer : _____

⑬ Sally had 5 valuable quarters. They were worth 116¢ each. The rest were worth 76¢ each. What was the value of her quarters?

Answer : _____

⑭ What was the value of her collection?

Answer : _____

⑮ Would it be a good idea to sell her entire collection for 25 cents for each coin?

Answer : _____

September is the first month of school. Wanda's class had homework assigned every day of the month. The homework took 2 hours to complete every night including weekends. All 17 girls in the class thought that this was too much. They only wanted to do 25 hours of homework every 15 days.

⑯ How many hours did Wanda spend on doing homework in September?

Answer : _____

⑰ How many hours did all the girls spend on doing homework in September?

Answer : _____

⑱ If there were 20 school days in September, how many hours of homework would be assigned each school day?

Answer : _____

⑲ If the teacher reduced the amount of homework as the girls requested, how many hours of homework would Wanda have to do in September?

Answer : _____

⑳ How many hours of homework would all the girls have to do in September then?

Answer : _____

Lisa makes 4 phone calls a day to her friends. The telephone company charges for telephone calls at a rate of 2 for $3.00. Each week, Lisa tries to keep track of the amount of money she spends on calling her friends.

㉑ How much does Lisa spend each week on phone calls?

Answer : _____

㉒ How many phone calls would she make in January?

Answer : _____

 ISBN: 978-1-897164-15-0

㉓ How much would her phone calls cost in October?

Answer : _____

㉔ If each day, each call was to a different friend, how much could she save each day by sending them a letter, if a stamp costs 46 cents?

Answer : _____

㉕ Another phone company is offering a rate of 4 calls for $5.00. How much would she save each week by switching companies?

Answer : _____

There are 936 paperbacks and 882 hardcover books in a small library. It takes 36 seconds to dust each book. They are stored on shelves with 26 paperbacks or 21 hardcover books on each shelf.

㉖ How long does it take to dust all the paperback books?

Answer : _____

㉗ How long does it take to dust all the hardcover books?

Answer : _____

㉘ How many shelves of paperback books will there be in the library?

Answer : _____

㉙ How many shelves of hardcover books will there be in the library?

Answer : _____

㉚ If Uncle Bill uses 6 boxes to store the paperback and hardcover books, how many books are in each box?

Answer : _____

Allan is taking stock of the items in his kitchen. He has 1242 grams of raisins, 1896 grams of peanuts, 4 bags of 63 figs each, 5 bags of 32 apricots each, and 486 cookies.

㉛ Allan divides his raisins into 6 bags. How many grams of raisins are there in each bag?

Answer : ______________________

㉜ Allan divides his peanuts into 8 servings. How many grams of peanuts are there in each serving?

Answer : ______________________

㉝ If each fig weighs 15 g, how heavy do Allan's figs weigh?

Answer : ______________________

㉞ Allan and his sister each eat 4 apricots after lunch every day. How long will Allan's apricots last?

Answer : ______________________

㉟ If Allan shares his cookies with 5 of his friends, how many cookies does each person get?

Answer : ______________________

㊱ Allan wants to put his cookies in bags of 5 or in bags of 7. Which way will there be more cookies left over?

Answer : ______________________

㊲ If Allan divides his figs into 3 bags, how many more figs does each bag hold than before?

Answer : ______________________

㊳ If Allan divides his peanuts into small bags each holding 25 grams, how many bags does he need to hold all the peanuts?

Answer : ______________________

㊴ If every 18 grams of raisins costs 12 cents, how much do Allan's raisins cost?

Answer : ______________________

- ***Question 39 is a 2-step problem. First, find how many portions of 18 grams each there are in 1242 grams of raisins. Then multiply the number of portions by the cost.***

ISBN: 978-1-897164-15-0

Solve the problems. Show your work.

40) Karen was collecting pebbles on the beach. After a couple of hours, she collected 308 pebbles. Karen wanted to take them home, but couldn't carry all those pebbles at once. She was going to be at the beach for 4 days. How many pebbles would she have to carry each day?

Answer : _____

41) Larry had 17 CDs. He played them 4 times each on average in a month. If each CD was 1 hour long, how much time would he spend in a year listening to the CDs?

Answer : _____

42) Don's dad had 1648 books. If he could fit 24 books on each shelf, how many shelves would he need?

Answer : _____

43) Peter was planting pansies in his garden. The pansies were planted in rows of 35. There were 23 rows across the garden. How many plants did Peter need?

Answer : _____

44) Peter uses about 45 L of water each day to water his plants. How much water will Peter use in a month of 31 days?

Answer : _____

The number of ants in Quincey's garden seems to double each day. Quincey saw 100 ants on Monday, how many ants might there be on Thursday?

Answer : _____

EXAMPLE

Two students were comparing their marks. Sylvia had 80 and Tim had half of Sylvia's mark plus 10. What was Tim's mark?

Tim's mark: $80 \div 2 + 10 = 40 + 10 = 50$

Answer: Tim's mark was 50.

Use the table below to solve the problems. Show your work.

A group of friends were playing a game. They threw a ball as far as they could in the park, and measured the distances. The person who threw the ball third farthest won 1 point, second farthest, 3 points and farthest, 5 points.

Name	Mario	Sandy	Danny	Jimmy	Dolores
Distance (m)	12	18	14	19	16

① How much farther did Jimmy throw than Sandy?

Jimmy threw _____ farther
Answer: than Sandy. _____

② How far did everyone throw altogether?

Answer: _____

③ If Mario and Jimmy formed a team against Sandy and Dolores, which team threw the ball farther?

Answer: _____

④ If Danny got to double his distance because he had no one on his team, how much farther did the winning team throw than Danny did?

Answer: _____

⑤ The friends thought of a new game. They got to multiply their distance by their score. Who got the highest number? What is the number?

Answer: _____

ISBN: 978-1-897164-15-0

Solve the problems. Show your work.

⑥ How many days are there in a leap year?

Answer: _____

⑦ If there were 56 marbles in a bag, how many marbles would Frank have if he bought 6 bags?

Answer: _____

⑧ A theatre has 47 seats in each row. How many people would fill 12 rows?

Answer: _____

⑨ Bill's father buys paper in 250 sheet packages. If he wants to print 1371 pages, how many packages of paper must he buy?

Answer: _____

⑩ George can ride his bike around a park in 4 minutes. How many times can he ride his bike around the park in 1 hour 20 minutes?

Answer: _____

⑪ Sally collects stamps. She has 482 stamps in her first album, 561 in her second one, and 398 in her third one. How many stamps does she have in all?

Answer: _____

⑫ A jacket costs $75.00. A pair of jeans costs $34.00. If John bought 2 jackets and 3 pairs of jeans, how much should he pay?

Answer: _____

Lorraine was helping out in a lumber yard. There were 2352 pieces of pine, 598 pieces of oak and 28 pieces of maple. Each piece of lumber was 2 metres long.

⑬   How many pieces of lumber did they have in all?

Answer: _____

⑭   How many more pieces of pine did they have than maple?

Answer: _____

⑮   How many more pieces of pine did they have than oak ?

Answer: _____

⑯   How many metres of lumber did they have at the lumber yard?

Answer: _____

⑰   If they sold 269 pieces of oak on Wednesday, how many metres of oak did they have left to sell?

Answer: _____

⑱   If they sold 1568 metres of pine per day, how many days would it take to sell all their pine pieces?

Answer: _____

⑲   If there are 414 metres of oak left over, how many pieces of oak were sold?

Answer: _____

   ISBN: 978-1-897164-15-0

Solve these problems in your head and write the statements.

⑳ Jean works part-time at the mall. She works 2 hours a day for $9.00 an hour. How much did she earn in a five-day week?

Answer: _____

> • The product of multiplication will be the same no matter what order the numbers are in.   ← **Read this first.**
>
> e.g. $4 \times 17 \times 5 = 17 \times 4 \times 5$
> $= 17 \times 20$
> $= 340$

㉑ Tim started his homework at 4:00 p.m. It took him 25 minutes to finish his Math, 17 minutes for his Social Studies and 28 minutes to read the next part of his English book. When did he finish his homework?

Answer: _____

㉒ Mario wanted two CDs. The first one was on sale for $15.00 and the other's regular price was $18.00. If all the prices included taxes and Mario had a twenty-dollar bill, a ten-dollar bill and a five-dollar bill, could he afford the two CDs?

Answer: _____

㉓ It takes Sandy 20 minutes to walk to school and 14 minutes to run to school. How much time could she save each week, if she ran to school and ran home each day instead of walking?

Answer: _____

㉔ Brian collects baseball cards. He read in a collector's magazine that one of his rare cards should double in price every seven years. How many times should its present value be worth in 21 years?

Answer: _____

CHALLENGE

① George was born in a leap year. If George is 11 years old this year, how many days old is he?

Answer: _____

② A small company bills one of their clients $158 920.00 each quarter. How much money would the client pay them for 9 months' work?

Answer: _____

EXAMPLE

Sally walks $\frac{2}{3}$ of a block to school. Kari walks $\frac{3}{4}$ of a block. Who walks the farther? *(Hint: The L.C.M. of 3 and 4 is 12.)*

Sally walks: $\frac{2}{3} = \frac{2 \times 4}{3 \times 4} = \frac{8}{12}$ Kari walks: $\frac{3}{4} = \frac{3 \times 3}{4 \times 3} = \frac{9}{12}$

Answer: Kari walks farther.

Solve the problems. Show your work.

① Peter and Joe were comparing hat sizes. Peter's hat was $6\frac{1}{2}$ and Joe's hat was $6\frac{3}{8}$. Who had the larger hat size?

_____

Answer: _____ had the larger hat size. _____

② If Mary spent $\frac{1}{2}$ hour reading a History chapter and Jill spent 42 minutes, who read the chapter faster?

_____

Answer: _____

③ Douglas had 1 quarter, 1 dime, and 3 pennies. Jill had 1 dime, 6 nickels, and 1 penny. Who had the larger fraction of a dollar?

_____

Answer: _____

④ Mary's mother served $\frac{2}{7}$ of a cake and kept $\frac{1}{4}$ of it. Did she save more cake than she serve?

_____

Answer: _____

⑤ Henry and Ann each had a chocolate bar of the same size. Henry ate $\frac{1}{3}$ of his bar and Ann ate $\frac{2}{5}$ of her bar. Who ate less?

_____

Answer: _____

The young people on Single Street wanted to raise money for charity. They decided that any time any member of their family raised their voice, they would have to put one coin in a special box. The louder the voice, the larger the coin. At the end of the month, they would meet and put all their coins together.

⑥ Patricia had 63 pennies. What fraction of a dollar did she have?

Answer: _____

⑦ Dolores brought in a dollar and 7 quarters. What fraction of a dollar did she have?

Answer: _____

⑧ Milly had 1 quarter, 4 dimes and 12 nickels. What fraction of a dollar did she have?

Answer: _____

⑨ Gerry had 7 quarters, 2 dimes and 6 nickels. What fraction of a dollar did he have?

Answer: _____

⑩ Who raised the most money for charity?

Answer: _____

⑪ How much money did they raise for charity in all?

Answer: _____

CHALLENGE

Sam has 147 trading cards, Hindy 216, Kelly 98, and Oliver 166. They went to a trading card show where an expert told them that Sam had 21 valuable cards, Hindy 54, Kelly 28 and Oliver 2.

① Who had the largest fraction of valuable cards in his or her collection?

Answer: _____

② Who had the second smallest fraction of valuable cards in his or her collection?

Answer: _____

③ List the people from the one with the largest fraction of valuable cards to the one with the smallest.

Answer: _____

Addition and Subtraction of Fractions

EXAMPLE

Frank had $\frac{1}{5}$ of a bag of marbles, Jerry has $\frac{3}{5}$ of a bag of marbles and Kelly has $\frac{4}{5}$ of a bag of marbles. Yesterday they lost $\frac{2}{5}$ of a bag playing at recess. How many marbles do they still have in all?

No. of marbles they have in all : $\frac{1}{5} + \frac{3}{5} + \frac{4}{5} = \frac{8}{5}$

After losing, they still have : $\frac{8}{5} - \frac{2}{5} = \frac{6}{5} = 1\frac{1}{5}$

Answer : They still have $1\frac{1}{5}$ bags of marbles in all.

Solve the problems. Show your work.

Ann, Dolores and Mario were working on a project together. Ann spent $1\frac{5}{6}$ hours, Dolores $1\frac{4}{6}$ hours and Mario $\frac{1}{6}$ of an hour working on it.

① How many hours did they spend in all working on the project?

Answer : They spent _____ hours in all.

② How many more hours did Dolores spend on the project than Mario?

Answer : _____

③ How many more hours did Ann and Dolores spend on the project than Mario?

Answer : _____

④ How many hours did Ann and Mario spend on the project in all?

Answer : _____

⑤ Compare the number of hours Dolores spent on the project with that spent by Ann and Mario together.

Answer : _____

⑥ How much more time would Mario have to spend to equal the time spent by Ann?

Answer : _____

 ISBN: 978-1-897164-15-0

Harry's class was collecting bottles for recycling. They put them in large plastic bags. Harry filled $\frac{3}{7}$ of a bag the first day, $\frac{5}{7}$ the second and $\frac{1}{7}$ the third. Barry filled $\frac{5}{7}$ of a bag the first day, $\frac{3}{7}$ the second and $\frac{2}{7}$ the third. Mary filled $\frac{6}{7}$ of a bag the first day, $\frac{6}{7}$ the second and 1 the third.

⑦ How many bags of bottles did Harry collect in all?

Answer : _____

⑧ How many bags of bottles did Barry collect in all?

Answer : _____

⑨ How many bags of bottles did Mary collect in all?

Answer : _____

⑩ Who collected the most bottles?

Answer : _____

⑪ How many bags of bottles did the children collect in all?

Answer : _____

⑫ How many more bags of bottles did Mary collect than Harry?

Answer : _____

⑬ How many more bags of bottles did Mary collect than Barry?

Answer : _____

⑭ How many more bags of bottles does Harry need to collect if he wants to have 2 bags?

Answer : _____

⑮ How many more bags of bottles does Barry need to collect if he wants to have 3 bags?

Answer : _____

⑯ How many more bags of bottles does Mary need to collect if she wants to have 5 bags?

Answer : _____

• **To subtract from a whole number, change the whole number into a mixed number, e.g.**

$$5 = 4\frac{7}{7}$$

Read this first.

Gary was looking at the breakfast cereals in his kitchen. He had $\frac{2}{5}$ of a box of corn flakes, $\frac{4}{5}$ of a box of bran flakes and $\frac{3}{5}$ of a box of rice flakes.

⑰ How much cereal did he have in all?

Answer : _____

⑳ If Gary's mother used $\frac{1}{5}$ of a box of each type of cereal to make healthy cookies, how much cereal would be left?

Answer : _____

⑱ How much more bran flakes did he have than corn flakes?

Answer : _____

㉑ If Gary bought a box of granola and ate $\frac{1}{5}$ of it, how much cereal would he have altogether?

Answer : _____

⑲ How much more rice and corn flakes did he have than bran flakes?

Answer : _____

Answer : _____

Kim's class was running for charity. Kim ran $2\frac{7}{20}$ km. Lori ran $3\frac{19}{20}$ km. Freda ran $2\frac{11}{20}$ km. Toni ran 5 km.

㉒ How far did they run in all?

Answer : _____

㉕ If Lori and Freda ran as a team, how far did they run in total?

Answer : _____

㉓ How much farther did the person who ran the farthest run than the one who ran the shortest distance?

㉖ How much farther did Toni run than Lori?

Answer : _____

Answer : _____

㉔ If Kim and Freda ran as a team, how far did their team run?

㉗ How much farther did Freda run than Kim?

Answer : _____

Answer : _____

 ISBN: 978-1-897164-15-0

Yvon has a collection of magazines. $\frac{7}{19}$ of his collection is from 1980 to 1989, $\frac{9}{19}$ from 1970 to 1979, $\frac{1}{19}$ from before 1970 and the rest new.

㉘ What fraction of his magazines are new?

Answer : _____

㉙ What fraction of his magazines were printed between 1980 and the present?

Answer : _____

㉚ What fraction of his magazines were printed between 1970 and 1990?

Answer : _____

㉛ Yvon was told that magazines printed before 1980 should be stored in protective envelopes. What fraction of his magazines need this protection?

Answer : _____

㉜ What fraction of his magazines do not need protective envelopes?

Answer : _____

㉝ If Yvon gives $\frac{3}{8}$ of his collection of magazines to his friends, what fraction of his magazines are left?

Answer : _____

㉞ Yvon has 190 magazines. 113 of them are in English and the rest in French. What fraction of his magazines are in English?

Answer : _____

㉟ What fraction of his magazines are in French?

Answer : _____

CHALLENGE

Ralph's cat knocked a cup of hot chocolate over onto his Math book. It stained the page with his homework. Ralph knew the answer to the last question was $\frac{9}{13}$, and that one of the two numbers was $\frac{3}{13}$. If he had to add to find the number, what was the fraction under the chocolate stain?

Answer : _____

UNIT 5 Addition and Subtraction of Decimals

EXAMPLE

Frank's score on the English test was 79.8 and Jerry's was 92.3. How much higher was Jerry's score than Frank's?

Difference: 92.3 – 79.8 = 12.5

Answer : Jerry's score was 12.5 higher than Frank's.

Solve the problems. Show your work.

Franco was trying out a recipe. He needed 0.75 kg of egg-plant, 0.007 kg of salt, 1.28 kg of sliced raw onions, 0.95 kg of chopped tomato and 0.01 kg of parsley to add to the liquid ingredients.

① How much would the raw solid ingredients weigh?

Answer : The raw solid ingredients would weigh _____ .

② Franco knew that he couldn't put more than 4 kg into a shopping bag before the handles broke. How much more weight could he add to his dry ingredients and still carry the bag by the handles?

Answer : _____

③ What weight of vegetables does this recipe require?

Answer : _____

④ What weight of herbs and spices does this recipe require?

Answer : _____

⑤ If Franco required 0.599 kg of liquid ingredients, how much would the entire dish weigh before cooking?

Answer : _____

ISBN: 978-1-897164-15-0

Hortense received $7.50 each week for an allowance. She spent $3.49 for entertainment, $1.78 for snacks, $2.00 for transportation and saved the rest.

⑥ How much money did she save each week?

Answer : _____

⑦ How much money did she spend for entertainment and snacks each week?

Answer : _____

⑧ How much more money did she spend for entertainment than transportation each week?

Answer : _____

⑨ If she got a $0.68 raise in allowance on the condition that she save it all, how much would she save each week?

Answer : _____

⑩ If she needed $2.23 for snacks one week and wanted to take that money from her entertainment budget, how much would she have left for entertainment that week?

Answer : _____

- **Align the decimal points when you add or subtract the decimal numbers,**

e.g. 1.78 + 2.00

```
  1. 78
+ 2. 00
─────────
```
align

Read this first.

CHALLENGE

① If Kim had completed 1.78 km of a 5.78 km trip and wanted to travel 1.97 km before stopping for the day, how much farther would he have to go?

Answer : _____

② Harriette made deposits of $5.78 and $1.99, and withdrawals of $3.14 and $2.67 from her bank account. If the bank charged her $0.15 per transaction and her initial balance was $15.02, what was her final balance?

Answer : _____

Multiplication and Division of Decimals

EXAMPLE

Every day for one week, Gary ate 2 cookies, each weighing 27.8 grams. He also drank 10.5 litres of milk that week. How many grams of cookies and litres of milk did he consume each day?

Cookies Gary ate each day : $2 \times 27.8 = 55.6$

Milk Gary drank each day : $10.5 \div 7 = 1.5$

Answer : Gary ate 55.6 grams of cookies and drank 1.5 litres of milk each day.

Solve the problems. Show your work.

Eddie was saving for a special game, which cost $75.60. He was planning on saving $5.75 per month for a year. His father suggested that he save $6.45 per month instead, but Eddie wasn't sure if he could afford that.

① Would Eddie save up enough money to buy the game by putting aside $5.75 per month for a year?

Answer : Eddie _____ save up enough money to buy the game.

② If he couldn't save the money within the year, how much would he be short of?

Answer : _____

③ Would his father's suggestion allow him to buy the game on time?

Answer : _____

④ How much extra would he have to save each month above the $5.75 a month to buy the game in a year?

Answer : _____

⑤ If the game went on sale for $59.88, how much less than $5.75 would he have to save each month to buy the game in a year?

Answer : _____

ISBN: 978-1-897164-15-0

Jenny was building a project out of wood. She needed 2.16 metres of pine, 0.3 metres of oak and 2.4 metres of walnut. Pine was $2.00 a metre, oak was $4.70 a metre and walnut was $5.65 a metre.

⑥ How much would she spend for pine?

Answer : _____

⑦ How much would she spend for oak?

Answer : _____

⑧ How much would she spend for walnut?

Answer : _____

⑨ How much would she spend for wood altogether?

Answer : _____

⑩ If it cost $0.50 per metre for finishing the wood, what would be the total cost?

Answer : _____

⑪ What was the total cost for the wood plus finishing?

Answer : _____

⑫ If Jenny shared the total cost of the wood with 2 friends, how much would each person pay?

Answer : _____

⑬ If Jenny cut the pine into 3 equal parts, how long was each part?

Answer : _____

⑭ If Jenny cut off 0.04 metres of the walnut and divided the rest into 4 equal parts, how long was each part?

Answer : _____

⑮ How many metres of pine can you buy for $16.50?

Answer : _____

• For decimals, ◀ Read this first.
multiply or divide as with whole numbers, but remember the rule for placing the decimal point in the product or quotient.

ISBN: 978-1-897164-15-0

Oliver travelled the following distances on his vacation. Read the table and solve the problems. Show your work.

Day	1	2	3	4	5
Distance travelled (km)	271	305	652	186	395
Cost (per km)	$0.04	$0.06	$0.05	$0.05	$0.04

⑯ What was the travel cost on Day 2?

Answer : _____

⑰ What was the difference in travel cost between Day 1 and Day 4?

Answer : _____

⑱ On which day was his travel cost the lowest? What was the cost?

Answer : _____

⑲ On which day was his travel cost the highest? What was the cost?

Answer : _____

⑳ If Oliver had budgeted $12.00 per day for travel costs, would Day 5 have exceeded his budget?

Answer : _____

㉑ Which days exceeded Oliver's travel budget?

Answer : _____

㉒ If the travel cost on Day 6 was $4 and the distance travelled was 100 km, what would be the cost per km?

Answer : _____

㉓ The travel cost and the distance travelled on Day 7 was the same as that on Day 6, but Oliver had used a $2 gas coupon. What was the actual cost per km?

Answer : _____

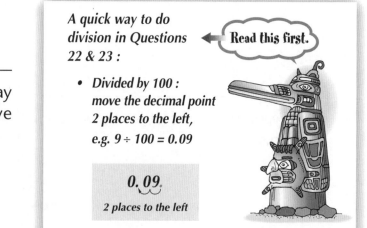

A quick way to do division in Questions 22 & 23 :   ← **Read this first.**

• **Divided by 100 :** move the decimal point 2 places to the left, e.g. 9 ÷ 100 = 0.09

0.09

2 places to the left

ISBN: 978-1-897164-15-0

Solve the problems. Show your work.

24 Matthew paid $8.76 to buy 4 boxes of juice. How much does each box of juice cost?

Answer : _____

25 The capacity of a box of juice is 1.25 L. If the box of juice can fill up 5 glasses, what is the capacity of each glass?

Answer : _____

26 How much juice is there in 7 boxes?

Answer : _____

27 Which size is the better buy, regular size distilled water 2 L for $1.38 or jumbo size 10 L for $5.90?

Answer : _____

28 How much should Matthew pay for buying 8 bottles of regular size distilled water?

Answer : _____

29 If Matthew drinks 1.75 L of water a day, how much water will he drink in a week?

Answer : _____

Darlene is going to paint a wall 16.8 m long and 2.4 m high. If 1L of paint covers 32 square metres, how much paint will she need for 2 coats of paint for the wall?

— *length* —

width (height)

Read this first.

Area of a rectangle = length x width (height)

Answer : _____

Solve the problems. Show your work.

Last Sunday, Mr Stanley held a Food Fair at Asna Park. His bakery baked different kinds of food for the Food Fair. Mr Stanley decided to donate half of the money collected to the Children's Hospital.

① There were 9 groups of girls and 12 groups of boys helping out at the fair. Each group had 4 people. How many helpers were there?

Answer : _____

② The baker, Mrs White, baked 64 cakes. If each cake was cut into 8 pieces, how many pieces of cake did Mrs White make?

Answer : _____

③ Each piece of cake was sold for $0.75. How much did a whole cake cost?

Answer : _____

④ If it cost $2.16 to bake each cake, what would be the total cost for baking all the cakes?

Answer : _____

⑤ There were 1064 chocolate doughnuts and 898 honey doughnuts. How many doughnuts were there in all?

Answer : _____

⑥ The chocolate doughnuts were sold in packages of 4. How many packages of chocolate doughnuts were there?

Answer : _____

⑦ At the end of the fair, 159 honey doughnuts were left. How many honey doughnuts had been sold?

Answer : _____

⑧ Gary bought 8 honey doughnuts for $5.04. How much did 1 honey doughnut cost?

Answer : _____

⑨ Each tray had 4 rows of 6 cookies. There were 15 trays altogether. How many cookies were there?

Answer : _____

⑩ 218 cookies were sold. How many cookies were left?

Answer : _____

⑪ The weight of a bag of 5 cookies was 486.5 grams. How much did 1 cookie weigh?

Answer : _____

⑫ Gary bought $\frac{1}{8}$ of a cake and Sally bought $\frac{5}{8}$ of the same cake. How much of the cake did they buy in all?

Answer : _____

⑬ How much more of the cake did Sally buy than Gary?

Answer : _____

⑭ Jill paid $4.16 for the cake. What was her change from a $10 bill?

Answer : _____

⑮ A bag of 5 bagels costs $1.30 and a bag of 8 bagels costs $1.76. Which bag is a better buy?

Answer : _____

⑯ Each stall collected $459.00. There were 8 stalls at the Food Fair. How much money did the stalls collect in all?

Answer : _____

⑰ How much money did Mr Stanley donate to the Children's Hospital?

Answer : _____

⑱ The total cost for organizing the fair was $1285.00. Did Mr Stanley make a profit after the donation?

Answer : _____

⑲ How much did Mr Stanley gain or lose?

Answer : _____

Inger's family want to redecorate their home. There are 4 bedrooms, 1 living room, 1 kitchen and 3 bathrooms in the house.

⑳ If each bedroom needs 3.48 L of paint, how many litres of paint are needed for all the bedrooms?

Answer : _____

㉑ A can of paint is 4 L. How many cans of paint does Inger need for all the bedrooms?

Answer : _____

㉒ Each bathroom needs $1\frac{3}{5}$ boxes of tiles. How many boxes of tiles are needed to cover all the bathrooms?

Answer : _____

㉓ If the tiles have to be bought in full boxes, how many boxes does Inger need to buy?

Answer : _____

㉔ If there are 100 tiles in each box, how many boxes of tiles will be left over?

Answer : _____

㉕ For the living room, they want to buy a couch for $798.65 and a rug for $268.47. How much do they spend in all to furnish the living room?

Answer : _____

㉖ Inger wants to buy 6 chairs and 1 dining table. Store A charges $102.00 each for the chairs and store B charges $621.00 for 6 chairs. Which store offers a better buy?

Answer : _____

㉗ The dining table is priced at $1295.00. How much will Inger pay for the dining table and 6 chairs at the lowest price?

Answer : _____

   ISBN: 978-1-897164-15-0

Circle the correct answer in each problem.

㉘ Mary drank $\frac{3}{7}$ of a bottle of milk. Kevin drank $\frac{5}{7}$ of a bottle and Lori drank an entire bottle. How many bottles of milk did they drink in all?

A. $\frac{8}{7}$ B. $2\frac{1}{7}$ C. $2\frac{3}{7}$ D. None of the above

㉙ Peter spent $1.68 for lunch. If he brought 1 loonie, 2 quarters and 4 dimes to school, how much would he have after lunch?

A. $2.20 B. $0.32 C. $0.22 D. $0.02

㉚ Billy went shopping with 3 of his friends. Each of them bought 4 shirts. How many shirts did they buy altogether?

A. 4 B. 8 C. 12 D. 16

㉛ Jim and Jane want to buy a gift for their parents and share the cost equally. The price of the gift is $44.00. If they have a $5 off coupon, how much does each person pay?

A. $19.50 B. $19.05 C. $24.50 D. $24.05

㉜ Each cake costs $8.00. If Kim paid for 3 cakes with 2 $20 bills, how much change would he get?

A. $4.00 B. $8.00 C. $16.00 D. $24.00

㉝ A pail of water weighs $1\frac{4}{5}$ kg. A pail of sand weighs $\frac{3}{5}$ kg heavier. How heavy is a pail of sand?

A. $2\frac{2}{5}$ kg B. $2\frac{1}{5}$ kg C. $1\frac{2}{5}$ kg D. $1\frac{1}{5}$ kg

㉞ How heavy are the pail of water and the pail of sand together?

A. $2\frac{2}{5}$ kg B. 3 kg C. $3\frac{3}{5}$ kg D. $4\frac{1}{5}$ kg

㉟ Ray bought 24 packets of gum each containing 12 pieces. Ray gave his 18 classmates 4 pieces each. How many pieces of gum were left over?

A. 206 B. 264 C. 216 D. 240

㊱ How many packets of gum were left over?

A. 18 B. 22 C. 16 D. 20

UNIT 7 Operations with Decimals

EXAMPLE

Terry wants to make a table 1.2 metres long and 0.6 metre wide. He wants to attach a rare wood edging around the table top. How many square metres would he need for the table top? How many metres of rare wood would he need for the edging?

Area of the table top : $1.2 \times 0.6 = 0.72$

Perimeter of the table top : $(1.2 + 0.6) \times 2 = 3.6$

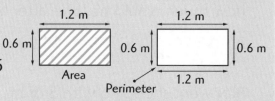

Answer : Terry would need 0.72 m² of wood for the table top and 3.6 m rare wood for the edging.

Solve the problems. Show your work.

The Orange and Black Department Store is having a sale. The prices shown below are taxes included.

① What would be the cost of 3 shirts and 1 CD?

Answer : The cost would be _____ .

② What is the amount Joan would save if she bought 5 CDs on sale?

Answer : _____

③ Can Mr Ray buy a shirt and a 17" colour TV with $230.00?

Answer : _____

④ Jenny bought 2 pairs of running shoes. What was her change from $150.00?

Answer : _____

⑤ Mr Winter bought a shirt, a CD and a pair of running shoes. What is the average price of these 3 items?

Answer : _____

ISBN: 978-1-897164-15-0

Mary and Sally went shopping on Wednesday. They spent $5.88 for apples, $3.35 for lettuce, $4.32 for carrots and $8.37 for candies.

⑥   How much did they spend in all?

Answer : _____

⑦   How much change should they receive from a $50 bill?

Answer : _____

⑧   Mary and Sally shared the bill. How much should each person pay?

Answer : _____

⑨   The store offers a special discount every Tuesday. Customers get $1.05 off every $10.00 spent. How much would Mary and Sally have paid by shopping one day earlier?

Answer : _____

⑩   The apples weighed 6 kg. What was the cost of 1 kg of apples?

Answer : _____

⑪   The candies weighed 3 kg. What was the cost of 1kg of candies?

Answer : _____

⑫   They bought 5 heads of lettuce. What was the cost of 1 head of lettuce?

Answer : _____

⑬   A 5-pound bag of potatoes costs $6.45. An 8-pound bag of potatoes costs $9.28. Which bag is a better buy?

- _To compare the prices of 2 items, find the price per unit first._   ← **Read this first.**

Answer : _____

Use the map to solve the problems. Show your work.

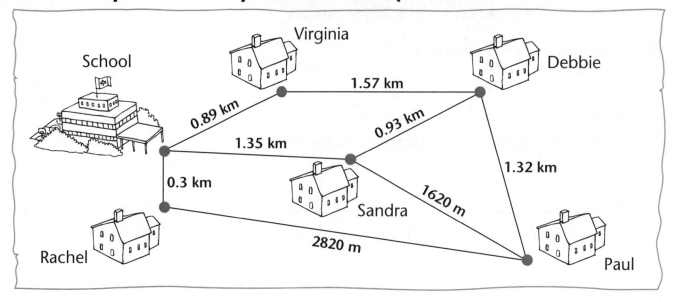

⑭ Who lives the closest to the school? What is the distance in metres?

Answer : _____

⑮ What is the distance in kilometres between Sandra's house and Paul's house?

Answer : _____

⑯ How far is it from Debbie's house to the school if she walks by Virginia's house?

Answer : _____

⑰ What is the shortest distance in metres from Debbie's house to the school?

Answer : _____

⑱ What is the shortest distance in kilometres from Rachel's house to Debbie's house?

Answer : _____

⑲ Yesterday Sandra walked to school in 5 minutes. What was the average distance she walked per minute?

Answer : _____

   ISBN: 978-1-897164-15-0

⑳ Debbie went from home to school passing Virginia's house in 6 minutes. What was the average distance she travelled per minute?

Answer : _____

㉑ Rachel went from home to Debbie's house passing Paul's house in 9 minutes. What was the average distance she travelled per minute?

Answer : _____

㉒ If Sandra shuttles between her house and school 4 times a day, how many kilometres will she travel in 5 days?

Answer : _____

㉓ Virginia and Sandra decide to meet at the school and walk over to Rachel's house together. How far do they walk in total?

Answer : _____

㉔ On a map, each centimetre represents 0.3 km. What is the actual distance if it is 2.5 cm on the map?

Answer : _____

Mr Headley's class was going to see a play. Each student ticket costs $3.75 and each adult ticket costs $6.90, taxes included. If 30 or more students attended, the theatre would give them $12.60 off and a free ticket for the teacher.

① If 25 students attended, how much would the students and Mr Headley have to pay in total?

Answer : _____

② If 35 students attended, how much would the students and Mr Headley have to pay in total?

Answer : _____

Two-Step Problems

EXAMPLE

Mark bought 3 packages of trading cards for $0.99 each. He paid with a $5 bill. What was his change?

Cost of 3 packages of cards : 0.99 × 3 = 2.97

Change : 5.00 – 2.97 = 2.03

Answer : His change was $2.03.

Solve the problems. Show your work.

The theatre has 26 rows of seats with 48 seats in each row. Tickets are $4.50 for adults and $3.00 for children. On Tuesdays, the $2.00 box of popcorn is free with the purchase of 1 adult and 1 children's ticket.

① If 952 people attended a show, how many empty seats were there?

Answer : There were _____ empty seats.

② Yesterday the theatre sold 462 adult tickets and the total amount from ticket sales was $2475.00. How many children's tickets were sold?

Answer : _____

③ If the entire theatre was filled with children and each bought a popcorn, how much money would be collected for that show?

Answer : _____

④ If the entire theatre was filled with adults and each bought a popcorn, how much money would be collected for that show?

Answer : _____

⑤ If Mrs Harris brought 4 children to the theatre on Tuesday, and bought each child a popcorn, how much would she pay in all?

Answer : _____

There was a sale at Smirdley's Discount Department Store. All shirts were on sale for 2 for $9.00. All blouses were on sale for 3 for $18.00. All dresses were on sale for $19.00 each. All trousers were on sale for $14.00 each. The store decided to give a $4.00 discount for every 6 items bought. All the prices included taxes.

⑥ Peter bought 2 shirts and 1 pair of trousers. How much would he pay for his purchases?

Answer : _____

⑦ Miranda bought 6 blouses and 1 dress. She paid with a $100 bill. How much change would she get?

Answer : _____

⑧ Jerome's mother bought 4 shirts and 3 blouses for her children. She had a twenty-dollar bill and a ten-dollar bill in her wallet and the rest of her money loose in her purse. How much money would she need from her purse?

Answer : _____

⑨ Wayne bought 2 pairs of trousers and 4 shirts. How much would he pay for his purchases?

Answer : _____

⑩ Mrs Von bought 9 blouses and 3 pairs of trousers. How much would she pay for her purchases?

Answer : _____

⑪ Frances wanted to buy 4 dresses. She had saved up $50.00 for her clothing and would borrow the rest from her father. How much would she need to borrow from her father?

Answer : _____

⑫ What was the price difference between 6 blouses and 4 dresses?

Answer : _____

⑬ Amy paid $71.00 for buying a pair of trousers and some dresses. How many dresses did she buy?

Answer : _____

⑭ There were 128 blue shirts and 224 white shirts. If the salesman put them in packages of 4, how many packages of 4 did he make?

Answer : _____

⑮ If the salesman put them in packages of 3, how many packages of 3 did he make?

Answer : _____

A radio station plays music and ads according to a formula. Every half hour, they play 8 minutes of ads, 16 minutes of music and the rest is talk. The station broadcasts 16 hours a day.

⑯ How much talk will there be every hour?

Answer : _____

⑰ If an ad costs $120 per 30 seconds, how much will the station earn per hour?

Answer : _____

⑱ If the average song is 4 minutes long, how many songs can be played between 4:00 p.m. and 9:00 p.m.?

Answer : _____

⑲ How many minutes of non-ad time will there be in a day?

Answer : _____

⑳ If a disc Jockey speaks at a rate of 12 words every 10 seconds, how many words will he say in each hour's talk time?

Answer : _____

Anna received a chain letter, telling her to make 4 copies of it and send them to 4 friends. Each of her friends was to do the same, and so on. Stamps cost $0.46 each.

㉑ Anna had no stamps at home and had to buy them to send her letters. How much change would she get from a $5 bill?

Answer : _____

   ISBN: 978-1-897164-15-0

㉒ If Anna sent out her letters and each of her friends sent out their letters, how much would have been spent in postage by all of them?

Answer : _____

㉓ If Anna's chain was 3 friends long, how many people were involved in the chain?

Answer : _____

㉔ If Anna's chain was 3 friends long, and everybody did as they were requested, how much would they all pay for postage?

Answer : _____

㉕ If it took 6 minutes to copy the letter and 2 minutes to fold and put it in an envelope, how much time would be spent by Anna and her 4 friends in doing this?

Answer : _____

① Ellen reads 38 pages each night before going to sleep and 29 pages each morning before breakfast. If she was reading a 249-page book, and started it on a Monday afternoon, how many pages would she have left to read on Thursday at noon?

Answer : _____

② A television set is on sale for $2120.50. It can also be bought for 24 payments of $92.60 each. How much more does Wayne pay by purchasing it on the instalment plan?

Answer : _____

EXAMPLE

Gary entered a contest. The skill-testing question was:

Take a number. Multiply it by 8. Subtract 6. Divide by 2. Add 15. Divide by 4. Subtract 3. What pattern did you find in Gary's number and the answer?

If Gary chose 14 as his number:

$14 \times 8 = 112$ ➡ $112 - 6 = 106$ ➡ $106 \div 2 = 53$ ➡ $53 + 15 = 68$ ➡

$68 \div 4 = 17$ ➡ $17 - 3 = 14$

Answer :   Gary's number and the answer are the same.

Solve the problems. Show your work.

Dorothy and Gladys are playing a pattern game. Dorothy would think of a pattern like "add 2 and multiply by 3" and keep it secret. Gladys would say a number like "2" and Dorothy would answer "12". Gladys would have to guess the pattern.

① If Gladys said "4", what would Dorothy answer?

Answer : Dorothy would answer _____ .

② If Gladys said "6", what would Dorothy answer?

Answer : _____

③ If Gladys said "5.5", what would Dorothy answer?

Answer : _____

④ Gladys wanted a turn to think of a pattern. When Dorothy said "4", she would answer "14". Which of the following is Gladys' pattern?

A.   Divide by 2. Add 10.

B.   Multiply by 6. Subtract 10.

C.   Subtract 3. Multiply by 10.

D.   Add 8. Divide by 2.

Answer : _____

⑤ If Dorothy said "2.4", what would Gladys answer?

Answer : _____

ISBN: 978-1-897164-15-0

Billy was practising shooting hoops. He kept track of the number of baskets he scored each day he played.

Day	1st	2nd	3rd	4th	5th
Number of Baskets	1	3	5	7	9

⑥ Was Billy improving as the week progressed?

Answer : _____

⑦ There was a pattern in his improvement. Look at the data and write out the pattern in words.

Answer : _____

⑧ Following the pattern, how many baskets would Billy score on the 6th day?

Answer : _____

⑨ On which day would Billy score 19 baskets?

Answer : _____

⑩ What was the total number of baskets Billy scored in the first 2 days?

Answer : _____

⑪ What was the total number of baskets Billy scored in the first 3 days?

Answer : _____

⑫ What was the total number of baskets Billy scored in the first 4 days?

Answer : _____

⑬ What was the total number of baskets Billy scored in the first 5 days?

Answer : _____

⑭ If this pattern were to continue, what would be the total number of baskets Billy scored in the first 9 days?

Answer : _____

⑮ If this pattern were to continue, how many days would Billy take to get 121 baskets in all?

Answer : _____

Sandy and Andy were on a long walk. To make sure that they did not get bored, they made up some problems for each other to solve.

⑯　Sandy gave Andy this list of number : 1, 3, 9, 27, ... She asked Andy to tell her the pattern and the next 2 numbers.

Answer : _____

⑰　Andy wanted to stump Sandy. He used this list of numbers : 1, 1.9, 2.8, 3.7, ... What is the pattern? What are the next 2 numbers?

Answer : _____

⑱　Sandy wanted to find a series that Andy could not figure out. She asked him to try this one : a, c, f, j, ... What is the pattern? What are the next 2 letters?

Answer : _____

⑲　Andy was in trouble. He could not stump Sandy. So he tried this one : 3, 6, 10, 15,... What is the pattern? What are the next 2 numbers?

Answer : _____

⑳　Andy used this list of numbers : 1, 1, 2, 2, 2, 4, 3, 3, 6, ... to stump Sandy. What is the pattern? What are the next 6 numbers?

Answer : _____

㉑　Sandy had the last laugh. She said : 1, 2, 3, 5, 8, 13, 21, ... What is the pattern? What are the next 2 numbers?

Answer : _____

Solve the problems. Show your work.

㉒ Hortense's parents have strange ideas about allowances. They offered her $0.10 the first day and doubled that each day for a week or Hortense could receive $12.00 per week. Which was a better deal for Hortense's parents?

Answer : _____

㉓ Karen got only 52 in Math. The Math teacher, Mr Finley, said that if she worked hard to improve, he would double any improvement she made on the next test to reach a final mark. Karen got 58 on the next test. What score would Mr Finley give her?

Answer : _____

㉔ On Jerry's 12th birthday, he received a gift from his grandparents. It was a $25.00 bond that doubled in value every 10 years. What will the bond be worth when Jerry is 72 years old?

Answer : _____

CHALLENGE

Donald and Ronald invented a pattern machine. It had a door to put numbers in, 4 dials to set and a door to take numbers out. The first example would be : (5 + 12) × 3 = 51. Help them complete the table.

	Number in	1st Operation		2nd Operation		Number out
		Number	Operation	Number	Operation	
	5	12	Addition	3	Multiplication	51
①	8	4	Multiplication	8	Addition	
②	45	3	Division	7		8
③	1	17		9	Division	2

EXAMPLE

A magic rabbit jumps 1.6 metres with its first jump, and half that distance each jump after. The problem is that the magic rabbit cannot jump less than 0.3 of a metre. How many jumps can the magic rabbit take?

1st jump	2nd jump	3rd jump	4th jump
1.6	1.6 ÷ 2 → 0.8	0.8 ÷ 2 → 0.4	0.4 ÷ 2 → 0.2

But 0.2 < 0.3, so the magic rabbit can only take 3 jumps.

Answer : The magic rabbit can take 3 jumps.

Solve the problems. Show your work.

The price of a savings bond doubles every 10 years. Use this fact to complete the table.

①

Year	1940	1950	1960	1970	1980	1990	2000
Price ($)			250.00		1000.00		

② What would the price of the savings bond be in 2020?

Answer :

③ In which year would the price of the savings bond be $64 000.00?

Answer :

④ How many times more was the price of the bond in 1960 than that in 1940?

Answer :

⑤ How much would you have earned if you bought the bond in 1980 and sold it in 2020?

Answer :

ISBN: 978-1-897164-15-0

Matthew buys trading cards each week. He buys as many as he can with the money left over after paying for everything else.

⑥   Complete the table to see what pattern you can find.

Week	1	2	3	4	5	6	7
No. of cards bought	5	6	8	5			
Money spent ($)	2.25	2.70	3.60		2.70		2.25
No. of cards in collection	5	11					

⑦   How many cards will Matthew buy in week 9?

Answer : _____

⑧   How much money will Matthew spend in week 10 on buying cards?

Answer : _____

⑨   How many cards will Matthew collect in the first 3 weeks?

Answer : _____

⑩   How many cards will Matthew collect in the first 6 weeks?

Answer : _____

⑪   How many cards will Matthew collect from week 1 to week 9?

Answer : _____

⑫   How many cards will Matthew collect from week 1 to week 30?

Answer : _____

⑬   If Matthew buys 5 cards in week 22, how many cards will he buy in week 23?

Answer : _____

⑭   How much money will Matthew spend in the first 3 weeks?

Answer : _____

⑮   How much money will Matthew spend in the first 6 weeks?

Answer : _____

Tony has 12 yellow marbles and 5 blue marbles. Each day Tony buys 2 yellow marbles and 3 blue marbles.

⑯ Help Tony complete the table.

Day	1st	2nd	3rd	4th	5th	6th
No. of yellow marbles	12					
No. of blue marbles	5					

⑰ How many yellow marbles does Tony have on the 7th day?

Answer : Tony has _____ yellow marbles on the 7th day. _____

⑱ How many blue marbles does Tony have on the 7th day?

Answer : _____

⑲ How many days does Tony take to have 32 yellow marbles?

Answer : _____

⑳ How many days does Tony take to have 32 blue marbles?

Answer : _____

㉑ How many days does Tony take to have the same number of yellow and blue marbles?

Answer : _____

㉒ How many marbles does Tony have in all in the first 6 days?

Answer : _____

㉓ What is the pattern of increase in the number of marbles?

Answer : _____

ISBN: 978-1-897164-15-0

Mrs Faam's class is studying a table. The numbers in column or row follow a pattern.

㉔ Help them complete the table.

Column / Row	1	2	3	4	5	6
1	0	0	0		0	
2	2	4		8		12
3					20	
4			18			36
5	8			32	40	
6	10	20	30			60

㉕ What is the pattern in column 3? What would the next 3 numbers be after 30?

Answer : _____

㉖ What is the pattern in row 3? What would the next 3 numbers be after 24?

Answer : _____

㉗ Which of the columns has the same pattern as that in row 6? What is the pattern?

Answer : _____

㉘ Joe has 10 cards. The number of cards that Joe collects increases by 10 each day. Which of the rows above can show the counting pattern of Joe's cards? How many cards will he have after 5 days?

Answer : _____

㉙ Raymond uses $8.00 every day. Which of the rows above can show the total amount of money he has spent? How much money will Raymond have spent after 4 days?

Answer : _____

The Johnson twins are setting up an agency to take care of dogs. Read the rate card. Then complete the table and answer the questions.

Simple care	:	$4.00 for the first hour; $5.00 per hour thereafter
Walking	:	$2.00 each time, plus $0.50 per km
Washing	:	2 times total charges
Drying	:	Free with care over 3 hours; $2.00 otherwise

㉚ Simple care :

Hour(s)	1	2	3	4	5	6
Charge ($)						

㉛ Walking :

Distance(km)	1	2	3	4	5	6
Charge ($)						

㉜ Tina had the twins look after her dog, Dorfus, for 10 hours. What was the charge?

Answer : _____

㉝ Kevin asked the twins to look after his dog for 4 hours and take her for a 3 km walk. How much did the twins earn for the service?

Answer : _____

㉞ Lily wanted her poodle walked for 4 km and washed. What was her bill?

Answer : _____

㉟ Dolly's parents asked the twins to look after their dog for 8 hours. They wanted the dog washed and dried. What was their total bill?

Answer : _____

ISBN: 978-1-897164-15-0

Keri and Harry were so impressed with the Johnson twins' business, they decided to start one of their own. They would look after cats. Use the following tables to complete their rate card and answer the questions.

Simple Care				
Hour(s)	1	2	3	4
Charge ($)	3.50	8.00	12.50	17.00

Feeding				
No. of meals	1	2	3	4
Charge ($)	5.00	10.00	15.00	20.00

㊱

Simple care : $_____ for the first hour;

$_____ per hour thereafter

Chasing cat : $12.00 per hour, plus $0.75 a km

Feeding cat : $_____ per meal

㊲ Ralph had a cat that was a little wild. His bill showed 3 hours' care and 1 hour and 6 km of chasing . What was his total bill?

Answer : _____

㊳ Mr and Mrs Quorley had a very well-behaved cat. They wanted it cared for 7 hours and fed two meals. What was their total bill?

Answer : _____

CHALLENGE

Willy and Billy set up a baby-sitting service. They charged $1.00 for the first hour and $1.50 per hour after that. If the children were under 3, there was a surcharge of $2.00 for the first hour.

Mr and Mrs Jones wanted them to babysit their two children for 5 hours. One was 2 years old and the other 4 years old. How much would their bill be?

Answer : _____

ISBN: 978-1-897164-15-0

Solve the problems.   Show your work.

This is a map of a section of Squaretown. Each block in Squaretown is 1.96 km^2 and each side of the block is 1.4 km. On this map, Allan lives at A. Bobby lives at B. Carol lives at C and Doris lives at D.

① What is the area bounded by Grand Ave. on the north, Bottom Ave. on the south, Mountain Blvd. on the west and Desert Blvd. on the east?

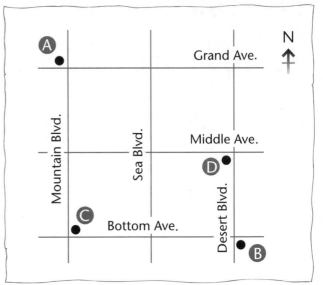

Answer : _____

② If Doris walks along Middle Ave. and then turns right on Mountain Blvd. to Allan's house, how far has she walked?

Answer : _____

③ If Bobby walks along Desert Blvd., and then turns left on Grand Ave. to Allan's house, how far has he walked?

Answer : _____

④ If both Allan and Carol walk to Doris' house by the shortest route, how far have they travelled in all?

Answer : _____

⑤ Carol was walking to Bobby's house by the shortest route. If she completed 1.86 km, how much farther would she have to walk?

Answer : _____

⑥ If Bobby walked to Doris' house in 5 minutes, how far did he travel in 1 minute?

Answer : _____

⑦ If Doris walked to Bobby's house in 4 minutes, how much farther did she walk in 1 minute than Bobby?

Answer : _____

ISBN: 978-1-897164-15-0

Bobby was cycling along Desert Blvd. He kept track of the time he took to travel each block.

⑧ Complete the table.

No. of blocks	1	2	3	4	5	6
Distance travelled (km)	1.4	2.8				
Time (min)	3	6				

⑨ What is the pattern of the time taken by Bobby to travel each block?

Answer : _____

⑩ What is the pattern of the distance travelled by Bobby?

Answer : _____

⑪ How long would Bobby take to travel 8 blocks?

Answer : _____

⑫ If Bobby rode for 36 min, how many blocks would he pass?

Answer : _____

⑬ If Bobby passed 9 blocks, how many kilometres would he travel?

Answer : _____

⑭ If Bobby drank $\frac{1}{4}$ L of water every 15 minutes, how many litres of water would he have drunk after 75 minutes?

Answer : _____

⑮ If Bobby drank $1\frac{3}{4}$ L of water, for how long would he have travelled on his bike?

Answer : _____

SuperSave Department Store is having a sale and all the prices include taxes. They take $3.25 off purchases between $10.00 and $20.00, $7.15 off purchases between $20.01 and $40.00, and $15.50 off purchases $40.01 and over.

⑯ The price of a sweater is $29.45. How much do you have to pay?

Answer : _____

⑰ Jane paid $53.25 for a pair of jeans. What is its original price?

Answer : _____

⑱ Richard buys 3 packs of socks at $10.80 each. How much can he save?

Answer : _____

⑲ The regular price of a book is $15.99. If Jim buys 2 books, how much will he pay?

Answer : _____

⑳ Billy pays $50.00 for 2 CDs at $22.99 each. How much change will he get?

Answer : _____

㉑ Tina pays $60.00 for 1 pair of shoes at $59.99 and 1 pair of socks at $3.99. How much change will she get?

Answer : _____

㉒ A box of chocolates costs $19.87. If Gary has 1 $10 bill, 3 toonies and 3 quarters, will he have enough money to buy a box of chocolates?

Answer : _____

㉓ There are 329 customers in the store. If 251 customers are female, how many male customers will there be?

Answer : _____

㉔ On average, each customer spends $5.00 in the store. How much money can be collected from 215 customers?

Answer : _____

㉕ Ray wants to buy either sweater A or sweater B. The price of sweater A is $34.87. The price of sweater B is $40.05. What is the price difference between sweater A and sweater B after the discount?

Answer : _____

㉖ Which sweater should Ray buy? Explain.

Answer : _____

Circle the correct answer in each problem.

Frank has invented a machine. If he drops a number in the top, a related number comes out from the side.

㉗ If you drop a 1 in the top, a 5 comes out from the side. A 2 produces an 8 and a 3 produces an 11. Which of the following is the machine's pattern?

A. Add 4

B. Multiply by 3 and add 2

C. Add 2 and multiply by 3

D. Multiply by 2 and add 3

㉘ If you drop 4 in the top, what number will come out from the side?

A. 8

B. 11

C. 14

D. 18

㉙ Frank dreams of a machine that works on the same pattern, but turns 1 loonie into 5, 2 loonies into 8 and so on. How much money would he make if he dropped 7 loonies into his machine?

A. 23

B. 42

C. 17

D. 11

㉚ To make 29 loonies, how many loonies would Frank have to drop into the machine?

A. 8

B. 9

C. 25

D. 13

㉛ What pattern would Frank have to create for the machine to turn 2 toonies into $17.00 and 3 toonies into $27.00?

A. Add 3 and multiply by 3

B. Multiply by 5 and add 3

C. Multiply by 4 and add 9

D. Multiply by 5 and subtract 3

㉜ If the machine made $47.00, how many toonies would Frank have dropped into the machine?

A. 7

B. 6

C. 5

D. 4

㉝ What pattern would Frank have to create for the machine to turn 6 nickels into $9.00 and 8 nickels into $10.00?

A. Multiply by 1.5

B. Multiply by 10 and add 6

C. Multiply by 1.25 and add 1.5

D. Add 4.2 and multiply by 2

There are 72 seats in the Virtual Reality Game Centre. Each adult ticket costs $6.49 and each children's ticket is $2.90 less than an adult ticket.

㉞ If all the seats were occupied by adults, how much money would the centre collect?

A. $467.28   B. $487.28   C. $457.28   D. $367.28

㉟ If all the seats were occupied by children, how much money would the centre collect?

A. $248.48   B. $258.48   C. $348.48   D. $358.48

㊱ If 46 seats were occupied by children and the rest by adults, how much money would the centre collect?

A. $391.88   B. $398.78   C. $268.98   D. $333.88

㊲ Mrs Faam buys 8 tickets for $46.12. The number of children's tickets she intends to buy is fewer than 5, how many adult tickets does she buy?

A. 4   B. 5   C. 6   D. 7

㊳ How many children's tickets does she buy?

A. 1   B. 2   C. 3   D. 4

㊴ Game A lasts $6\frac{7}{12}$ minutes and Game B lasts $5\frac{11}{12}$ minutes. How long do these two games last?

A. $11\frac{8}{12}$ minutes   B. $12\frac{6}{12}$ minutes

C. $11\frac{18}{24}$ minutes   D. $13\frac{8}{12}$ minutes

㊵ By how many minutes is Game A longer than Game B?

A. $1\frac{8}{12}$ B. $\frac{9}{12}$ C. $1\frac{3}{12}$ D. $\frac{8}{12}$

㊶ Joe played Game A twice. How long did he play Game A?

A. $12\frac{1}{12}$ minutes   B. $12\frac{14}{24}$ minutes   C. $12\frac{7}{12}$ minutes   D. $13\frac{2}{12}$ minutes

Section IV

Overview

In the previous section, problem-solving strategies were applied in the context of the four arithmetic operations and pattern recognition.

In this section, word problems involve finding perimeter, area, volume, speed and time. Geometry units include applications of coordinate systems and transformations. Statistics topics covered are the interpretation of circle graphs and line graphs. Students also practise solving problems involving mean and mode, and probability.

Operations with Money

EXAMPLE

Mary buys 2 desk pads at $14.95 each and 5 binders at $2.97 each. If Mary gets a $2.18 discount on desk pads and a $1.48 discount on binders, how much will she spend in all?

Cost of desk pads : (14.95 × 2) – 2.18 = 27.72

Cost of binders : (2.97 × 5) – 1.48 = 13.37

Cost in all : 27.72 + 13.37 = 41.09

Answer : Mary will spend $41.09 in all.

Solve the problems. Show your work.

Ben wants to make some money by doing odd jobs.

Excellent Service	
Call Ben • 725-JOBS	
Raking Leaves	$ 4.98
Sweeping Sidewalks	$ 2.84
Mowing Lawns	$12.49
Cleaning Garages	$20.18
Washing Cars	$ 5.39

* $4.50 off for 3 jobs or more at the same time.

① If Mrs Donovan hired Ben to rake her leaves and mow her lawn, what would her bill be?

Answer : Her bill would be ____ .

② If Mr Kell hired Ben to clean his garage and wash his car, what would his bill be?

Answer : ____

③ If Mr Ryan hired Ben to do all the jobs except car washing, what would his bill be?

Answer : ____

④ If Mr Ryan gave Ben a $100 bill, how much change would he get?

Answer : ____

⑤ Mrs Winter hired Ben to do 2 jobs and her bill was $23.02. Which 2 jobs did Ben do?

Answer : ____

⑥ If Mrs Winter gave Ben a $50 bill, how much change would she get?

Answer : ____

ISBN: 978-1-897164-15-0

⑦ If Ben took 2 hours to clean a garage, how much money would he earn per hour?

Answer : _____

⑧ Ben decided to give a quarter of his earnings to charity. He earned $37.65 the first week, $35.94 the second and $31.53 the third. How much would he have after his donation?

Answer : _____

Edward's Emporium is having a year-end sale. There is a $1.50 rebate for every $10 spent. If a customer spends over $100.00, he or she gets an additional $0.30 off every $10. All prices include taxes.

⑨ Ann buys a blouse at $82.97. What is her change from a $100 bill?

Answer : _____

⑩ Tim buys a shirt at $120.45. What is his change from a $100 bill?

Answer : _____

⑪ Ray buys 3 sweaters at $16.99 each. How much rebate does he get? What is his change from a $50 bill?

Answer : _____

⑫ A pair of boots costs $92.85. If Sally wants to buy 2 pairs of boots, should she buy them separately or together? Explain.

Answer : _____

⑬ Jacket A costs $98.27. Jacket B costs $102.95. If Eric wants to buy a cheaper jacket, which one should he buy?

Answer : _____

Donna and her friends went to a new candy store to buy their favourite candies. The prices included taxes.

⑭ Donna wanted to buy some lollipops. It was $0.97 each or $ 10.80 for a package of 12. How much would Donna save by buying a package of lollipops?

Answer : _____

⑮ Donna bought 2 packages of lollipops. What was her change from $25.00?

Answer : _____

⑯ Gary wanted some jellybeans. A box of 6 packages was sold at $3.24. How much did 1 package cost?

Answer : _____

⑰ Gary bought 18 packages of jelly-beans. What was his change from a $20 bill?

Answer : _____

⑱ Louis paid $23.76 to buy a package of lollipops and a few boxes of jelly-beans. How many boxes of jellybeans did Louis buy?

Answer : _____

⑲ There was a sign in the shop. 'Buy 2 chocolate bars at $1.26 each and get the third one free.' How much did each chocolate bar cost on average?

Answer : _____

⑳ Alexander took 9 chocolate bars. How much did he pay?

Answer : _____

㉑ Each jar of candies cost $12.96. Jeffrey had $40.00. Would he have enough money to buy 3 jars of candies?

Answer : _____

㉒ If Jeffrey bought 2 jars of candies, how much money would he have left?

Answer : _____

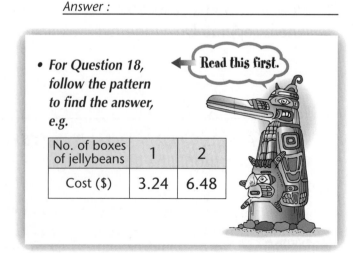

• For Question 18, follow the pattern to find the answer, e.g.

Read this first.

No. of boxes of jellybeans	1	2
Cost ($)	3.24	6.48

ISBN: 978-1-897164-15-0

Help the candy store owner write out the profits in the past 4 weeks in numbers and in words. Then put the weeks in order.

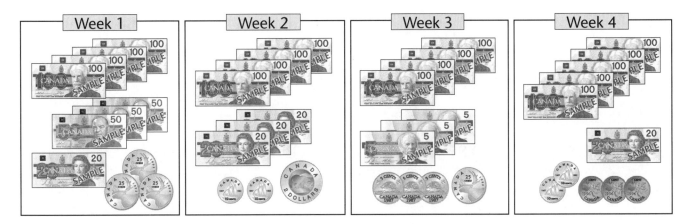

㉓ Money earned in week 1 : $ _____ ; the total amount earned in week 1 was

_____ .

㉔ Money earned in week 2 : $ _____ ; the total amount earned in week 2 was

_____ .

㉕ Money earned in week 3 : $ _____ ; the total amount earned in week 3 was

_____ .

㉖ Money earned in week 4 : $ _____ ; the total amount earned in week 4 was

_____ .

㉗ List the weeks in order from the greatest amount earned to the least.

Answer : _____

CHALLENGE

Mr Tiff buys 12 toy cars for $187.20 and re-sells them at $20.94 each.

① How much money will Mr Tiff get?   ② How much will he gain or lose?

Answer : _____   *Answer :* _____

ISBN: 978-1-897164-15-0

EXAMPLE

What is the perimeter and area of this figure?

Perimeter : 1.5 + 1.2 + 2 + 0.8 + 3.5 + 2 = 11

Area : (1.5 × 2) + (2 × 0.8) = 4.6

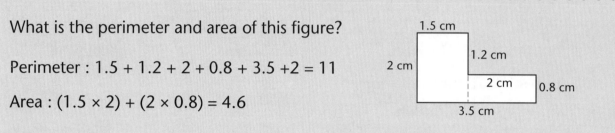

Answer : The perimeter of this figure is 11 cm and its area is 4.6 cm².

The diagrams below show the dimensions of 6 flower beds. Use the diagrams to solve the problems. Show your work.

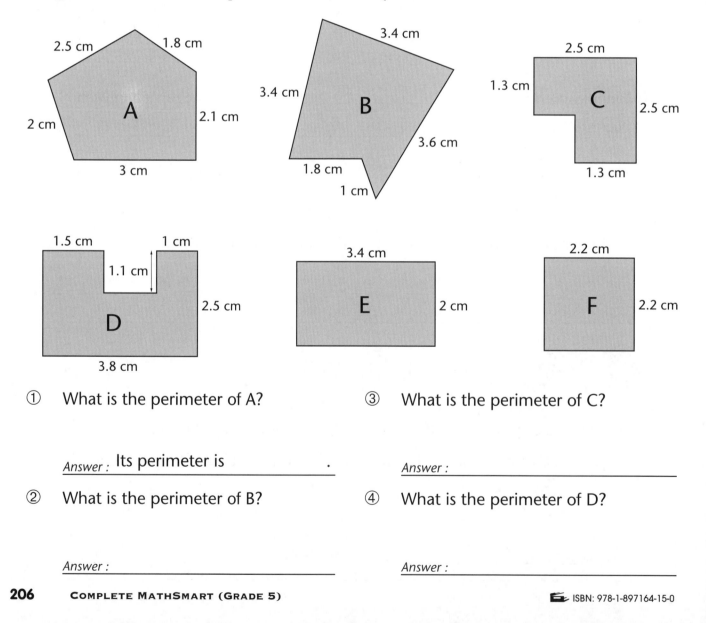

① What is the perimeter of A?

Answer : Its perimeter is _____ .

② What is the perimeter of B?

Answer : _____

③ What is the perimeter of C?

Answer : _____

④ What is the perimeter of D?

Answer : _____

ISBN: 978-1-897164-15-0

⑤ What is the perimeter of E?

Answer : _____

⑥ What is the perimeter of F?

Answer : _____

• Use these formulas to find the perimeter of a square and a rectangle. ← Read this first.

length

Perimeter of a square
= length × 4

length

width

Perimeter of a rectangle
= (length + width) × 2

⑦ The actual size of each garden is 100 times bigger than the diagram. Find the actual perimeter of each garden and write in metres.

Garden	A	B	C	D	E	F
Actual Perimeter						

Darren wants to divide his backyard into parts. The actual size is 100 times greater than the diagram below. Measure the diagram to solve the problems. Show your work.

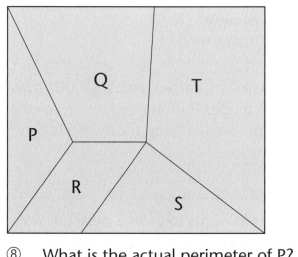

⑧ What is the actual perimeter of P?

Answer : _____

⑨ What is the actual perimeter of Q?

Answer : _____

⑩ What is the actual perimeter of R?

Answer : _____

⑪ What is the actual perimeter of S?

Answer : _____

⑫ What is the actual perimeter of T?

Answer : _____

⑬ Put the parts in order from the greatest perimeter to the smallest.

Answer : _____

Look at the floor plan and dimensions of the first floor of Darren's house. All the ceilings are 2.8 m high. Solve the problems. Show your work.

	Dimension		Dimension
Library	5 m × 6.5 m	Side Garden	2.3 m × 5 m
Porch	5 m × 2.9 m	Wash-room	2.6 m × 5 m
Dining Room	5 m × 13 m	Living Room	7.9 m × 7.9 m
Hall	3 m × 7.3 m	Kitchen	5 m × 6.4 m

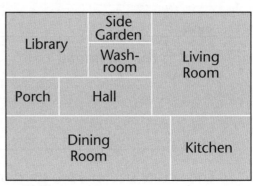

⑭ What is the area of the library?

Answer : _____

⑮ What is the area of the hall?

Answer : _____

⑯ What is the area of the living room?

Answer : _____

⑰ How many times of the area of the washroom is the area of the dining room?

Answer : _____

⑱ What is the area of the first floor of Darren's house?

Answer : _____

⑲ How many square metres of carpet would cover the living room and the library?

Answer : _____

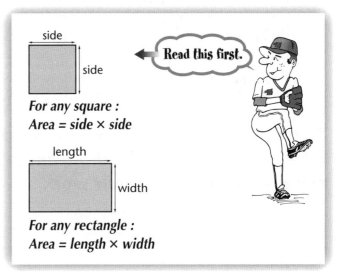

For any square :
Area = side × side

For any rectangle :
Area = length × width

⑳ If 1 m² of carpet costs $2.00, how much does Darren need to pay for the carpet for his living room and library?

Answer : _____

㉑ Darren wants to paint 2 adjacent walls in the kitchen. If 1 L of paint covers 4 m², how many litres of paint are needed for the 2 walls?

Answer : _____

㉒ If paint comes in 2 L cans, how many cans of paint does Darren need to buy?

Answer : _____

ISBN: 978-1-897164-15-0

Solve the problems. Show your work.

㉓ A table is 2.5 m long and 1.2 m wide. What is its perimeter and area?

2.5 m

1.2 m

Answer : _____

㉔ The length of a square coffee table is 60 cm. What is its perimeter and area?

60 cm

Answer : _____

㉕ A square has a perimeter of 120 cm. How long is each side?

Answer : _____

㉖ A rectangular backyard has an area of 450 m². If its length is 25 m, what is its width?

Answer : _____

㉗ A piece of rectangular cardboard has a perimeter of 45 cm. If its width is 5 cm, what is its area?

Answer : _____

CHALLENGE

The outside dimensions of a framed picture are 25 cm by 40 cm. If the border is 2 cm wide,

① what is the length and width of the picture?

FINISH

Answer : _____

② what is the area and perimeter of the picture?

Answer : _____

ISBN: 978-1-897164-15-0

EXAMPLE

School starts at 8:45 a.m. and finishes at 3:20 p.m. How long is the school day?

1st From 8:45 a.m. to noon : 3 h 15 min

2nd From noon to 3:20 p.m. : 3 h 20 min

Total time : 3 h 15 min + 3 h 20 min = 6 h 35 min

1st	2nd
12 h 00 min	3 h 20 min
− 8 h 45 min	− 0 h 00 min
3 h 15 min	3 h 20 min

Answer : The school day is 6 h 35 min.

Solve the problems. Show your work.

Jimmy and his grandparents like to walk for exercise. Last Saturday, they left home at 9:40 a.m. for the park, which took 57 minutes at their usual pace. After spending 40 minutes there, they walked to the convenience store for groceries, which took 32 minutes. After shopping, they arrived home at 12:42 p.m.

① At what time did Jimmy and his grandparents reach the park?

They reached the park
Answer : at   .

② At what time did they leave the park?

Answer :

③ At what time did they reach the convenience store?

Answer :

④ They shopped in the store for 35 minutes. At what time did they leave the store?

Answer :

⑤ How long did they take to walk home after shopping?

Answer :

⑥ It took Jimmy's grandmother 26 min to cook their lunch. If she finished cooking at 1:17 p.m., at what time did she start?

Answer :

⑦ Larry has an assignment due on Nov. 29. If he starts to work on it on Nov. 3, how many days does he have to complete the assignment?

Answer : _____

⑧ If Larry starts doing his assignment at 8:16 a.m. and stops at 4:05 p.m., how long has he worked on it?

Answer : _____

⑨ Larry spent 2 h 20 min looking for reference materials in the school library. He left there at 5:32 p.m. When did he start working in the library?

Answer : _____

⑩ Mrs Smith has an appointment with her doctor at 2:15 p.m. It takes her 23 minutes to walk to the doctor's office. If Mrs Smith leaves home at 1:48 p.m., will she be there on time?

Answer : _____

⑪ Ben's favourite TV show starts at 11:45 a.m. and lasts 1 h 35 min, when will the show be over?

Answer : _____

⑫ Movie A lasts 1 h 43 min; movie B lasts 1 h 16 min. If movie A starts at 11:45 a.m. and movie B starts at 12:10 p.m., which movie finishes first?

Answer : _____

⑬ Peter travelled from City A to City B in 170 h. How many days and hours did he spend on travelling?

Answer : _____

⑭ Gary wanted to go to the theatre. He left home at 11:26 a.m. First he took a bus for 37 min. Then he walked for 16 min. At what time did he reach the theatre?

Answer : _____

A flight from Jonesville to Littletown takes 2 h 16 min. A flight from Norhead to Littletown takes 1 h 45 min. If flight A leaves Jonesville for Littletown at 11:55 a.m., about what time must flight B leave Norhead to reach Littletown at the same time as flight A?

Answer : _____

EXAMPLE

Mr Ford drove his car at an average speed of 60 km/h. Mr Coleman drove his car at an average speed of 75 km/h. They both started at the same time from the same place but drove in opposite directions. How far apart would they be after 3 hours?

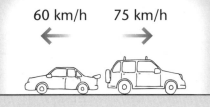

Distance travelled by Mr Ford : 60 × 3 = 180

Distance travelled by Mr Coleman : 75 × 3 = 225

Distance apart : 180 + 225 = 405

Answer : They would be 405 km apart after 3 hours.

Solve the problems. Show your work.

Sally and her family were going on a motoring trip. They planned to drive to Centretown, a distance of 600 km, and from there to Middleberg, a distance of 880 km and then drive the 780 km home.

① If they drove at an average speed of 60 km/h, how long would it take to drive from home to Centretown?

Answer : It would take _____ .

② If they drove at an average speed of 80 km/h, how long would it take to drive from Centretown to Middleberg?

Answer : _____

③ The trip from Middleberg to home took 10 hours. What was their average speed on this part of the trip?

Answer : _____

④ If they drove at an average speed of 60 km/h, how long would it take to drive from Middleberg to home?

Answer : _____

⑤ If they drove at an average speed of 80 km/h, how long would it take to drive the whole trip?

Answer : _____

⑥ If they took 20 hours to complete the trip, what would be the average speed?

Answer : _____

ISBN: 978-1-897164-15-0

Doris can cycle at 20 km/h and run at 12 km/h. Use the diagram to solve the problems. Show your work.

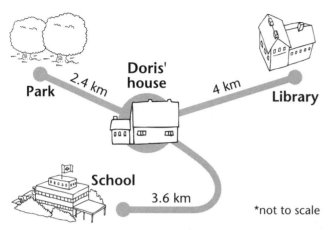

Park — 2.4 km — Doris' house — 4 km — Library

School — 3.6 km

*not to scale

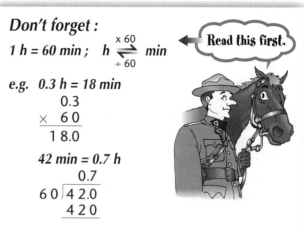

Don't forget :

$1 h = 60 min$; $h \overset{\times 60}{\underset{\div 60}{\rightleftharpoons}} min$

← Read this first.

e.g. 0.3 h = 18 min

$$\begin{array}{r} 0.3 \\ \times\ 60 \\ \hline 18.0 \end{array}$$

42 min = 0.7 h

$$\begin{array}{r} 0.7 \\ 60\overline{)42.0} \\ 420 \end{array}$$

⑦ How long will Doris take to cycle to and from the library?

Answer : _____

⑧ How long will Doris take to run to the park from home?

Answer : _____

⑨ How many minutes can Doris save by riding the bicycle to the park instead of running?

Answer : _____

⑩ How many minutes will Doris take to cycle to school?

Answer : _____

⑪ Last Thursday, Doris took 15 min to cycle to school. What was her cycling speed in kilometres per minute?

Answer : _____

⑫ What was her cycling speed in kilometres per hour?

Answer : _____

CHALLENGE

Ricky, Raymond and Sam each have a 180-page story book. Ricky plans to read 20 pages each day. Raymond plans to read 36 pages every 2 days. Sam plans to read 15 pages every half day. How many days does each of them take to finish the whole book? Who is the first to finish the book?

Answer : _____

ISBN: 978-1-897164-15-0

EXAMPLE

Gary has an aquarium 50 cm long, 30 cm wide and 45 cm high. What is its volume? How many litres of water does it hold?

Volume : 50 × 30 × 45 = 67500

Capacity : 67500 ÷ 1000 = 67.5

Answer : The volume of his aquarium is 67 500 cm^3. It holds 67.5 L of water.

Solve the problems. Show your work.

Sandy had a new aquarium 60 cm long, 25 cm wide and 40 cm high. She was told to fill it with 20 L of water on Monday, 15 L of water on Wednesday and 10 L of water on Friday. On Saturday, she could put her fish in the aquarium.

① Before filling the aquarium with water, what was the volume of air inside?

Answer : _____

② How many litres of water could the aquarium hold?

Answer : _____

③ What volume of air would be in the aquarium on Monday?

Answer : _____

④ What volume of air would be in the aquarium on Wednesday?

Answer : _____

$cm^3 / mL \underset{\times 1000}{\overset{\div 1000}{\rightleftarrows}} L$

e.g.   *415 mL = 0.415 L*

5.12 L = 5120. mL

← Read this first.

⑤ What volume of air would be in the aquarium on Friday?

Answer : _____

⑥ Sandy's old aquarium was 45 cm long, 15 cm wide and 20 cm high. How many more litres of water could the new aquarium hold than the old one?

Answer : _____

ISBN: 978-1-897164-15-0

Alan has a tank full of 160 000 cm^3 of water. He is trying to empty it with a pail in the shape of a rectangular prism. The pail is 25 cm long, 20 cm high and 10 cm wide.

⑦   What is the volume of the pail?

Answer : _____

⑧   How many litres of water does the pail hold?

Answer : _____

⑨   How many litres of water does the tank hold?

Answer : _____

⑩   After Alan has removed 8 pailfuls of water, what volume of air will be in the tank?

Answer : _____

⑪   How many litres of water will remain in the tank?

Answer : _____

⑫   How many pailfuls of water must be removed to half empty the tank?

Answer : _____

⑬   How many pailfuls of water must be removed to empty the entire tank?

Answer : _____

⑭   If Alan was emptying the water into an aquarium 1 m long and 0.25 m wide, how high would it be to just hold all the water from the tank?

Answer : _____

⑮   If Alan puts 6 metal balls into the tank and 75 000 cm^3 of water overflows, what is the volume of each metal ball?

Answer : _____

ISBN: 978-1-897164-15-0

Carol has 2 aquariums. The big one is 1 m long, 0.5 m wide and 0.6 m high. The small one is only 0.6 m long, but has the same height and width as the big one.

⑯ How much water can the big aquarium hold?

Answer : _____

⑰ How much water can the small aquarium hold?

Answer : _____

⑱ How much more water does the big aquarium hold than the small one?

Answer : _____

⑲ Each side of a cube is 10 cm long. If Carol tries to put the cubes into the small aquarium, how many cubes can the small aquarium hold?

Answer : _____

⑳ If Carol pumps 25 000 cm³ of water each minute into the big aquarium, how long does it take to fill up the whole aquarium?

Answer : _____

㉑ If it takes Carol 30 minutes to fill up the small aquarium with pails of water, how much water will she pour into the aquarium in one minute?

Answer : _____

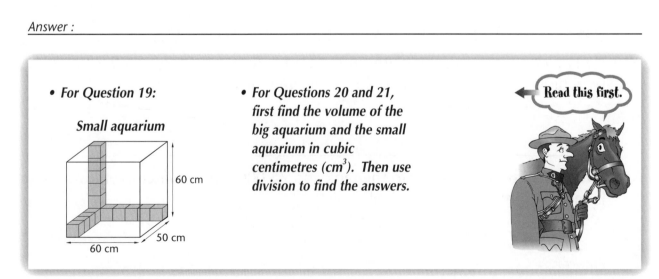

• For Question 19:

Small aquarium

60 cm
50 cm
60 cm

• For Questions 20 and 21, first find the volume of the big aquarium and the small aquarium in cubic centimetres (cm³). Then use division to find the answers.

Read this first.

ISBN: 978-1-897164-15-0

Look at the floor plan of Francis' new house. All the ceilings are 3 m high. Use the table to solve the problems. Show your work.

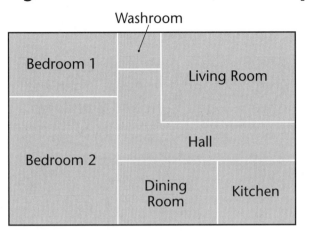

Washroom

Bedroom 1

Living Room

Bedroom 2

Hall

Dining Room

Kitchen

	Dimension
Bedroom 1	4 m × 7 m
Bedroom 2	8 m × 7 m
Washroom	2.3 m × 2.8 m
Dining room	4 m × 6.4 m
Kitchen	4 m × 5 m
Living room	5.6 m × 8.6 m

㉒ How much air is in the living room?

Answer : _____

㉓ How much air is in bedroom 2?

Answer : _____

㉔ How much more air is in bedroom 1 than in the washroom?

Answer : _____

㉕ Francis' father has built a store room in the kitchen. The area of the store room is one-eighth of the kitchen. What is its volume in cubic metres?

Answer : _____

㉖ What is the volume of the store room in cubic centimetres?

Answer : _____

CHALLENGE

Tina used 60 cubes each to build 2 models as shown. Each side of the cube was 1 cm long. Help her complete the table.

	Model	Volume (cm³)	Capacity (mL)
①	A		
②	B		

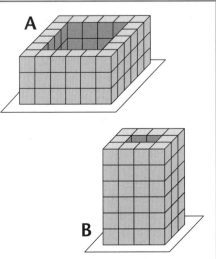

A

B

EXAMPLE

Kari was at position (2, 1). First she went 6 units right and 4 units up. Then she went 4 units left and 3 units down. Finally, she went 1 unit right and 2 units up. Show Kari's route on the grid and tell where she is now.

1st   : 6 units right & 4 units up ⟶ (8, 5)

2nd : 4 units left & 3 units down ⟶ (4, 2)

Final: 1 unit right & 2 units up ⟶ (5, 4)

Answer: She is at position (5, 4) now.

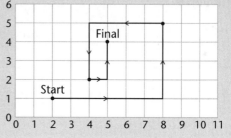

Solve the problems. Show your work.

Jerry calls out numbers and Lori has to guess the shape he is describing. Help Lori graph each set of ordered pairs and join them to form polygons. Then identify each polygon.

① (9, 5), (9, 1), (1, 1), (1, 5)

③ (3, 5), (10, 5), (9, 1), (2, 1)

② (6, 1), (9, 4), (2, 5)

④ (2, 5), (8, 5), (6, 1), (4, 1)

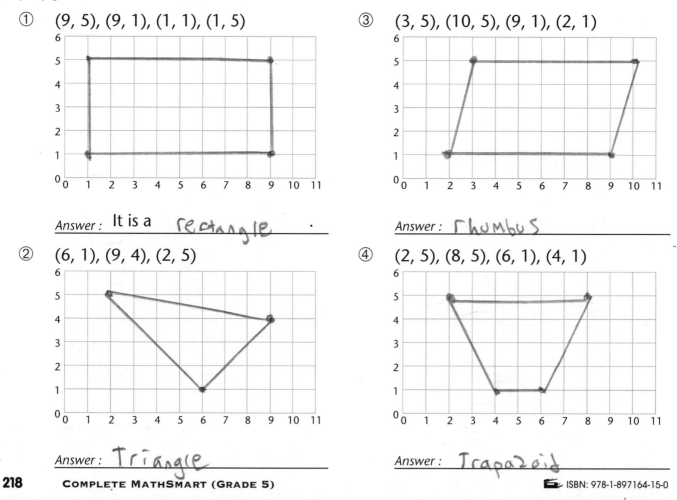

Answer: It is a ___rectangle___ .

Answer: ___rhombus___

Answer: ___Triangle___

Answer: ___Trapazoid___

ISBN: 978-1-897164-15-0

Jerry draws some incomplete shapes on the grid. Help Lori find the missing vertex to complete each shape and solve the problems.

⑤ The missing vertex is 3 units right and 2 units up from (7, 3).

a.
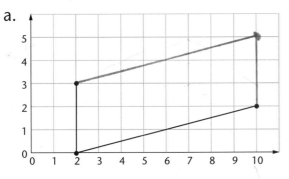

b. What is the ordered pair of the missing vertex?

Answer : (10, 5)

c. What shape is it?

Answer : rhumbyse

⑥ The missing vertex is 2 units right and 3 units up from (0, 2).

a.
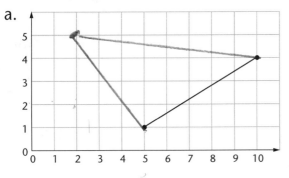

b. What is the ordered pair of the missing vertex?

Answer : (2, 5)

c. What shape is it?

Answer : Triangle

⑦ The missing vertex is 2 units up from (3, 0).

a.
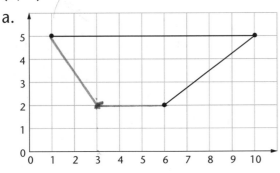

b. What is the ordered pair of the missing vertex?

Answer : (3, 2)

c. What shape is it?

Answer : Trapozoid

⑧ The missing vertex is between the ordered pairs (0, 4) and (4, 4).

a.
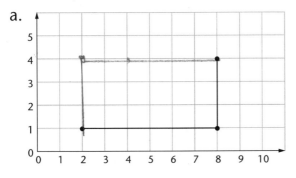

b. What is the ordered pair of the missing vertex?

Answer : (2, 4)

c. What shape is it?

Answer : rectengyle

ISBN: 978-1-897164-15-0

Dory's class is having a treasure hunt. They have a grid drawn over the map of an island. To find the treasure, they should follow Dory's instructions. Help the children find the coordinates of all the places and locate the traps on the grid. Then complete Dory's instructions and draw the route on the grid.

⑨ The origin is at (____ , ____) .

⑩ The temple is at _____ .

⑪ The castle is at _____ .

⑫ The arena is at _____ .

⑬ The cave is at _____ .

⑭ The treasure is at _____ .

⑮ There are 5 traps on the island. They are at (4, 2), (6, 4), (6, 7), (10, 4) and (12, 5). Label them with A, B, C, D and E respectively.

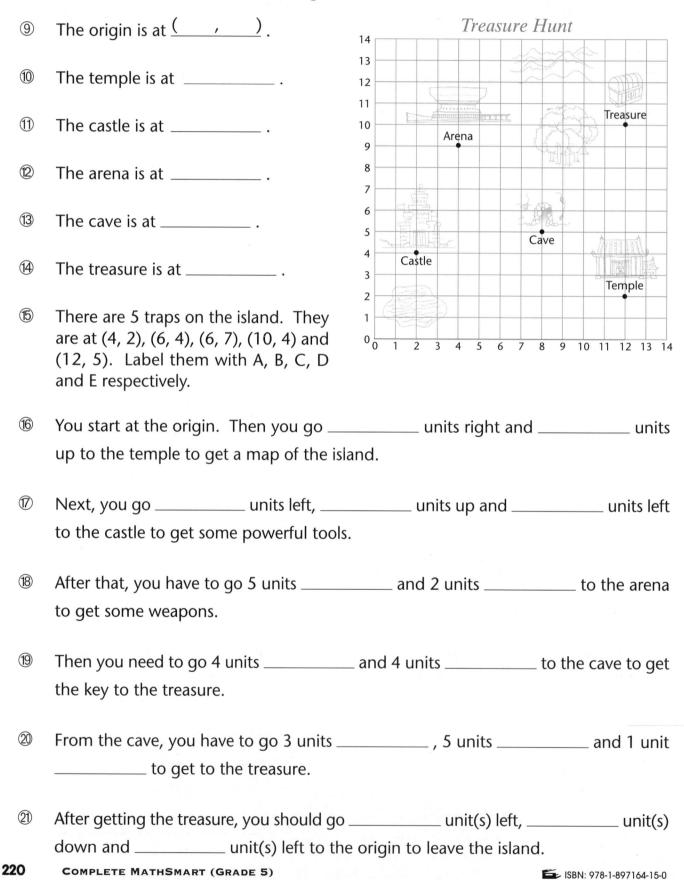

Treasure Hunt

⑯ You start at the origin. Then you go _____ units right and _____ units up to the temple to get a map of the island.

⑰ Next, you go _____ units left, _____ units up and _____ units left to the castle to get some powerful tools.

⑱ After that, you have to go 5 units _____ and 2 units _____ to the arena to get some weapons.

⑲ Then you need to go 4 units _____ and 4 units _____ to the cave to get the key to the treasure.

⑳ From the cave, you have to go 3 units _____ , 5 units _____ and 1 unit _____ to get to the treasure.

㉑ After getting the treasure, you should go _____ unit(s) left, _____ unit(s) down and _____ unit(s) left to the origin to leave the island.

ISBN: 978-1-897164-15-0

Use the clues to find the seats for the children. Write their names in the boxes and find the ordered pairs.

- Mary is sitting 2 units left from Lori; Daisy is sitting 2 units right from Lori.
- Matthew is sitting between Daisy and Jerry.
- George is sitting 2 units up from the origin; Susan is sitting 1 unit down from George.
- Alvin is sitting between Mary and Gary; Ray is sitting 1 unit left from Alvin.
- Walk 2 units down and 1 unit left from Michael and you can find Amy's seat.
- Emily is sitting between Michael and Sarah; Jessica is sitting 1 unit right from Emily.
- John is sitting 1 unit up from Jessica, and Emily is sitting between John and Elaine.

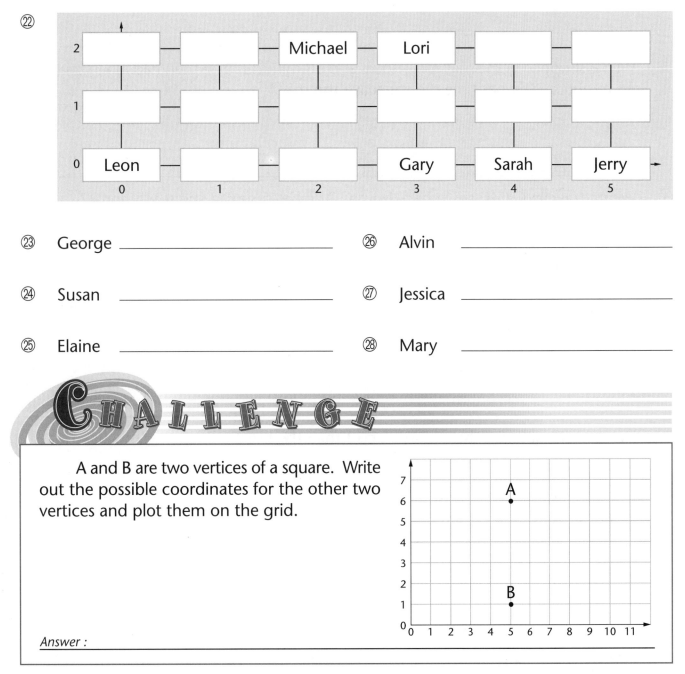

㉒

| | | Michael | Lori | | |
2

| | | | | | |
1

| Leon | | | Gary | Sarah | Jerry |
0

㉓ George _____ ㉖ Alvin _____

㉔ Susan _____ ㉗ Jessica _____

㉕ Elaine _____ ㉘ Mary _____

CHALLENGE

A and B are two vertices of a square. Write out the possible coordinates for the other two vertices and plot them on the grid.

Answer : _____

Solve the problems. Show your work.

Wilma went to the mall to buy some containers and an aquarium. She left home at 10:47 a.m. and travelled at an average speed of 50 km/h to get to the mall.

① Wilma reached the mall at 11:11 a.m. How long did she take to go from her home to the mall?

Answer : _____

② How far away was the mall from her house?

Answer: _____

③ Wilma shopped in the mall for 2 hours and 18 minutes. She then had lunch there for 45 minutes. At what time did she leave the mall?

Answer : _____

④ Wilma travelled at 40 km/h back home. At what time did she reach home?

Answer : _____

⑤ Wilma bought 1 box and 1 aquarium. The box cost $18.27 and the aquarium cost $52.49. What was her change from a $100 bill?

Answer : _____

⑥ How much more did the aquarium cost than the box?

Answer : _____

⑦ The box was 45 cm wide, 60 cm long and 50 cm high. Wilma wanted to cover the bottom of the box with felt. How much felt would she need?

Answer : _____

⑧ Wilma wanted to decorate the edges of the top sides of the box by drawing a border. How long would her border be?

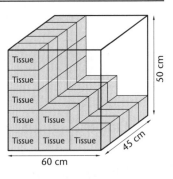

Answer : _____

⑨ What was the volume of the box?

Answer : _____

⑩ A box of tissue was 9 cm wide, 20 cm long and 10 cm high. How many boxes of tissue would the box hold?

Answer : _____

⑪ The aquarium was 20 cm wide, 40 cm long and 30 cm high. How many litres of water could the aquarium hold?

Answer : _____

⑫ Wilma turned on the tap to fill the aquarium with water from 4:29 p.m. until 4.34 p.m. How long did it take to fill up the whole aquarium?

Answer : _____

⑬ Wilma poured some water from the aquarium until the water level in the aquarium dropped 5 cm. How much water was in the aquarium?

Answer : _____

⑭ Wilma put 8 pebbles into the aquarium and the water level rose 0.5 cm. On average, what was the volume of each pebble?

Answer : _____

ISBN: 978-1-897164-15-0

Darlene has a grid drawn over the map of her neigbourhood. Follow Darlene's instructions to write the places in the boxes.

⑮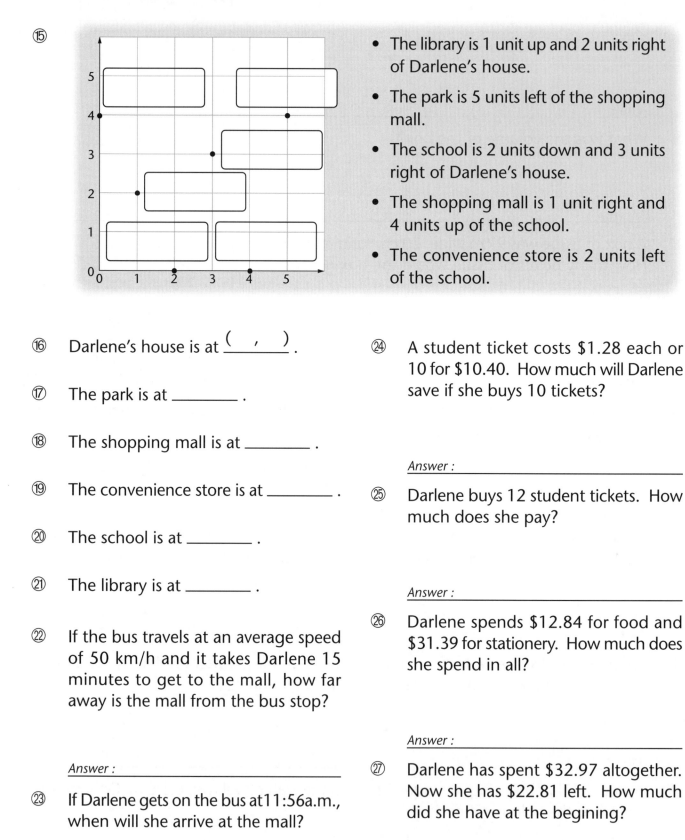

- The library is 1 unit up and 2 units right of Darlene's house.
- The park is 5 units left of the shopping mall.
- The school is 2 units down and 3 units right of Darlene's house.
- The shopping mall is 1 unit right and 4 units up of the school.
- The convenience store is 2 units left of the school.

⑯ Darlene's house is at (___ , ___) .

⑰ The park is at _____ .

⑱ The shopping mall is at _____ .

⑲ The convenience store is at _____ .

⑳ The school is at _____ .

㉑ The library is at _____ .

㉒ If the bus travels at an average speed of 50 km/h and it takes Darlene 15 minutes to get to the mall, how far away is the mall from the bus stop?

Answer : _____

㉓ If Darlene gets on the bus at 11:56 a.m., when will she arrive at the mall?

Answer : _____

㉔ A student ticket costs $1.28 each or 10 for $10.40. How much will Darlene save if she buys 10 tickets?

Answer : _____

㉕ Darlene buys 12 student tickets. How much does she pay?

Answer : _____

㉖ Darlene spends $12.84 for food and $31.39 for stationery. How much does she spend in all?

Answer : _____

㉗ Darlene has spent $32.97 altogether. Now she has $22.81 left. How much did she have at the begining?

Answer : _____

Circle the correct answer in each problem.

㉘ Gary is drawing a square on a grid. The vertices of the square are at (2, 0), (6, 0) and (2, 4). Where is the 4th vertex?

A. (4, 6)   B. (0, 6)   C. (6, 4)   D. (0, 4)

㉙ John is drawing a rectangle on a grid. The vertices of the rectangle are at (6, 2), (3, 5) and (1, 3). Where is the 4th vertex?

A. (0, 4)   B. (4, 0)   C. (5, 0)   D. (0, 5)

㉚ How much water would it take to half fill a rectangular box 1.6 m long, 0.6 m wide and 0.8 m high?

A. 384 L   B. 38.4 L   C. 3.84 L   D. 0.384 L

㉛ A bicycle and a car start at the same time from Bayville to Meadowview. The average speeds of the bicycle and the car are 20 km/h and 55 km/h. How far ahead is the car after 1 hour and 30 minutes?

A. 45.5 km   B. 54.5 km   C. 52.5 km   D. 30 km

㉜ A car takes 3 h 16 min to travel from Bayville to Meadowview. It leaves Bayville at 3:47 p.m. When will it arrive at Meadowview?

A. 6:33 p.m.   B. 8:03 p.m.   C. 6:03 p.m.   D. 7:03 p.m.

㉝ Georgia is planting her garden. Her plot is 4.2 m long and 3.5 m wide. She wants to put a fence around her plot. What length of fencing will she need?

A. 7.7 m   B. 14.7 m   C. 16.1 m   D. 15.4 m

㉞ If the fence costs $2.5 per metre, what will the cost of fencing be?

A. $19.25   B. $38.50   C. $36.75   D. $40.25

㉟ Georgia wants to plant one-seventh of her garden as lettuce. How much space will the lettuce take up?

A. 2.1 m^2 B. 7.7 m^2 C. 13 m^2 D. 14.7 m^2

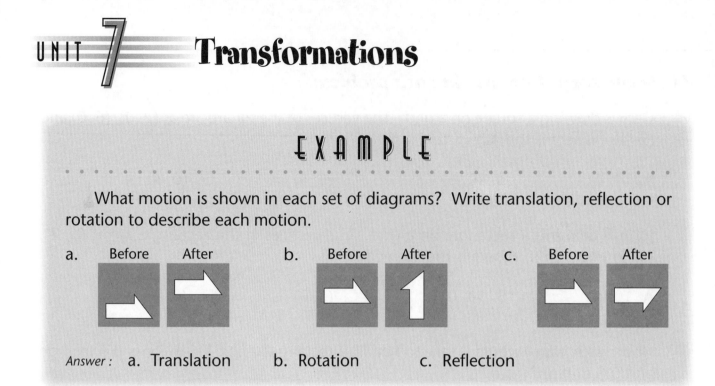

EXAMPLE

What motion is shown in each set of diagrams? Write translation, reflection or rotation to describe each motion.

a. Before After   b. Before After   c. Before After

Answer: a. Translation   b. Rotation   c. Reflection

Solve the problems. Show your work.

① Draw the reflection image of each polygon.

a.   b.   c.

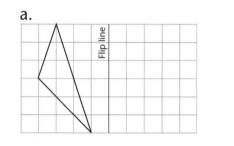
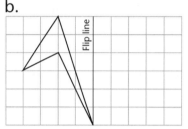

② Draw the rotation image of each polygon.

a. $\frac{1}{4}$ turn clockwise   b. $\frac{1}{2}$ turn clockwise   c. $\frac{1}{4}$ turn counterclockwise

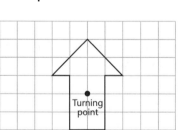
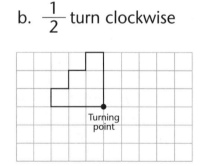
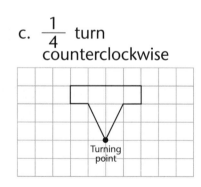

③ Draw the translation image of each polygon.

a. 2 units right
   1 unit down

b. 3 units right
   1 unit up

c. 3 units left
   2 units down

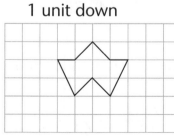
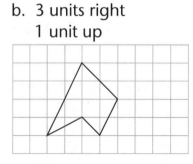
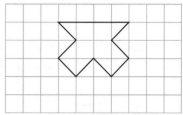

ISBN: 978-1-897164-15-0

④ Draw the flip line for the reflection image of each shaded polygon.

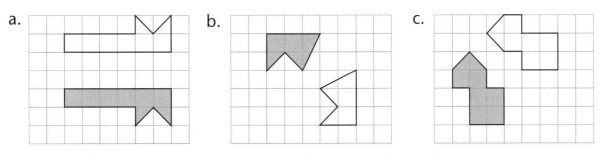

a.   b.   c.

⑤ Draw the turning point for the rotation image of each shaded polygon and tell whether the turn is $\frac{1}{4}$ turn, $\frac{1}{2}$ turn or $\frac{3}{4}$ turn clockwise.

a.

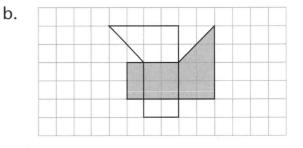

b.

Answer : _____   *Answer :* _____

⑥ Describe the translation image of each shaded polygon.

a.

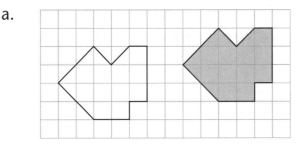

b.

Answer : _____   *Answer :* _____

⑦ Draw the reflection image of each shaded polygon over the flip lines l, m and n.

a.

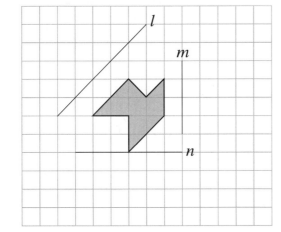

b.

Solve the problems.

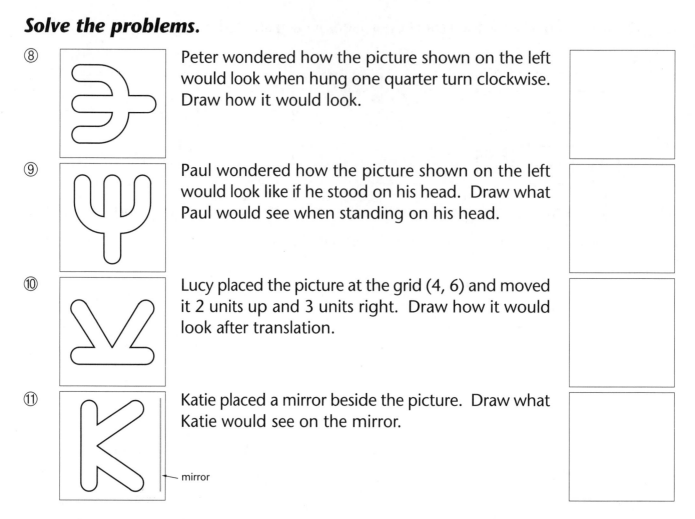

⑧ Peter wondered how the picture shown on the left would look when hung one quarter turn clockwise. Draw how it would look.

⑨ Paul wondered how the picture shown on the left would look like if he stood on his head. Draw what Paul would see when standing on his head.

⑩ Lucy placed the picture at the grid (4, 6) and moved it 2 units up and 3 units right. Draw how it would look after translation.

⑪ Katie placed a mirror beside the picture. Draw what Katie would see on the mirror.

mirror

Look at the polygons on the grid. Solve the problems. Show your work.

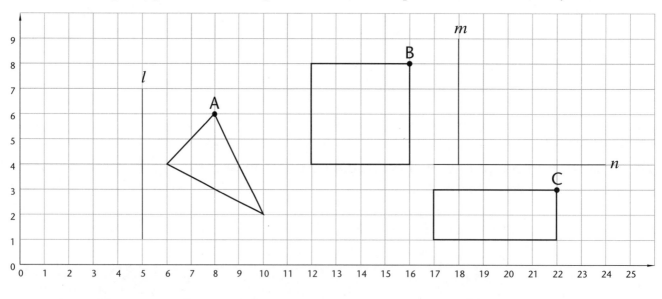

⑫ If Darren makes a $\frac{1}{4}$ turn clockwise about the point (6, 4) of the triangle, what will be the ordered pair of vertex A of the turned image?

Answer : _____

ISBN: 978-1-897164-15-0

⑬ If Darren flips the triangle over line *l*, what will be the ordered pair of vertex A of the flipped image?

Answer : _____

⑭ If the ordered pair of the translation image of vertex B is (10, 6), describe how Terry translates the square to its image.

Answer : _____

⑮ If Terry flips the square over the line *m*, what will be the ordered pair of vertex B of the flipped image?

Answer : _____

⑯ If Grace makes a $\frac{1}{4}$ turn counterclockwise about the point (17, 3) of the rectangle, what will be the ordered pair of vertex C of the turned image?

Answer : _____

⑰ If the ordered pair of the translation image of vertex C is (23, 7), describe how Grace translates the rectangle to its image.

Answer : _____

⑱ If Grace flips the rectangle over line *n*, what will be the ordered pair of vertex C of the flipped image?

Answer : _____

CHALLENGE

Sam is turning his sticker counterclockwise. Which set of the diagrams below shows the movement of the sticker? Circle the correct answer.

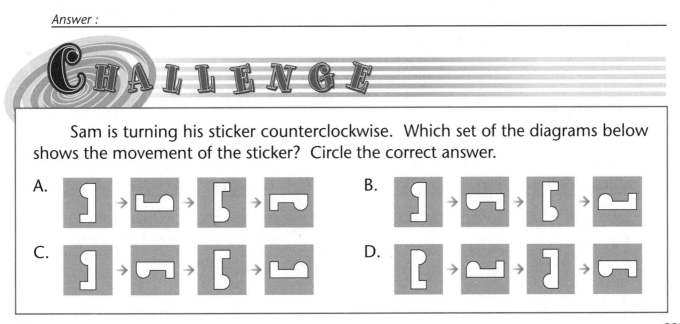

A.

B.

C.

D.

EXAMPLE

Mary used a line graph to show the number of stamps she had. How many more stamps did Mary have in December than in August?

No. of stamps in Dec : 25

No. of stamps in Aug : 5

Difference : 25 − 5 = 20

Answer : Mary had 20 more stamps in December than in August.

Use the graphs to solve the problems. Show your work.

Larry recorded the number of toy cars produced by the factory last week.

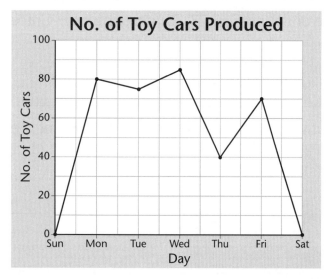

③ How many more toy cars were produced on Wednesday than on Thursday?

Answer : _____

④ One of the production lines in the factory broke down last week. Which day did it happen? Explain.

Answer : _____

① How many toy cars were produced last Monday?

 toy cars were produced

Answer : last Monday. _____

⑤ On which days was the factory closed? Explain.

Answer : _____

② How many toy cars were produced last Friday?

⑥ On average, how many toy cars were produced each working day?

Answer : _____

Answer : _____

ISBN: 978-1-897164-15-0

Larry's factory produces 3 types of toy cars. He kept track of the production in the past year.

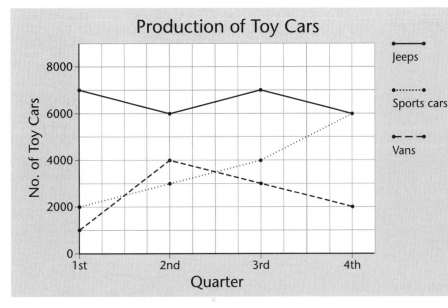

⑦ How many sports cars were produced in the 1st quarter?

Answer : _____

⑧ How many vans were produced in the 2nd quarter?

Answer : _____

⑨ How many jeeps were produced in the 3rd quarter?

Answer : _____

⑩ How many more vans were produced in the 4th quarter than in the 1st quarter?

Answer : _____

⑪ How many jeeps were produced from the 1st quarter to the 4th quarter?

Answer : _____

⑫ How many vehicles were produced in the 4th quarter?

Answer : _____

⑬ In which quarter was the number of jeeps 3 times the number of vans?

Answer : _____

⑭ In which quarter did Larry's factory produce more vans than sports cars?

Answer : _____

⑮ What did the line for sports cars indicate?

Answer : _____

⑯ If Larry wanted to cut one of his production lines, which one should be cut? Explain.

Answer : _____

Darcy and Horace wanted to buy a gift for their sister. They used a table to record their savings. Use their table to make a line graph and solve the problems.

⑰ **Darcy's and Horace's Savings**

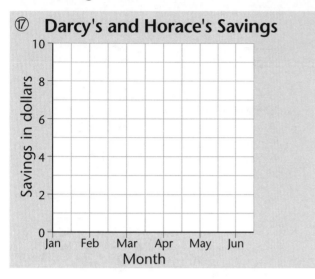

	Darcy's savings	Horace's savings
JAN	$4.50	$4.50
FEB	$2.00	$6.00
MAR	$8.50	$3.50
APR	$4.50	$7.00
MAY	$7.00	$6.00
JUN	$6.50	$5.50

⑱ How much more did Darcy save than Horace in March?

Answer : _____

⑲ How much more did Horace save than Darcy in February?

Answer : _____

⑳ In which months did Darcy save more than Horace?

Answer : _____

㉑ How many months were Darcy's savings more than Horace's?

Answer : _____

㉒ In which month were their savings the same?

Answer : _____

• *Don't forget to label the lines on the line graph. e.g.*

Read this first.

Amy
John

㉓ How much did Darcy save in the six months?

Answer : _____

㉔ How much did Horace save in the six months?

Answer : _____

㉕ If the birthday gift for their sister cost $65.39, would they have enough money to buy it?

Answer : _____

ISBN: 978-1-897164-15-0

Mrs Harding sold her nuts in bags. She recorded the sales of cashews and almonds in the past year. Use her table to make a line graph and solve the problems.

	JAN	FEB	MAR	APR	MAY	JUN	JUL	AUG	SEP	OCT	NOV	DEC
No. of bags of cashews sold	250	350	300	450	350	300	250	250	250	300	200	200
No. of bags of almonds sold	150	150	100	150	200	250	300	300	350	400	400	450

㉖
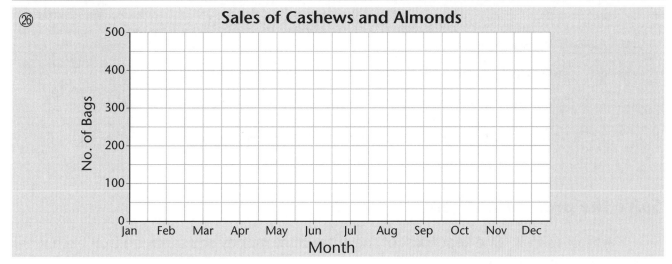

㉗ How many more bags of cashews were sold than almonds in April?

Answer : _____

㉘ How many more bags of almonds were sold than cashews in September ?

Answer : _____

㉙ How many bags of nuts did Mrs Harding sell in June?

Answer : _____

㉚ During which month did the sales of cashews increase the most?

Answer : _____

CHALLENGE

Look at the above line graph. Describe the trend of sales of cashews and the trend of sales of almonds.

Answer : _____

ISBN: 978-1-897164-15-0

EXAMPLE

Dora's parents were looking at Dora's circle graph. It showed the time she was awake and the time she spent sleeping. They said that Dora should be getting more sleep. How did they know?

Answer : They found that only $\frac{1}{4}$ of the circle represented sleeping. Since $\frac{1}{4}$ of 24 hours is 6 hours, they thought that Dora did not have enough sleep.

Dora's Day

Solve the problems. Show your work.

Karin loves fruit. She kept track of the amount of money she spent on fruit each week and drew the circle graph.

① Which fruit did Karin spend the most money on?

Answer : Karin spent the most money on _____.

② Which section represents the fruit that Karin spent the most money on? Colour it red.

③ Which fruit did Karin spend the least money on?

Answer : _____

④ Which section represents the fruit that Karin spent the least money on? Colour it green.

⑤ If Karin spent $100.00 on fruit, how much would she spend on pears?

Answer : _____

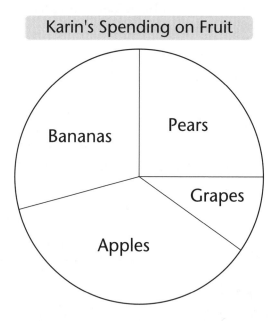

Karin's Spending on Fruit

⑥ List the fruits from the one Karin spent the most money on to the one she spent the least money on.

Answer : _____

ISBN: 978-1-897164-15-0

Gary's teacher, Mr Milne, made a circle graph to represent the number of students in each group that scored an A on the test.

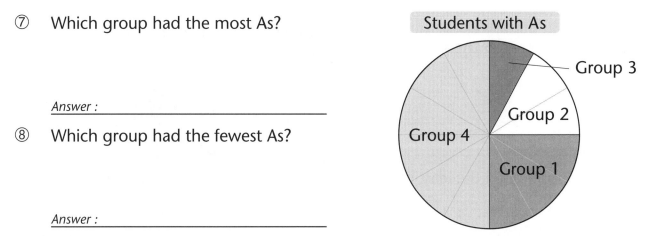

Students with As

⑦ Which group had the most As?

Answer : _____

⑧ Which group had the fewest As?

Answer : _____

⑨ Altogether, there were 12 students who scored an A. How many students with an A were in group 4?

Answer : _____

⑩ How many students with an A were in group 1?

Answer : _____

⑪ Half of the students in group 4 got an A on the test. How many students were there in group 4?

Answer : _____

⑫ Each group had the same number of students. How many students took the test?

Answer : _____

⑬ There were 5 students with Bs in group 1, 1 in group 2, 4 in group 3 and 2 in group 4. Colour the circle graph and the boxes with matching colours to show the number of students in each group that scored a B on the test.

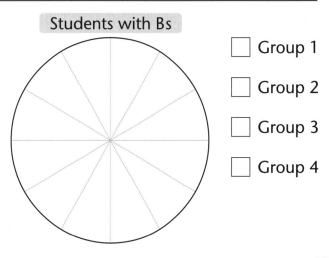

Students with Bs

☐ Group 1

☐ Group 2

☐ Group 3

☐ Group 4

Four groups of children sold apples to raise money for charity. Lori, John, Mario and Shirley were the group representatives. Their teacher, Mrs Carter, recorded the results in the circle graph.

⑭ Which group raised the second most money?

Answer : _____

⑮ Which group raised the least money?

Answer : _____

⑯ List the group representatives from the most money raised to the least.

Answer : _____

⑰ John's group raised $24.00. How much money did Mario's group raise?

Answer : _____

⑱ How much money did Shirley's group raise?

Answer : _____

⑲ How much money did Lori's group raise?

Answer : _____

⑳ How much money did the children raise altogether?

Answer : _____

Money Raised in Apple Sale

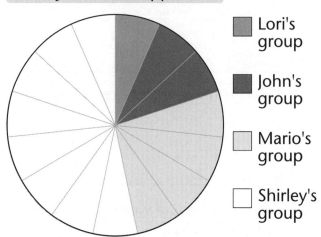

Lori's group

John's group

Mario's group

Shirley's group

㉑ If the cost of each apple was the same, which group sold the most number of apples? Explain.

Answer : _____

㉒ Which group sold the second most number of apples? Explain.

Answer : _____

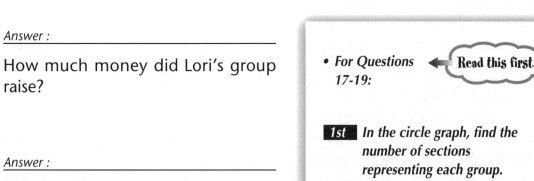

- **For Questions 17-19:**   ← Read this first.

1st In the circle graph, find the number of sections representing each group.

2nd Compare each group with John's group and calculate.

ISBN: 978-1-897164-15-0

Willy drew a circle graph to show how much time he spent on video games each day last week.

㉓ Which day did Willy spend the most time on video games?

Answer : _____

㉔ Which day did he spend the second most time on video games?

Answer : _____

㉕ Which days did he not play video games?

Answer : _____

㉖ Willy spent 1 hour playing video games on Friday. How many hours did he play video games on Monday?

Answer : _____

Time Spent on Video Games

■ Sunday
□ Monday
■ Wednesday
■ Friday
□ Saturday

㉗ How many hours did he play video games on Saturday?

Answer : _____

㉘ How many more hours did he play video games on Sunday than on Wednesday?

Answer : _____

CHALLENGE

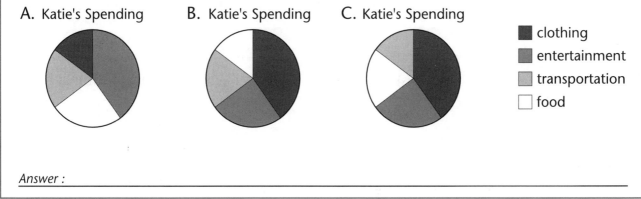

Katie had $20.00. She spent $8.00 on clothing, $5.00 on entertainment, $3.00 on food and $4.00 on transportation. Which of the circle graphs below is the best to show Katie's spending? Explain.

A. Katie's Spending   B. Katie's Spending   C. Katie's Spending

■ clothing
■ entertainment
■ transportation
□ food

Answer : _____

ISBN: 978-1-897164-15-0

EXAMPLE

Ken got his report card with the following marks : 87, 75, 78, 56, 78 and 88. What were his mean and mode marks?

Mean : (87 + 75 + 78 + 56 + 78 + 88) ÷ 6 = 462 ÷ 6 = 77

Mode : 87, 75, 78, 56, 78, 88 ——— 78 occurs the most often.

Answer : His mean mark was 77 and his mode mark was 78.

Solve the problems. Show your work.

Lori was trying to improve her running speed. She practised in the park every morning for the past 4 weeks. Her times were recorded in the table.

① What was Lori's mean running time in the 1st week?

Her mean running time was

Answer : _____ s.

② What was her mean running time in the 2nd week?

Answer : _____

Lori's Running Time				
Day \ Week	1st	2nd	3rd	4th
Sun	127s	110s	124s	100s
Mon	117s	126s	106s	125s
Tue	120s	112s	98s	105s
Wed	105s	104s	110s	104s
Thu	110s	108s	106s	100s
Fri	105s	110s	106s	104s
Sat	100s	121s	106s	104s

③ What was her mean running time in the 3rd week?

Answer : _____

④ What was her mean running time in the 4th week?

Answer : _____

⑤ What was her mode running time in the 3rd week?

Answer : _____

⑥ What was her mode running time in the 4th week?

Answer : _____

ISBN: 978-1-897164-15-0

Mr Layton grouped the children and listed their allowances.

Group A	
Frank	$5.00
Kelly	$6.75
Ray	$5.37
Peter	$5.00

Group B	
Ron	$6.80
Amy	$9.15
Rachel	$4.16
Beatrice	$4.16
Tim	$4.18

Group C	
George	$3.83
Ringo	$7.37
Elaine	$3.83

Group D	
Lily	$4.75
Donny	$8.13
Terry	$4.75
Cindy	$4.75
Mark	$8.13
Wayne	$0.69

⑦ Who had the highest allowance in the class?

Answer : _____

⑧ Who had the lowest allowance in the class?

Answer : _____

⑨ What was the mean allowance received by the students in group A?

Answer : _____

⑩ What was the mean allowance received by the students in group C?

Answer : _____

⑪ Was the mean allowance received by the students in group B higher than that by group D?

Answer : _____

⑫ What was the mode allowance in group B?

Answer : _____

⑬ What was the mode allowance in group D?

Answer : _____

⑭ If Tim was placed in group A, what would the mean allowance of group A be?

Answer : _____

⑮ If one of the students in group D joined group C and changed the mean allowance of group C to $5.79, who were the possible students?

Answer : _____

Henry, Larry, Michael and Elaine were comparing their trading cards. Henry had 258 cards, Larry 426, Michael 426 and Elaine 678.

⑯ What was the mean number of cards that the 4 children had?

Answer : _____

⑰ What was the mode number of cards that the 4 children had?

Answer : _____

⑱ If Elaine gave Henry 126 cards, what would be the mean number of cards that the 4 children had?

Answer : _____

⑲ What would be the mode number of cards that the 4 children had?

Answer : _____

⑳ If Larry gave Michael 252 cards, what would be the mean number of cards that the 4 children had?

Answer : _____

㉑ What would be the mode number of cards that the 4 children had?

Answer : _____

㉒ If Michael gave Larry 60 cards and Henry gave Elaine 40 cards, what would be the mean number of cards that the 4 children had?

Answer : _____

㉓ If Larry bought 28 cards and Henry bought 120 cards, what would be the mean number of cards that the 4 children had?

Answer : _____

㉔ If Elaine lost 88 cards, what would be the mean number of cards that the 4 children had?

Answer : _____

㉕ If the 4 children gave 160 cards to their friends, Ray, what would be their mean number of cards afterwards?

Answer : _____

㉖ If Michael lost 48 cards and Henry bought 12 cards, what would be the mean number of cards that the 4 children had?

Answer : _____

ISBN: 978-1-897164-15-0

㉗ Tim has an average of 135 cards in 4 boxes. Which 4 of these boxes are his?

Ⓐ 110   Ⓑ 150   Ⓒ 120   Ⓓ 130   Ⓔ 180

Answer : _____

㉘ If all the above boxes belonged to Tim, what would be the mean number of cards in each box?

Answer : _____

㉙ Elaine has an average of 12.35 kg of flour in 4 bags. Which 4 of these bags are hers?

Ⓐ Flour 10.68 kg   Ⓑ Flour 12.37 kg   Ⓒ Flour 13.25 kg   Ⓓ Flour 11.89 kg   Ⓔ Flour 14.46 kg

Answer : _____

㉚ If all the above bags belonged to Elaine, what would be the mean amount in each bag?

Answer : _____

CHALLENGE

Don spilled some hot chocolate onto his report card, covering his mark in Math. He got 78 in English, 86 in Social Studies, 92 in Science and 68 in Physical Education. His average mark was 76.

① What was his mark in Math?

Answer : _____

② If he wanted an average mark of 77, how much would he have to get in Math?

Answer : _____

ISBN: 978-1-897164-15-0

Probability

EXAMPLE

Harry has a bag with 5 red balls and 7 blue balls. If he takes out one ball, what is the probability that the ball will be red?

Think : There are 12 balls altogether; 5 out of 12 balls are red.

Answer : The probability that the ball will be red is 5 out of 12, or $\frac{5}{12}$.

Solve the problems. Show your work.

Donny and Sari drew a circle on a piece of cardboard and divided it into 4 sections. Then they mounted a pointer in the centre and spun 100 times.

Section	Ice cream	Pop	Lollipop	Popsicle
No. of times occurred	40	10	30	20

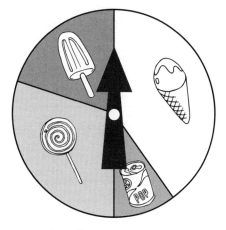

① Complete the bar graph to show the number of times each outcome occurred.

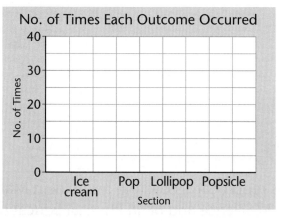

② What fraction of times did the pointer stop on 'ice cream'?

Answer : _____

③ What fraction of times did the pointer stop on 'pop'?

Answer : _____

④ What fraction of times did the pointer stop on 'lollipop'?

Answer : _____

⑤ On which section do you think the spinner is least likely to stop?

Answer : _____

⑥ On which section do you think the spinner is most likely to stop?

Answer : _____

   ISBN: 978-1-897164-15-0

See how many marbles each child has. Help them solve the problems. Show your work.

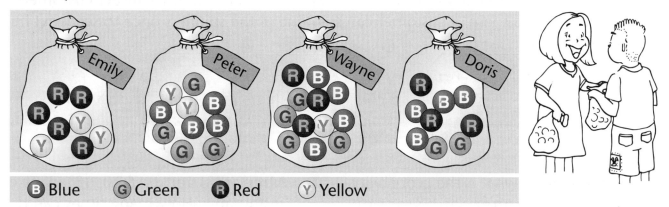

B Blue   **G** Green   **R** Red   **Y** Yellow

⑦ If Emily draws out a marble from her bag, what is the probability that the marble will be red?

Answer : _____

⑧ If Peter draws out a marble from his bag, what is the probability that the marble will be blue?

Answer : _____

⑨ If Wayne draws out a marble from his bag, what is the probability that the marble will be green?

Answer : _____

⑩ If Doris draws out a marble from her bag, what is the probability that the marble will be yellow?

Answer : _____

⑪ If Emily puts all her marbles into Peter's bag and draws out a marble from his bag, what is the probability that the marble will be blue?

Answer : _____

⑫ Doris says, 'If I draw out a marble from my bag, the most likely marble is red.' Is she correct? Explain.

Answer : _____

Solve the problems. Show your work.

The Fisher King Restaurant is holding a 'Spin and Win' event to attract customers. For every ten dollars spent, a customer can spin one of the spinners once to see what he or she can get.

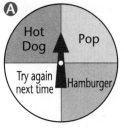 

⑬ For spinner A, what is the probability that the spinner will stop on 'hamburger'?

Answer : _____

⑭ For spinner B, what is the probability that the spinner will stop on 'sandwich'?

Answer : _____

⑮ For spinner C, what is the probability that the spinner will stop on 'pop'?

Answer : _____

⑯ For spinner C, what is the probability that the spinner will stop on 'hot dog'?

Answer : _____

⑰ Which spinner has the greatest probability that the spinner will stop on 'hot dog'?

Answer : _____

⑱ Which spinner has the least probability that the spinner will stop on 'try again next time'?

Answer : _____

⑲ Michael spends $20.08 in the restaurant. How many times can he spin?

Answer : _____

⑳ If Michael wants to have a free hot dog, which spinner should he spin? Explain.

Answer : _____

㉑ If Michael chooses spinner A, what is the probability that the spinner will stop on 'hot dog', 'pop', 'hamburger' or 'try again next time'?

Answer : _____

㉒ If Michael chooses spinner C, what is the probability that the spinner will stop on 'coffee'?

Answer : _____

- **The sum of the probability of all possible outcomes must be equal to 1.**
- **If an event never occurs, then the probability is zero.**

Read this first.

ISBN: 978-1-897164-15-0

Joe has 1 yellow marble, 1 blue marble and 1 red marble in his bag. Tim has a penny. They try to take a marble from the bag and flip the coin once.

㉓ Complete the tree diagram to show all the possible outcomes.

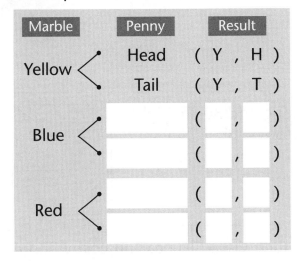

Marble	Penny	Result
Yellow	Head	(Y , H)
	Tail	(Y , T)
Blue		(,)
		(,)
Red		(,)
		(,)

㉔ How many possible outcomes are there?

Answer : _____

㉕ What is the probability that they will get a red marble and a head?

Answer : _____

㉖ What is the probability that they will get a blue marble and a tail?

Answer : _____

㉗ Joe says, 'The probability of getting a blue marble and a head is greater than the probability of getting a red marble and a tail.' Is he correct? Explain.

Answer : _____

㉘ If Joe and Tim played the games 60 times, about how many times would they get a yellow marble and a head?

Answer : _____

CHALLENGE

Which 2 of the 4 spinners below show the same probability of getting each letter? Explain.

Spinner A

Spinner B

Spinner C

Spinner D

Answer : _____

Solve the problems. Show your work.

Mrs Quinn, the convenience store owner, was packing cereal boxes into a carton 20 cm wide, 60 cm long and 90 cm high.

① What was the volume of the carton?

Answer : _____

② Each cereal box was 5 cm wide, 15 cm long and 30 cm high. How many boxes of cereal would the carton hold?

Answer : _____

③ If each box of cereal cost $2.99, how much would the carton cost when it was packed full?

Answer : _____

④ Mrs Quinn filled the carton with 18 boxes of bran flakes, 8 boxes of rice flakes, 10 boxes of corn flakes and some boxes of granola. How many boxes of granola were there?

Answer : _____

⑤ If Mrs Quinn took out 1 box of cereal from the carton, what would be the probability that it was a box of rice flakes?

Answer : _____

⑥ If Mrs Quinn took out 1 box of cereal from the carton, what would be the probability that it was not a box of corn flakes?

Answer : _____

⑦ Which type of cereal had the greatest probability that it would be taken out by Mrs Quinn? Explain.

Answer : _____

ISBN: 978-1-897164-15-0

⑧ Mrs Quinn wanted to use a circle graph to show the different kinds of cereal in the carton. Each sector in the circle graph represents 2 boxes. Colour the circle graph and the boxes with matching colours to show the number of each kind of cereal in the carton.

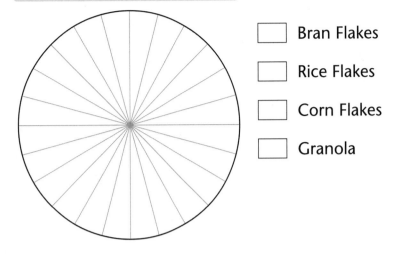

Number of Boxes of Cereal

☐ Bran Flakes

☐ Rice Flakes

☐ Corn Flakes

☐ Granola

Mrs Quinn recorded the number of cartons of cereal sold last year. Use the table to make a line graph.

	Jan	Feb	Mar	Apr	May	Jun	Jul	Aug	Sep	Oct	Nov	Dec
No. of cartons of cereal sold	125	100	150	50	25	75	150	125	100	100	75	125

⑨ **No. of Cartons of Cereal Sold**

(line graph grid — No. of Cartons vs Month, Jan–Dec)

⑩ How many more cartons were sold in August than in May?

Answer : _____

⑪ On average, how many cartons were sold each month?

Answer : _____

⑫ If the delivery charge for 1 carton was $0.25, how much would be the cost of delivery in November?

Answer : _____

ISBN: 978-1-897164-15-0

Look at the report cards of some of the students in Miss Bliss' class.

Sarah		
English	:	80
Math	:	86
French	:	86
Art	:	75
Science	:	79
Drama	:	86

Molly		
English	:	78
Math	:	91
French	:	78
Art	:	65
Science	:	85
Drama	:	89

Stanley		
English	:	76
Math	:	88
French	:	97
Art	:	72
Science	:	76
Drama	:	83

Elaine		
English	:	82
Math	:	97
French	:	69
Art	:	96
Science	:	80
Drama	:	80

⑬ What was Sarah's mean mark?

Answer : _____

⑭ What was Molly's mean mark?

Answer : _____

⑮ What was Stanley's mean mark?

Answer : _____

⑯ What was Elaine's mean mark?

Answer : _____

⑰ What was Sarah's mode mark?

Answer : _____

⑱ Which students had their mean mark higher than their mode mark?

Answer : _____

⑲ What was the mean mark in English for these 4 students?

Answer : _____

⑳ What was the mean mark in Drama for these 4 students?

Answer : _____

㉑ The children shuffled their report cards and placed them face down. If Elaine picked a card, what was the probability that she would pick her own card?

Answer : _____

㉒ If Molly picked a card, what was the probability that she would not pick her own card?

Answer : _____

㉓ If Stanley played the game 40 times, about how many times would he get his own card?

Answer : _____

   ISBN: 978-1-897164-15-0

Circle the correct answer in each problem.

㉔ Which of the diagrams below is the same as its reflection image?

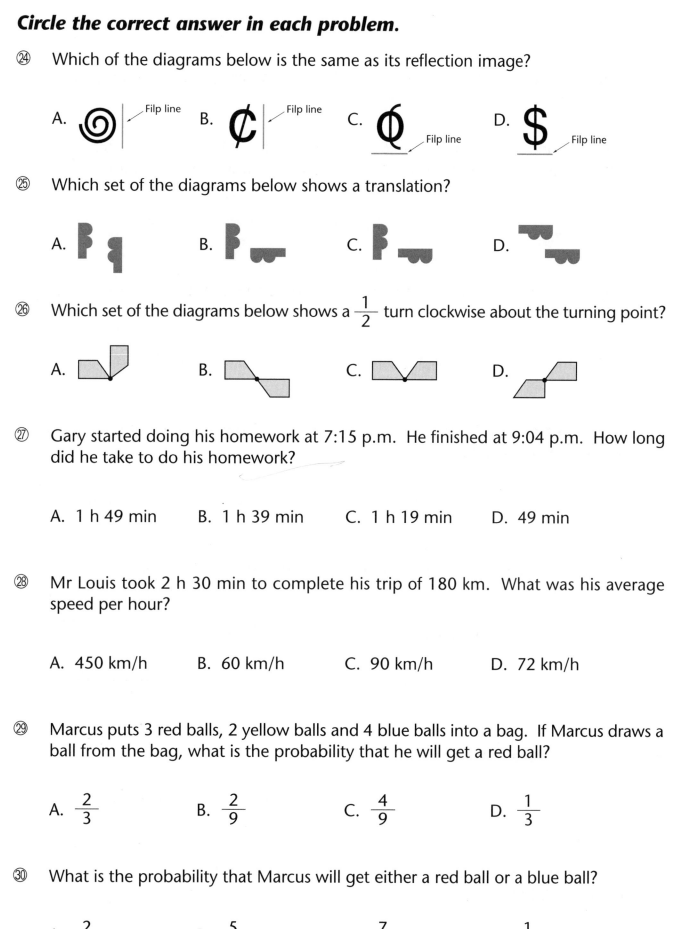

A. ⊚ — Flip line   B. ¢ — Flip line   C. ¢ Flip line   D. $ Flip line

㉕ Which set of the diagrams below shows a translation?

A. ▶ ▮   B. ▶ ▬   C. ▶ ▬   D. ▬ ▬

㉖ Which set of the diagrams below shows a $\frac{1}{2}$ turn clockwise about the turning point?

A.   B.   C.   D.

㉗ Gary started doing his homework at 7:15 p.m. He finished at 9:04 p.m. How long did he take to do his homework?

A. 1 h 49 min   B. 1 h 39 min   C. 1 h 19 min   D. 49 min

㉘ Mr Louis took 2 h 30 min to complete his trip of 180 km. What was his average speed per hour?

A. 450 km/h   B. 60 km/h   C. 90 km/h   D. 72 km/h

㉙ Marcus puts 3 red balls, 2 yellow balls and 4 blue balls into a bag. If Marcus draws a ball from the bag, what is the probability that he will get a red ball?

A. $\frac{2}{3}$ B. $\frac{2}{9}$ C. $\frac{4}{9}$ D. $\frac{1}{3}$

㉚ What is the probability that Marcus will get either a red ball or a blue ball?

A. $\frac{2}{3}$ B. $\frac{5}{9}$ C. $\frac{7}{9}$ D. $\frac{1}{3}$

③① How many minutes are there from 11:49 a.m. to 1:07 p.m.?

   A. 68 minutes   B. 78 minutes   C. 18 minutes   D. 118 minutes

③② Paul is looking at his watch. The 6 is nearest to him. If he gave the watch a quarter turn counterclockwise, what number would be farthest away from him?

   A. 3   B. 6   C. 9   D. 12

③③ Kelly has a swimming pool 16 m long, 12 m wide and 2 m deep. She wants to fill it right up to the top with water. How many cubic metres of water will she need?

   A. 384 m^3 B. 192 m^3 C. 30 m^3 D. 768 m^3

③④ The hose carries 6 cubic metres of water a minute. How many minutes will it take to fill Kelly's swimming pool?

   A. 5 minutes   B. 32 minutes   C. 64 minutes   D. 128 minutes

③⑤ Look at the shape on the right. What is the perimeter of the shape?

   A. 10.4 cm   B. 9.7cm

   C. 7.9 cm   D. 12.2 cm

③⑥ What is the area of the shape?

   A. 4.5 cm^2 B. 7.2 cm^2 C. 6.48 cm^2 D. 5.4 cm^2

③⑦ The heights of three boys are 1 m 2 cm, 1 m 9 cm and 1 m 16 cm. What is their average height?

   A. 1 m 4 cm   B. 1 m 5 cm   C. 1 m 6 cm   D. 1 m 9 cm

   ISBN: 978-1-897164-15-0

1. Large Numbers

- → Children learn how to write and read large numbers up to a hundred million.
- → Advise children to start writing a number from the ones digit, and leave a space between every three numerals counted from the right.

  Example   Write 14 803 765 instead of 14803765.

- → When rounding a number to a certain place value, the digit immediately to the right of that place has to be considered.

  Example   Round 14 803 765 and 2 497 382 to the nearest thousand.

  14 803 765 ← The hundreds digit 7 is greater than 5, so round up to 14 804 000.

  2 497 382 ← The hundreds digit 3 is less than 5, so round down to 2 497 000.

2. Distributive Property of Multiplication

- → Encourage children to apply the distributive property of multiplication to simplify their calculation.

  Example   42 x 7 + 42 x 3

  = 294 + 126 ← Multiply in the usual   = 42 x (7 + 3) ← Apply the distributive
  way; then add.

  = 420   = 42 x 10   property of multiplication.

  = 420

- → Remind children that the distributive property does not apply to division.

  Example   24 ÷ 2 + 24 ÷ 4

  = 12 + 6   24 ÷ 2 + 24 ÷ 4

  = 18 ✔   = 24 ÷ (2 + 4)

  = 24 ÷ 6

  = 4 ✘

3. Prime and Composite Numbers

- → Children learn the difference between prime and composite numbers. Parents may emphasize the following points:

  a. 1 is neither a prime number nor a composite number.

  b. All prime numbers except 2 are odd numbers.

  c. All numbers with the ones digit equal to 5 are composite numbers except for 5.

  d. A number with only 1 and itself as factors is a prime number.

  e. A number with more than two factors is a composite number.

  f. A number which can form a rectangle is a composite number.

4. Fractions

- → Remind children that the value of a fraction equals 1 if its numerator and denominator are equal, and that any whole number can be written as an improper fraction.

- → Make sure that children understand equivalent fractions have the same numerical value.

- To add or subtract fractions with like denominators, children should add or subtract the numerators only and keep the denominator the same. To add or subtract mixed numbers, they can either add or subtract the whole numbers and fractions separately, or change the mixed numbers to improper fractions before calculation.

- Reduce 1 to an improper fraction if necessary when subtracting fractions.

- To multiply two fractions, multiply their numerators and denominators respectively. To divide a fraction by another fraction, invert the fraction immediately after the ÷ sign and change ÷ to x.

- If the divisor is a whole number, remind children to change it to a fraction with denominator 1 before doing the division.

Example $\frac{4}{5} \div 2 = \frac{4}{5} \div \frac{2}{1} = \frac{\overset{2}{\cancel{4}}}{5} \times \frac{1}{\cancel{2}_1} = \frac{2}{5}$

5. Decimals

- Remind children to align the decimal points when doing vertical addition or subtraction.

- The number of decimal places in the product is the same as that in the question. Add enough "0"s before the non-zero digits if necessary to locate the decimal point, and the "0"s at the end of the product can be deleted after locating the decimal point.

Example   0.5 x 0.08 = ?

$$\begin{array}{r} 0.0\,8 \\ \times\quad 0.5 \\ \hline 4\,0 \end{array} \longrightarrow \begin{array}{r} 0.0\,8 \\ \times\quad 0.5 \\ \hline 0.0\,4\,0 \end{array}$$

This "0" can be deleted after ← locating the decimal point.

Add 2 "0"s to locate the decimal point.

- When dividing, don't forget to add a "0" before the decimal point if necessary to locate the decimal point. If there is a remainder, add "0"s to the right of the dividend after the decimal point and continue to divide until the remainder is zero or there are enough decimal places.

Example   4.8 ÷ 5 = ?

$$\begin{array}{r} 9 \\ 5\,\overline{)\,4.8} \\ 4\,5 \\ \hline 3 \end{array} \rightarrow \begin{array}{r} 9 \\ 5\,\overline{)\,4.8\,0} \\ 4\,5 \\ \hline 3\,0 \end{array} \rightarrow \begin{array}{r} 9\,6 \\ 5\,\overline{)\,4.8\,0} \\ 4\,5 \\ \hline 3\,0 \\ 3\,0 \end{array} \rightarrow \begin{array}{r} 0.9\,6 \\ 5\,\overline{)\,4.8\,0} \\ 4\,5 \\ \hline 3\,0 \\ 3\,0 \end{array}$$

There is a remainder.   Add a "0" to the right of the dividend and bring down.   Continue to divide until the remainder is zero.   Add a "0" to locate the decimal point.

- Encourage children to check if their answers are reasonable by rounding the decimals to the nearest whole numbers and estimating the answers.

    ISBN: 978-1-897164-15-0

6. Decimals and Fractions

- Remind children that a decimal is another way to represent a fraction, with a denominator of 10, 100, 1000 etc., and that a fraction can be changed to a decimal by first writing its equivalent fraction with a denominator of 10, 100, 1000 etc.

- A fraction can also be converted to a decimal by dividing the numerator by the denominator.

Example

$$7.5 = 7\frac{5}{10}$$
$$(0.5 = \frac{5}{10})$$

$$7\frac{1}{4} = 7\frac{25}{100} = 7.25 \quad \longleftarrow \quad (\frac{25}{100} = 0.25)$$
$$(\frac{1}{4} = \frac{1 \times 25}{4 \times 25} = \frac{25}{100})$$

7. Percent

- Children learn the conversion among percents, decimals and fractions. Parents should encourage them to make observations of the application of percent in everyday situations.

- Children should note that $1 = 100\%$ (one hundred percent) $= \frac{100}{100}$

8. Simple Equations

- Children may encounter difficulties in determining the value of an unknown in an equation using guess-and-test method. Parents can explain to them the balance principle in solving a simple equation, and encourage them to check the answer by substituting the answer for the unknown.

Example

1.
$$y + 30 = 70 \quad \longleftarrow \text{ an addition equation}$$
$$y + 30 - 30 = 70 - 30 \quad \longleftarrow \text{ subtract the same amount from both}$$
$$y = 40 \qquad\qquad \text{sides of the equation}$$

2.
$$y \times 4 = 28 \quad \longleftarrow \text{ a multiplication equation}$$
$$y \times 4 \div 4 = 28 \div 4 \quad \longleftarrow \text{ divide both sides of the equation}$$
$$y = 7 \qquad\qquad \text{by the same number}$$

9. Time and Speed

- Children recognize how to write the time and find a duration on a 12-hour clock and a 24-hour clock. Parents may remind children that when calculating a duration, they should trade 1 hour for 60 minutes if necessary.

10. Perimeter and Area

- Children practise using formulas to find the perimeter and area of some 2-D shapes. They may sometimes mistake the hypotenuse of a triangle or the slanted side of a parallelogram for the height. Remind them that the height of a 2-D shape must make a right angle with its base.

11. Factorization

- Children learn how to write a number as a product of prime factors, and determine the G.C.F. and L.C.M. of two numbers.

12. Inverse Proportion

➡ Make sure that children understand the difference between direct and inverse proportion. Encourage them to think and estimate whether one quantity is increasing or decreasing while the other quantity is increasing before writing the mathematical sentence for calculation. Remind them to check if their answers are reasonable.

13. Circles

➡ Children recognize the circumference, centre, radius, and diameter of a circle. At this stage, parents should not introduce to children the concept of π and the relationship between circumference and diameter/radius.

14. Volume and Capacity

➡ Children use a formula to calculate the volume of a cube. The method of determining the volume of an irregular object using the amount of water displaced is also practised.

➡ Point out to children that cm^3 is used to measure smaller volumes while m^3 is used to measure larger volumes.

15. Graphs

➡ Children learn to read bar graphs presenting data in large numbers.

➡ Besides learning to read and draw line graphs, children should be encouraged to make predictions following the trend of a line graph, and estimate data which have not been collected.

➡ At this stage, children learn to read and complete circle graphs divided into simple fractions only.

16. Transformations and Coordinate Systems

➡ When reading coordinates on a grid, children should read the number on the horizontal axis first, and then the number on the vertical axis.

17. Money

➡ Children practise how to write the amount of money using decimals and perform mathematical operations to find the change or money spent.

18. Probability

➡ At this stage, children are required to represent the probability of an event happening as a simple fraction.

Example   The probability of getting a 2 by rolling a die is $\frac{1}{6}$.

1 Introducing Decimals

1. $\frac{52}{100}$ 2. 0.05   3. 0.3   4. $\frac{9}{100}$

5. 7.2   6. $4\frac{1}{10}$

7.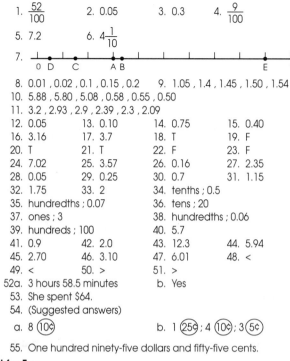

8. 0.01 , 0.02 , 0.1 , 0.15 , 0.2   9. 1.05 , 1.4 , 1.45 , 1.50 , 1.54
10. 5.88 , 5.80 , 5.08 , 0.58 , 0.55 , 0.50
11. 3.2 , 2.93 , 2.9 , 2.39 , 2.3 , 2.09

12. 0.05   13. 0.10   14. 0.75   15. 0.40
16. 3.16   17. 3.7   18. T   19. F
20. T   21. T   22. F   23. F
24. 7.02   25. 3.57   26. 0.16   27. 2.35
28. 0.05   29. 0.25   30. 0.7   31. 1.15
32. 1.75   33. 2   34. tenths ; 0.5
35. hundredths ; 0.07   36. tens ; 20
37. ones ; 3   38. hundredths ; 0.06
39. hundreds ; 100   40. 5.7
41. 0.9   42. 2.0   43. 12.3   44. 5.94
45. 2.70   46. 3.10   47. 6.01   48. <
49. <   50. >   51. >
52a. 3 hours 58.5 minutes   b. Yes
53. She spent $64.
54. (Suggested answers)

a. 8 (10¢)   b. 1 (25¢) ; 4 (10¢) ; 3 (5¢)

55. One hundred ninety-five dollars and fifty-five cents.

Just for Fun

■ = 3 or 1   ♠ = 1 or 3

♦ = 7   ♥ = 8

2 Operations with Whole Numbers

1. 700   2. 570   3. 800   4. 70 000
5. 290   6. 90   7. 200   8. 620
9. 100   10. 300   11. 1000   12. 40
13. 6580   14. 111   15. 6753   16. 8229
17. 85   18. 2512   19. 73

20.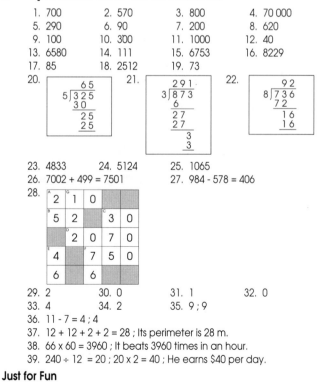

23. 4833   24. 5124   25. 1065
26. 7002 + 499 = 7501   27. 984 - 578 = 406
28.

	A	G		
2	1	0		
B 5	2		C 3	0
	D 2	0	7	0
E 4		F 7	5	0
6		6		

29. 2   30. 0   31. 1   32. 0
33. 4   34. 2   35. 9 ; 9
36. 11 - 7 = 4 ; 4
37. 12 + 12 + 2 + 2 = 28 ; Its perimeter is 28 m.
38. 66 x 60 = 3960 ; It beats 3960 times in an hour.
39. 240 ÷ 12 = 20 ; 20 x 2 = 40 ; He earns $40 per day.

Just for Fun

1a. 110 , 121 , 132   b. 108 , 120 , 132
2. 5790 ; 4563

3 Adding Decimals

1. 1.5   2. 10.6   3. 46.8   4. 65.0
5. 22.9   6. 13.7   7. 58.21   8. 34.23
9. 30.91   10. 107.14   11. 8.83   12. 108.10
13. 6.40   14. 326.00   15. 158.01   16. 26.23
17. 12.8   18. 6.68   19. 7.63   20. 8.23
21. 14.63   22. 7.93   23. 52.57   24. 29.15
25. 162.13   26. 811.82   27. 167.45   28. 370.42
29. 16.18   30. 115.9   31. 30.65   32. 9.09
33. 21.83   34. 21.14   35. 980
36. 20 + 5 + 0.8 + 0.07   37. 10 + 2 + 0.9 + 0.03
38. 570.8   39. 108.64   40. $10.27   41. $11.17
42. $11.32   43. $11.14   44. $60.07   45. $71.44
46. $69.83   47. $11.17 , $11.32 , $60.07 , $71.44
48. $154.00   49. $154.00   50. 18.7   51. 24.6
52. 23.3   53. 17.4   54. + ; +
55. 5.50 + 5.50 + 3.75 + 1.2 + 1.2 = 17.15 ; $17.15
56. 6.75 + 5.9 + 6.5 + 5 = 24.15 ;
   She gets $24.15 over the 4 week period.
57. 25.2 + 22.1 + 24.8 + 28.2 = 100.3 ;
   He cycled 100.3 km during the week.

Just for Fun

5 ; 7 ; 5

4 Subtracting Decimals

1. 0.5   2. 56.5   3. 6.3   4. 1.2
5. 28.4   6. 33.8   7. 5.04   8. 0.69
9. 3.06   10. 579.16   11. 23.71   12. 1.98
13. 5.03   14. 3.77   15. 8.27   16. 3.02
17. 11.38   18. 7.87   19. 1.82   20. 0.88
21. 0.22   22. 0.26   23. 0.81   24. 0
25. 0.06   26. 32.47   27. 26.4   28. 150.77
29. 50   30. 19.78   31. 199.4   32. 3
33. 1   34. 40   35. 9   36. 14
37. 14   38. 2.7   39. 1.8   40. 11.1
41. 18.4   42. 34.3   43. 12.6   44. 1.4
45. 8.0   46. 3.36   47. 2.4   48. 1.9
49. 2.61   50. 4.2   51. 1.23   52. 7
53. 0.6   54. 7.7   55. 7.38   56. 14.13
57. 9.46
58.

11.4	7.7	7.38	7.0	6.94
17.0	5.8	1.4	10.6	9.17
7.5	0.2	14.13	5.2	3.61
15.1	9.3	4.2	14.0	15.2
14.8	3.63	9.46	41.11	12.3
12.3	22.3	2.61	2.60	11.36
2.63	0.6	8.0	1.23	3.27

59. I
60. 35 - 32.85 ; 2.15 ; $2.15
61. 45.2 - 41.5 = 3.7 ; Sue is 3.7 kg heavier than her sister.
62. 0.55 - 0.19 = 0.36 ; The CN Tower is 0.36 km taller.
63. 12.13 - 11.87 = 0.26 ; Carl took 0.26 seconds longer.

Just for Fun

4	9	2
3	5	7
8	1	6

5 Multiplying Decimals by Whole Numbers

1. 1   2. 32   3. 0.7   4. 0.08
5. 12   6. 9.9   7. 24.06   8. 540
9. 91.5   10. 0.1   11. 10   12. 93
13. 200.8   14. 8   15. 6.2   16. 1
17. 248   18. 1   19. 14.1   20. 10.76
21. 54.5   22. 45.29   23. 44.40   24. 65.7

25. 34.3
26. 97.6
27. 28.60
28. 59.34
29. 10.8
30. 3.92
31. 33.81
32. 1.62
33. 29.25
34. 9.66
35. 23.2
36. 506.1
37. 29.97
38. 4.56
39. 35 ; 36.4
40. 8 ; 7.4
41. 50 ; 49.05
42. 48 ; 49.38
43. 12 ; 11.25
44. 3.2 ; 2.88
45. 1.8 ; 1.53
46. 32 ; 33.76
47. 13.86
48. ✓
49. 3.09
50. 100
51. 3
52. 10
53. 100
54. 159
55. 30.9
56. 23.99 x 3 ; 71.97 ; $71.97
57. 89.50 x 4 = 358 ; The total cost is $358.
58. 2.3 x 5 = 11.5 ; He walks 11.5 km in a 5-day week.
59. 3.2 x 8 = 25.6 ; They occupy 25.6 cm.
60. 12.95 x 3 = 38.85 ; 39.99 x 2 = 79.98 ; 38.85 + 79.98 = 118.83 ;
    She pays $119 altogether.

Just for Fun

444 + 44 + 4 + 4 + 4 = 500

6 Dividing Decimals by Whole Numbers

1. 0.98
2. 0.032
3. 0.75
4. 0.0092
5. 0.328
6. 0.0005
7. 0.008
8. 1.5493
9. 3.1645
10. 17.6
11. 0.12
12. 2.04
13. 0.52

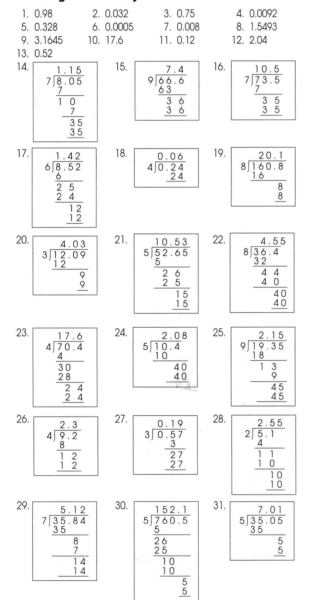

14–31. (long division worked solutions)

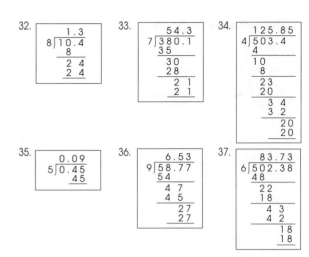

32–37. (long division worked solutions)

38. LITTLE STARS
39. 32.5 ÷ 10 ; 3.25 ; 3.25 kg
40. 7350 ÷ 100 = 73.5 ; He travelled 73.5 km each hour.
41. 36.4 ÷ 8 = 4.55 ; Each part is 4.55 m.
42. 394 ÷ 8 = 49.25 ; Each student pays $49.25.
43. 13.5 ÷ 3 = 4.5 ; The length of each side is 4.5 cm.

Just for Fun

21 ; 34 ; 55

7 More Addition and Subtraction of Decimals

1. 19.5
2. 2
3. 6.99
4. 14
5. 10.5
6. 1.5
7. 0
8. 15
9. 10
10. 28
11. 0.5
12. 17.5
13. 10
14. 100
15. 15.45
16. 3.28
17. 8.8
18. 5.01
19. 4.69
20. 4.8
21. 109.25
22. 20.33
23. 243.6
24. 1003.8
25. 0.93
26. 100.27
27. 14.56
28. 10.66
29. $15.44
30. $73.10
31. $24.80
32. $98
33. $10.24
34. $11.52
35. 59¢
36. 33¢
37. 22¢
38. 7¢
39. 8.1
40. 1.67
41. 1.5
42. 20
43. 0.65
44. 3.44
45. 25.00 - 4.55 - 6.99 = 13.46 ; $13.46
46. 35.00 - 5.95 - 17.45 = 11.60 ; She has $11.60 left.
47. 6.50 + 19.95 + 7.50 - 2.00 = 31.95 ; Each of them spent $31.95.
48. 17.5 + 17.5 + 17.5 = 52.50 ; 20.95 + 20.95 + 6.30 = 48.20 ;
    They have enough money.

Just for Fun

1¢ + 2¢ + 4¢ + 8¢ + 16¢ + 32¢ + 64¢ = 127¢ ($1.27)

8 More Multiplying and Dividing of Decimals

1. 73.4
2. 0.923
3. 1.234
4. 1.21
5. 12.3
6. 120
7. 0.03
8. 10.1
9. 3.429
10. 34 290
11. 125
12. 0.002
13. 4
14. 11.8
15. 4
16. 0.0125
17. 0.2
18. 635

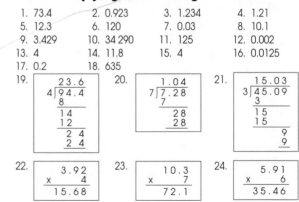

19–24. (worked solutions)

ISBN: 978-1-897164-15-0

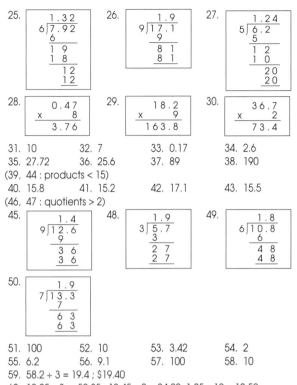

25.
```
    1.32
6)7.92
    6
    1 9
    1 8
      1 2
      1 2
```

26.
```
    1.9
9)17.1
    9
    8 1
    8 1
```

27.
```
    1.24
5)6.2
    5
    1 2
    1 0
      2 0
      2 0
```

28.
```
   0.47
 x    8
   3.76
```

29.
```
   1 8.2
 x     9
 1 6 3.8
```

30.
```
   3 6.7
 x     2
   7 3.4
```

31. 10   32. 7   33. 0.17   34. 2.6
35. 27.72   36. 25.6   37. 89   38. 190
(39, 44 : products < 15)
40. 15.8   41. 15.2   42. 17.1   43. 15.5
(46, 47 : quotients > 2)

45.
```
    1.4
9)12.6
    9
    3 6
    3 6
```

48.
```
    1.9
3)5.7
    3
    2 7
    2 7
```

49.
```
    1.8
6)10.8
    6
    4 8
    4 8
```

50.
```
    1.9
7)13.3
    7
    6 3
    6 3
```

51. 100   52. 10   53. 3.42   54. 2
55. 6.2   56. 9.1   57. 100   58. 10
59. 58.2 ÷ 3 = 19.4 ; $19.40
60. 19.95 x 3 = 59.85 ; 12.45 x 2 = 24.90 ; 1.25 x 10 = 12.50 ;
    59.85 + 24.90 + 12.50 = 97.25 ; She pays $97.25 altogether.
61. 12.99 x 2 = 25.98 ; 1.29 x 2 = 2.58 ; 1.49 x 2 = 2.98 ;
    25.98 + 2.58 + 2.98 = 31.54 ; 31.54 ÷ 5 = 6.308 ;
    They must pay $6.31 each.
62. 29.40 ÷ 3 = 9.80 ; 39.50 ÷ 5 = 7.90 ;
    A 5-kg bag for $39.50 is the better buy.

Just for Fun

0.5

Midway Review

1. 18.95   2. 11.76   3. 67.2   4. 1.05
5. 16.26   6. 0.62   7. 209.04   8. 3.2
9. 954.1   10. 14.59   11. 968.69   12. 149.5
13. 54.19   14. 95.31   15. 520 ; 5.2 16. 7 ; 0.07
17. 1.2 ; 0.012 18. 7.5 ; 0.75   19. 0.3 ; 0.03   20. 8 ; 80
21. 150 ; 1500   22. D   23. C   24. C
25. C   26. B   27. D   28. B
29. C   30. A   31. B   32. B
33. C   34. C   35. 9.0 + 3.2 + 3.2 = 15.4 ; 15.4
36. 20 x 15.4 = 308 ; The total cost is $308.
37. 9 + 3.2 + 9 + 3.2 = 24.4 ; The perimeter is 24.4 m.
38. 9 x 3.2 = 28.8 ; The area is 28.8 m².
39a. New length = 9.0 x 2 = 18.0 ; New width = 3.2 x 2 = 6.4 ;
     18.0 + 18.0 + 6.4 + 6.4 = 48.8 = 24.4 x 2 ;
     The perimeter is doubled as well.
  b. 9 x 2 x 3.2 x 2 = 9 x 3.2 x 2 x 2 = 28.8 x 4 ;
     The area is 4 times larger than before.

9   Introducing Fractions

1. $\frac{1}{6}$ 2. $\frac{1}{3}$ 3. $\frac{2}{3}$ 4. $\frac{5}{6}$

5. $\frac{1}{6}$ 6. $\frac{4}{6} = \frac{2}{3}$ 7. $\frac{5}{8}$ 8. $\frac{6}{16} = \frac{3}{8}$

9. $\frac{3}{8}$ 10. $\frac{1}{4}$

11. 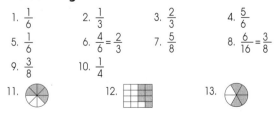   12.   13.

14.   15.   16.

17.
```
 1  1        2   1         4   9
20 10        5   2         5  10
0                                    1
```

18. $\frac{5}{9}$ 19. $\frac{5}{8}$ 20. $\frac{8}{11}$

21.   22.   23.

24. 5   25. 12   26. 6   27. 2

28. 2   29. 4   30. $\frac{3}{4}$ 31. $\frac{1}{3}$

32. $\frac{1}{2}$ 33. $\frac{2}{3}$ 34. $\frac{3}{8}$ 35. $\frac{4}{5}$

36. (Suggested answers) $\frac{1}{8}$; $\frac{1}{4}$; $\frac{1}{3}$

37a. $\frac{35}{100} = \frac{7}{20}$ b. $\frac{60}{100} = \frac{3}{5}$ 38. $\frac{3}{24} = \frac{1}{8}$ 39. $\frac{2}{8} = \frac{1}{4}$

40. $\frac{50}{250} = \frac{1}{5}$ 41. $\frac{15}{45} = \frac{1}{3}$ 42. $\frac{21}{26}$ 43. $\frac{18}{30} = \frac{3}{5}$

44. $\frac{50}{120} = \frac{5}{12}$ 45. $\frac{12}{16} = \frac{3}{4}$ 46a. $\frac{87}{100}$ b. $\frac{13}{100}$

Just for Fun

1. $\frac{1}{16}$; $\frac{1}{32}$; $\frac{1}{64}$ 2. No

10   Equivalent Fractions and Ordering of Fractions

1. 25   2. 25   3. 15   4. 75
5. 2   6. 77   7. $\frac{5}{6}$ 8. $\frac{1}{2}$

9. $\frac{2}{11}$ 10. $\frac{3}{7}$ 11. $\frac{1}{4}$ 12. $\frac{2}{3}$

13. $\frac{3}{4}$ 14. $\frac{1}{3}$ 15. $\frac{1}{6}$ 16. $\frac{2}{3}$

17. $\frac{8}{21}$ 18. $\frac{11}{15}$ 19. $\frac{1}{10} < \frac{1}{5} < \frac{1}{2} < \frac{3}{5} < \frac{7}{10} < \frac{4}{5}$

20. $\frac{1}{4} < \frac{1}{3} < \frac{2}{4} < \frac{2}{3} < \frac{3}{4}$ 21. T   22. F

23. T   24. F   25. 3 ; 12
26. 5 ; 2   27. 2 ; 4   28. 55 ; 4

29. – 32. (Suggested answers)   29. $\frac{2}{16}$; $\frac{3}{24}$; $\frac{4}{32}$

30. $\frac{4}{6}$; $\frac{6}{9}$; $\frac{8}{12}$ 31. $\frac{2}{8}$; $\frac{3}{12}$; $\frac{4}{16}$ 32. $\frac{10}{14}$; $\frac{15}{21}$; $\frac{20}{28}$

33. $\frac{7}{8} > \frac{3}{5} > \frac{5}{8} > \frac{1}{2} > \frac{3}{8} > \frac{1}{4} > \frac{3}{16}$

34. $\frac{5}{6} > \frac{13}{18} > \frac{2}{3} > \frac{1}{2} > \frac{7}{18} > \frac{1}{3} > \frac{1}{6}$

35. <   36. =   37. >   38. <
39. <   40. >   41. $\frac{3}{4}$ 42. $\frac{3}{5}$

43. $\frac{5}{6}$ 44. $\frac{4}{9}$ 45. $\frac{7}{9}$ 46. $\frac{6}{7}$

47. $\frac{200}{450}$; $\frac{75}{125}$; $\frac{15}{20}$; $\frac{14}{18}$; $\frac{45}{54}$; $\frac{150}{175}$

48. 14 ; 14   49. 8 ; 8   50. 88 ; 88
51. Nadine : $\frac{9}{12} = \frac{27}{36}$; Danielle : $\frac{14}{18} = \frac{28}{36}$; Danielle

52a. $\frac{682}{5421}$; $\frac{1583}{8474}$ b. Increasing

  c. $\frac{512}{5421}$; $\frac{542}{8474}$ d. Decreasing

Just for Fun

$\frac{1}{16}$; $\frac{1}{25}$; $\frac{1}{36}$

11 Improper Fractions and Mixed Numbers

1. $2\frac{1}{7}$ 2. $\frac{27}{8}$ 3. $3\frac{2}{3}$ 4. $\frac{45}{4}$

5. $1\frac{2}{5}$ 6. $\frac{4}{7}$; $\frac{5}{20}$; $\frac{7}{9}$; $\frac{11}{12}$

7. $\frac{9}{9}$; $\frac{25}{20}$; $\frac{15}{8}$; $\frac{16}{7}$ 8. $3\frac{3}{10}$; $3\frac{1}{2}$; $1\frac{5}{20}$; $1\frac{2}{5}$

9. $2\frac{2}{3}$; $\frac{8}{3}$ 10. $1\frac{1}{6}$; $\frac{7}{6}$

11.

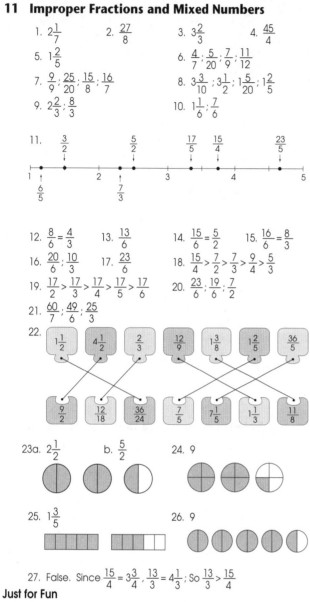

12. $\frac{8}{6} = \frac{4}{3}$ 13. $\frac{13}{6}$ 14. $\frac{15}{6} = \frac{5}{2}$ 15. $\frac{16}{6} = \frac{8}{3}$

16. $\frac{20}{6}$; $\frac{10}{3}$ 17. $\frac{23}{6}$ 18. $\frac{15}{4} > \frac{7}{2} > \frac{7}{3} > \frac{9}{4} > \frac{5}{3}$

19. $\frac{17}{2} > \frac{17}{3} > \frac{17}{4} > \frac{17}{5} > \frac{17}{6}$ 20. $\frac{23}{6}$; $\frac{19}{6}$; $\frac{7}{2}$

21. $\frac{60}{7}$; $\frac{49}{6}$; $\frac{25}{3}$

22.

$1\frac{1}{2}$ $4\frac{1}{2}$ $\frac{2}{3}$ $\frac{12}{9}$ $1\frac{3}{8}$ $1\frac{2}{5}$ $\frac{36}{5}$

$\frac{9}{2}$ $\frac{12}{18}$ $\frac{36}{24}$ $\frac{7}{5}$ $7\frac{1}{5}$ $1\frac{1}{3}$ $\frac{11}{8}$

23a. $2\frac{1}{2}$ b. $\frac{5}{2}$ 24. 9

25. $1\frac{3}{5}$ 26. 9

27. False. Since $\frac{15}{4} = 3\frac{3}{4}$, $\frac{13}{3} = 4\frac{1}{3}$; So $\frac{13}{3} > \frac{15}{4}$

Just for Fun

56

12 Adding Fractions with the Same Denominator

1. 1   2. 1   3. $\frac{2}{3}$ 4. $\frac{2}{5}$

5. $\frac{5}{9}$ 6. $\frac{4}{7}$ 7. $\frac{4}{5}$ 8. 1

9. 1   10. $\frac{8}{9}$ 11. $\frac{11}{13}$ 12. $\frac{8}{11}$

13. $\frac{7}{8}$ 14. $\frac{13}{20}$ 15. $\frac{9}{17}$ 16. $\frac{9}{19}$

17. $\frac{21}{25}$ 18. $\frac{10}{12} = \frac{5}{6}$ 19. $\frac{17}{21}$ 20. $\frac{8}{15}$

21. $\frac{6}{16} = \frac{3}{8}$ 22. $\frac{2}{4} = \frac{1}{2}$ 23. $\frac{12}{18} = \frac{2}{3}$ 24. $\frac{22}{23}$

25. $\frac{4}{6} = \frac{2}{3}$ 26. $\frac{25}{27}$ 27. $\frac{13}{20}$ 28. $\frac{12}{15} = \frac{4}{5}$

29. $\frac{3}{9} = \frac{1}{3}$ 30. $\frac{12}{14} = \frac{6}{7}$ 31. $\frac{6}{8} = \frac{3}{4}$ 32. $\frac{6}{10} = \frac{3}{5}$

33. $\frac{8}{16} = \frac{1}{2}$ 34. $\frac{6}{12} = \frac{1}{2}$ 35. $\frac{4}{20} = \frac{1}{5}$ 36. $\frac{2}{6} = \frac{1}{3}$

37. $\frac{4}{7}$ 38. $\frac{3}{18} = \frac{1}{6}$ 39. $\frac{6}{24} = \frac{1}{4}$ 40. $\frac{8}{32} = \frac{1}{4}$

41. $\frac{7}{7} = 1$ 42. $\frac{11}{11} = 1$

43. 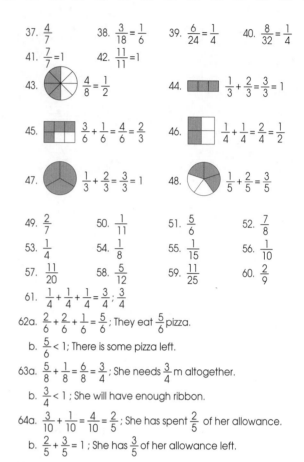 $\frac{4}{8} = \frac{1}{2}$ 44. $\frac{1}{3} + \frac{2}{3} = \frac{3}{3} = 1$

45. $\frac{3}{6} + \frac{1}{6} = \frac{4}{6} = \frac{2}{3}$ 46. $\frac{1}{4} + \frac{1}{4} = \frac{2}{4} = \frac{1}{2}$

47. $\frac{1}{3} + \frac{2}{3} = \frac{3}{3} = 1$ 48. $\frac{1}{5} + \frac{2}{5} = \frac{3}{5}$

49. $\frac{2}{7}$ 50. $\frac{1}{11}$ 51. $\frac{5}{6}$ 52. $\frac{7}{8}$

53. $\frac{1}{4}$ 54. $\frac{1}{8}$ 55. $\frac{1}{15}$ 56. $\frac{1}{10}$

57. $\frac{11}{20}$ 58. $\frac{5}{12}$ 59. $\frac{11}{25}$ 60. $\frac{2}{9}$

61. $\frac{1}{4} + \frac{1}{4} + \frac{1}{4} = \frac{3}{4}$; $\frac{3}{4}$

62a. $\frac{2}{6} + \frac{2}{6} + \frac{1}{6} = \frac{5}{6}$; They eat $\frac{5}{6}$ pizza.

b. $\frac{5}{6} < 1$; There is some pizza left.

63a. $\frac{5}{8} + \frac{1}{8} = \frac{6}{8} = \frac{3}{4}$; She needs $\frac{3}{4}$ m altogether.

b. $\frac{3}{4} < 1$; She will have enough ribbon.

64a. $\frac{3}{10} + \frac{1}{10} = \frac{4}{10} = \frac{2}{5}$; She has spent $\frac{2}{5}$ of her allowance.

b. $\frac{2}{5} + \frac{3}{5} = 1$; She has $\frac{3}{5}$ of her allowance left.

Just for Fun

$\frac{8}{15}$	$\frac{1}{15}$	$\frac{6}{15}$
$\frac{3}{15}$	$\frac{5}{15}$	$\frac{7}{15}$
$\frac{4}{15}$	$\frac{9}{15}$	$\frac{2}{15}$

13 Adding Improper Fractions and Mixed Numbers

1. 2   2. 3   3. 5   4. 3

5. 7   6. 3   7. 6   8. 7

9. 3   10. 2   11. 2   12. 3

13. 4   14. 2   15. $2\frac{1}{4}$ 16. $6\frac{3}{5}$

17. $3\frac{2}{5}$ 18. $5\frac{1}{2}$ 19. $3\frac{2}{5}$ 20. $3\frac{1}{2}$

21. $1\frac{1}{2}$ 22. $4\frac{1}{3}$ 23. $1\frac{3}{5}$ 24. $2\frac{7}{8}$

25. $3\frac{1}{4}$ 26. 2   27. $4\frac{3}{4}$ 28. $2\frac{1}{3}$

29. $9\frac{2}{5}$ 30. 6   31. $\frac{3}{4}$ 32. $\frac{5}{8}$

33. $1\frac{4}{5}$ 34. $1\frac{1}{2}$ 35. $\frac{1}{2}$ 36. $\frac{3}{5}$

37. $\frac{2}{3}$ 38. $\frac{7}{6}$ 39. $3\frac{1}{5}$ 40. $\frac{3}{4}$

41. T   42. T   43. F   44. T

45. T   46. F   47. T   48. F

50, 51, 55 : sum < 3   49. $3\frac{1}{3}$ 52. $3\frac{1}{2}$

53. $3\frac{1}{2}$ 54. $3\frac{1}{5}$ 56. $3\frac{5}{9}$

57. $1\frac{1}{4} + 2\frac{1}{4} + 1\frac{3}{4} = 5\frac{1}{4}$; They eat $5\frac{1}{4}$ cans of food per week.

58. $45\frac{3}{8} + 2\frac{1}{8} = 47\frac{1}{2}$; The new selling price is $47\frac{1}{2}$ ¢.

59a. $3\frac{1}{8} + 4\frac{3}{4} = 7\frac{7}{8}$; She must buy $7\frac{7}{8}$ m.　　b. Yes.

60. $1\frac{1}{4} + 1\frac{1}{4} + \frac{3}{4} + 1\frac{1}{4} + 2 + 1\frac{3}{4} + 2\frac{3}{4} = 11$;

She watched TV for 11 hours during the week.

Just for Fun

16

14 Subtracting Fractions with the Same Denominator

1. $\frac{2}{7}$　　2. $\frac{1}{12}$　　3. $\frac{7}{9}$　　4. $\frac{2}{11}$

5. $\frac{2}{7}$　　6. $\frac{1}{10}$　　7. $\frac{3}{17}$　　8. 0

9. $\frac{1}{15}$　　10. $\frac{1}{4}$　　11. $\frac{2}{13}$　　12. $\frac{2}{7}$

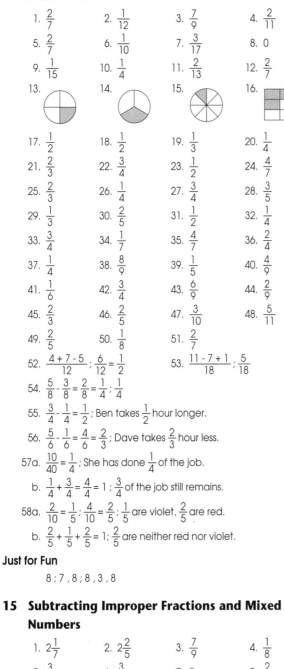

13.　　14.　　15.　　16.

17. $\frac{1}{2}$　　18. $\frac{1}{2}$　　19. $\frac{1}{3}$　　20. $\frac{1}{4}$

21. $\frac{2}{3}$　　22. $\frac{3}{4}$　　23. $\frac{1}{2}$　　24. $\frac{4}{7}$

25. $\frac{2}{3}$　　26. $\frac{1}{4}$　　27. $\frac{3}{4}$　　28. $\frac{3}{5}$

29. $\frac{1}{3}$　　30. $\frac{2}{5}$　　31. $\frac{1}{2}$　　32. $\frac{1}{4}$

33. $\frac{3}{4}$　　34. $\frac{1}{7}$　　35. $\frac{4}{7}$　　36. $\frac{2}{4}$

37. $\frac{1}{4}$　　38. $\frac{8}{9}$　　39. $\frac{1}{5}$　　40. $\frac{4}{9}$

41. $\frac{1}{6}$　　42. $\frac{3}{4}$　　43. $\frac{6}{9}$　　44. $\frac{2}{9}$

45. $\frac{2}{3}$　　46. $\frac{2}{5}$　　47. $\frac{3}{10}$　　48. $\frac{5}{11}$

49. $\frac{2}{5}$　　50. $\frac{1}{8}$　　51. $\frac{2}{7}$

52. $\frac{4+7-5}{12}$; $\frac{6}{12} = \frac{1}{2}$　　53. $\frac{11-7+1}{18}$; $\frac{5}{18}$

54. $\frac{5}{8} - \frac{3}{8} = \frac{2}{8} = \frac{1}{4}$; $\frac{1}{4}$

55. $\frac{3}{4} - \frac{1}{4} = \frac{1}{2}$; Ben takes $\frac{1}{2}$ hour longer.

56. $\frac{5}{6} - \frac{1}{6} = \frac{4}{6} = \frac{2}{3}$; Dave takes $\frac{2}{3}$ hour less.

57a. $\frac{10}{40} = \frac{1}{4}$; She has done $\frac{1}{4}$ of the job.

b. $\frac{1}{4} + \frac{3}{4} = \frac{4}{4} = 1$; $\frac{3}{4}$ of the job still remains.

58a. $\frac{2}{10} = \frac{1}{5}$; $\frac{4}{10} = \frac{2}{5}$; $\frac{1}{5}$ are violet, $\frac{2}{5}$ are red.

b. $\frac{2}{5} + \frac{1}{5} + \frac{2}{5} = 1$; $\frac{2}{5}$ are neither red nor violet.

Just for Fun

8 ; 7 , 8 ; 8 , 3 , 8

15 Subtracting Improper Fractions and Mixed Numbers

1. $2\frac{1}{7}$　　2. $2\frac{2}{5}$　　3. $\frac{7}{9}$　　4. $\frac{1}{8}$

5. $\frac{3}{4}$　　6. $\frac{3}{4}$　　7. 0　　8. $\frac{2}{9}$

9. 3　　10. $\frac{1}{9}$　　11. $\frac{3}{13}$　　12. 1

13. $\frac{7}{8}$　　14. $\frac{2}{3}$　　15. $\frac{4}{6} = \frac{2}{3}$　　16. 5

17. 0　　18. $2\frac{1}{2}$　　19. 1　　20. $1\frac{1}{2}$

21. $\frac{1}{2}$　　22. $\frac{1}{4}$　　23. 2　　24. $\frac{2}{5}$

25. $\frac{1}{3}$　　26. 1　　27. $1\frac{1}{4}$　　28. 0

29. 1　　30. $1\frac{2}{3}$　　31. 3　　32. $1\frac{1}{5}$

33. $\frac{1}{2}$　　34. $\frac{4}{5}$　　35. $\frac{1}{3}$　　36. 5

37. $1\frac{1}{2}$　　38. $\frac{3}{4}$　　39. 4　　40. $\frac{5}{3} = 1\frac{2}{3}$

41. $\frac{3}{4}$　　42. $2\frac{3}{7}$　　43. $\frac{2}{5}$　　44. $3\frac{1}{2}$

45. $\frac{2}{3}$　　46. 1　　47. $\frac{1}{2}$　　48. $\frac{4}{5}$

49. $3 + 4 - 2 + \frac{4+1-2}{6}$; $5\frac{1}{2}$　　50. $9 - 3 + 1 + \frac{2-1}{8}$; $7\frac{1}{8}$

51. $4 - 3 + 1 + \frac{1-3+4}{6}$; $2\frac{1}{3}$　　52. $3 + 2 - 1 + \frac{2+4-5}{7}$; $4\frac{1}{7}$

53. $3\frac{1}{4} - 2\frac{3}{4} = \frac{1}{2}$; Pat spent $\frac{1}{2}$ hour longer.

54. $8\frac{3}{8} - 6\frac{5}{8} = 1\frac{3}{4}$; He ran $1\frac{3}{4}$ km farther.

55. $3\frac{1}{5} - 2\frac{4}{5} = \frac{2}{5}$; The difference is $\frac{2}{5}$ dollar.

56. $1 - \frac{3}{8} - \frac{1}{8} = \frac{1}{2}$; The length of the third side is $\frac{1}{2}$ m.

57. $15\frac{1}{4} - 1\frac{1}{2} - 1\frac{1}{2} = 12\frac{1}{4}$; $10\frac{1}{2} - 1\frac{1}{2} - 1\frac{1}{2} = 7\frac{1}{2}$;

The dimensions of the unframed part of the picture are $12\frac{1}{4}$ cm by $7\frac{1}{2}$ cm.

Just for Fun

$\frac{1}{4}$

16 Relating Decimals and Fractions

1. 0.1　　2. 0.7　　3. 0.03　　4. 0.49

5. 0.09　　6. 0.73　　7. $\frac{3}{10}$　　8. $\frac{7}{10}$

9. $\frac{9}{10}$　　10. $\frac{1}{100}$　　11. $\frac{9}{100}$　　12. $\frac{7}{100}$

13. $\frac{31}{100}$　　14. $\frac{19}{100}$　　15. $\frac{47}{100}$　　16. $\frac{3}{100}$

17. 0.5　　18. 0.2　　19. 0.75　　20. 0.6

21. 0.125　　22. 0.625　　23. 0.375　　24. 0.8

25. 1.63　　26. 3.57　　27. 12.8　　28. 2.38

29. 3.83　　30. 5.44　　31. 1.67　　32. 2.6

33. 4.25　　34. 10.4　　35. 8.86　　36. 6.7

37. $\frac{13}{20}$　　38. $\frac{75}{100}$; $\frac{3}{4}$　　39. $\frac{5}{100}$; $\frac{1}{20}$　　40. $\frac{12}{100}$; $\frac{3}{25}$

41. $\frac{45}{100}$; $\frac{9}{20}$　　42. $\frac{36}{100}$; $\frac{9}{25}$　　43. $1\frac{45}{100}$; $1\frac{9}{20}$　　44. $6\frac{55}{100}$; $6\frac{11}{20}$

45. $2\frac{8}{10}$; $2\frac{4}{5}$　　46. $2\frac{25}{100}$; $2\frac{1}{4}$　　47. 25　　48. 75

49. 40　　50. 60　　51. 70　　52. 90

53. 0.65　　54. 0.9　　55. $1\frac{2}{5}$　　56. $\frac{2}{3}$

57. 4.26　　58. 0.57　　59. 3.69　　60. 8.38

61. $6\frac{3}{8}$　　62. 1.54 ; $1\frac{7}{8}$; $1\frac{8}{9}$

63. $2\frac{4}{7}$; $2\frac{3}{5}$; 2.68　　64. $5\frac{4}{5}$; 5.83 ; $5\frac{9}{10}$

65. 0.125 ; 0.25 ; 0.75 ; 0.375 ; 0.875 ; 0.2 ; 0.7

66. $\frac{1}{8}$; $\frac{1}{5}$; $\frac{1}{4}$; $\frac{3}{8}$; $\frac{7}{10}$; $\frac{3}{4}$; $\frac{7}{8}$　　67. $\frac{6}{25}$

68a. $\frac{5}{8}$　　b. 0.625　　69a. 0.4　　b. 30¢

Just for Fun

$\frac{3}{9}$; $\frac{3}{8}$; 0.56 ; $\frac{5}{6}$; $\frac{8}{9}$

Final Review

1. B   2. C   3. D   4. A

5. B   6. D   7. A   8. C

9. B   10. $\frac{3}{4}$; 0.75   11. $1\frac{2}{5}$; 1.4   12. $\frac{1}{5}$; 0.2

13. $\frac{3}{20}$; $\frac{1}{4}$; $\frac{1}{2}$; $\frac{3}{5}$; $\frac{4}{5}$ 14. 0.15 ; 0.25 ; 0.5 ; 0.6 ; 0.8

15. $3\frac{3}{4}$ 16. $1\frac{1}{2}$ 17. $3\frac{2}{5}$ 18. $2\frac{1}{9}$

19. $1\frac{1}{3}$ 20. $3\frac{1}{2}$ 21. $4\frac{2}{3}$ 22. $4\frac{1}{6}$

23. $4\frac{3}{8}$ 24. $1\frac{3}{4}$ 25. $2\frac{3}{5}$ 26. $4\frac{4}{5}$

27.

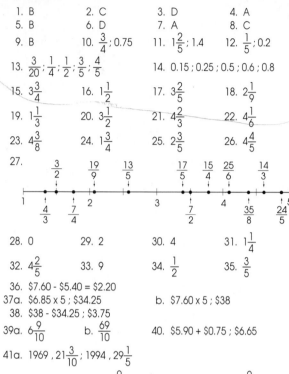

28. 0   29. 2   30. 4   31. $1\frac{1}{4}$

32. $4\frac{2}{5}$ 33. 9   34. $\frac{1}{2}$ 35. $\frac{3}{5}$

36. $7.60 - $5.40 = $2.20

37a. $6.85 x 5 ; $34.25   b. $7.60 x 5 ; $38

38. $38 - $34.25 ; $3.75

39a. $6\frac{9}{10}$ b. $\frac{69}{10}$ 40. $5.90 + $0.75 ; $6.65

41a. 1969 , $21\frac{3}{10}$; 1994 , $29\frac{1}{5}$

  b. 29.2 - 21.3 = 7.9 or $7\frac{9}{10}$; The increase was 7.9 or $7\frac{9}{10}$ million.

  c. 29.2 + 7.9 = 37.1 ;

   The population of Canada in 2019 will be 37.1 million.

42a. $\frac{35}{100} = \frac{7}{20}$ = 0.35 ; He has run $\frac{7}{20}$ or 0.35 of his monthly goal.

  b. 100 - 35 = 65 ; He still has to run 65 km.

  c. $1 - \frac{7}{20} = \frac{13}{20}$ = 0.65 ;

   He still has to run $\frac{13}{20}$ or 0.65 of the total distance.

  d. $\frac{65 - 35}{100} = \frac{30}{100} = \frac{3}{10}$;

   The difference between the fractions of the total distance
   run in the first week and during the rest of the month is $\frac{3}{10}$.

43a. $2\frac{1}{4} + 3\frac{3}{4}$ = 6 ; They drink 6 cups of tea.

  b. $3\frac{3}{4} - 2\frac{1}{4} = 1\frac{1}{2}$; The difference is $1\frac{1}{2}$ cups.

  c. $2\frac{1}{4}$ = 2.25 ; 2.25 x 7 = 15.75 ;

   Mr King will drink 15.75 cups per week.

  d. $3\frac{3}{4}$ = 3.75 ; 3.75 x 7 = 26.25 ;

   Mrs King will drink 26.25 cups per week.

44a. $8\frac{1}{5} + 9\frac{3}{5} + 7\frac{1}{5}$ = 25 ; They watch TV for 25 hours in a week.

  b. $9\frac{3}{5} - 8\frac{1}{5} = 1\frac{2}{5}$; David watches TV for $1\frac{2}{5}$ hours longer
   than Peter.

  c. $9\frac{3}{5} - 7\frac{1}{5} = 2\frac{2}{5}$; David watches TV for $2\frac{2}{5}$ hours longer
   than Ruth.

  d. $7\frac{1}{5} - 1\frac{3}{5} = 5\frac{3}{5}$; She can watch TV for $5\frac{3}{5}$ hours now.

Review

1. 4282	2. 1944
3. 6720	4. 75
5. 3558	6. 3641
7. 217	8. 2884
9. 8000	10. 900

11. 40 ; 50 ; 60 ; 70 ; 80 ; 90 ; 100
12. 12 ; 15 ; 18 ; 21 ; 24 ; 27 ; 30
13. 36 ; 45 ; 54 ; 63 ; 72 ; 81 ; 90
14. 28 ; 35 ; 42 ; 49 ; 56 ; 63 ; 70
15. 60 ; 75 ; 90 ; 105 ; 120 ; 135 ; 150

16. 42	17. 24
18. 50	19. 54
20. 56	21. 72
22. 63	23. 80
24. 120	25. 90
26. 7	27. 5
28. 72	29. 98
30. 24	31. 123
32. 48	33. 38
34. 8	35. 8
36. 4	37. 8
38. 6	39. 15
40. 13	41. 4
42. 30	43. 20
44. 19	45. 16
46. 138	47. 6.0
48. 4.2	49. 6.5
50. 3.6	51. 11.6
52. 32.5	53. 24.8
54. 57.1	55. 281.7
56. 158.1	57. 33.4
58. 31.2	59. 52.1
60. 89.1	61. Steve
62. Sue	63. No

64. Steve, Paul, Stan, Sue

65. $\frac{9}{10}$	66. $\frac{4}{100}$
67. 0.25	68. 0.4
69. 0.3	70. 0.37
71. 1.02	72. 1.04
73. 1.05	74. 1.08
75. $1\frac{4}{8}$	76. $\frac{5}{8}$
77. $\frac{3}{8}$	78. 0.30
79. 50	80. 48.25
81. 6.75	82. 3.75
83. Reflection	84. Rotation
85. Translation	86. Reflection
87. 12 ; 9	88. 14 ; 10
89. 10 ; 6	

1   Operations with Whole Numbers

1. 8690	2. 7369
3. 902	4. 4214
5. 2288	6. 2355

7.
```
    54
  x 27
  ----
   378
  1080
  ----
  1458
```
8.
```
    38
  x 49
  ----
   342
  1520
  ----
  1862
```
9.
```
    17
  x 65
  ----
    85
  1020
  ----
  1105
```

10.
```
      742
  9 )6678
     63
     ---
      37
      36
      ---
       18
       18
```
742 x 9 = 6678

11.
```
      93
  6 )559
     54
     ---
      19
      18
      ---
       1
```
93 x 6 + 1 = 559

12.
```
      702
  7 )4914
     49
     ----
       14
       14
```
702 x 7 = 4914

13. 1	14. 2
15. 0	16. 7
17. 8	18. 3
19. 4	20. 5
21. WELL DONE	22. ✔
23. ✔	24. 34
25. ✔	26. 20
27. ✔	28. ✔
29. ✔	30. 1
31. 20	32. 50
33. ✔	34. 4025
35. 1417	36. 980
37. 2265	38. 780
39. 81	40. 235
41. 1218	42. 3344
43. 120	44. 210
45. 4854	46. 8
47. 187	48. 29
49. 72	

50.

2	3	5	1	8	7
5	1	2	1	8	4
7	2	3	1	1	8
2	9	8	2	2	5
0	7	1	0	1	4
3	3	4	4	0	8

51. 16	52. 16

53. Time taken : 12 x 90 = 1080 ; 1080
54. Time taken : 15 x 75 = 1125
    He takes 1125 seconds to swim 15 lengths.
55. Difference : 1125 – 1080 = 45
    The difference between their times is 45 seconds.
56. Average number of swimmers : 1848 ÷ 7 = 264
    The average number of swimmers per day was 264.

Mind Boggler

40 ; 48

2   Fractions

1. 2	2. 2	3. 2	4. 14
5. 5	6. 1		
7. E	8. F	9. B	10. C
11. D	12. A		

13.

| $\frac{1}{3}$ | (shaded 1 of 3) |
| $\frac{1}{4}$ | (shaded 1 of 4) |

14.

| $\frac{1}{2}$ | (shaded 1 of 3) |
| $\frac{2}{5}$ | (shaded 2 of 5) |

15.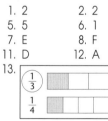

| $\frac{2}{3}$ | (shaded 2 of 3) |
| $\frac{3}{4}$ | (shaded 3 of 4) |

ISBN: 978-1-897164-15-0

16. T   17. T   18. F   19. T
20. F   21. T   22. F   23. T
24. F   25. F   26. F   27. T

28. $\frac{11}{4} > \frac{5}{2} > 2\frac{1}{5}$ 29. $\frac{7}{4} > \frac{6}{4} > \frac{7}{8}$

30. $3\frac{1}{3} > \frac{13}{4} > 3\frac{1}{6}$ 31. $\frac{13}{3} > \frac{4}{3} > \frac{3}{4}$

32. $\frac{3}{5}$; $\frac{17}{20}$; $\frac{27}{50}$; $\frac{9}{25}$; $\frac{3}{4}$; $3\frac{4}{5}$; $1\frac{1}{2}$

33. 0.6 ; 0.85 ; 0.54 ; 0.36 ; 0.75 ; 3.8 ; 1.5

34a. $\frac{1}{2}$; $\frac{1}{4}$; $\frac{3}{4}$ b. $\frac{1}{4} < \frac{1}{2} < \frac{3}{4}$

35a. $4\frac{1}{2}$ b. $1\frac{1}{2}$ c. $2\frac{1}{4}$

36a. 12   b. 5   c. $\frac{7}{10}$

   d. No.
    30 ÷ 4 = 7R2 ; 30 is not divisible by 4.

37a. Having snacks   b. Playing in the garden

38. (Suggested answers) $\frac{1}{4}$; $\frac{3}{12}$

39. $\frac{1}{3}$

40. $\frac{4}{16} = \frac{1}{4}$ 41. 0.18

42a. 0.3   b. 0.5   c. 0.2

Mind Boggler

   Jane

3   Decimals

1. 7.51   2. 9.00   3. 4.06   4. 7.52
5. 2.88   6. 2.38   7. 21.21   8. 20.52
9. 46.89   10. 49.07   11. 39.37   12. 41.46
13. 38.68   14. 33.73

15. $\frac{7}{100}$ 16. $\frac{9}{100}$; $\frac{49}{100}$ 17. 70 ; 7

18. $\frac{7}{10}$; $\frac{79}{100}$ 19. $\frac{65}{100}$ 20. $\frac{34}{100}$

21. $\frac{4}{10}$; $\frac{5}{100}$

22. 27.2   23. 18.5   24. 181.35   25. 27.12
26. 121.87   27. 5.58   28. 192.72   29. 37.5
30. ✔   31. ✗   32. ✗   33. ✗
34. ✔   35. ✗

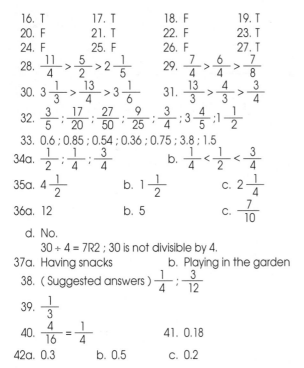

39. 12.31   40. 8.85   41. 6.75
42. 50 ÷ 5 ; 10   43. 56 ÷ 7 ; 8   44. 45 ÷ 9 ; 5
45. 983   46. 129.3   47. 4.52   48. 1.284
49. 912.3   50. 0.163   51. 80   52. 0.08
53. 0.12   54. 12   55. 72   56. 991
57. 48   58. 63.4   59. 480   60. 220
61. 154.5   62. 432   63. 5.68   64. 3.8
65. 2.1   66. 12.3   67. 0.72   68. 52.0
69. 100 − 29.95 = 70.05 ; 70.05
70. 20 x 3 − 52.99 = 7.01
    She gets $7.01 change.
71. 29.95 + 52.99 = 82.94
    Kim pays $82.94 altogether.

72. 12.75 x 3 = 38.25
    She pays $38.25 altogether.
73. 32.60 ÷ 10 = 3.26
    Each pair costs $3.26.
74. 6.93 x 2 = 13.86
    They pay $13.86 altogether.
75. 42.5 x 3 = 127.50
    She pays $127.50.
76. 78.5 ÷ 2 = 39.25
    Each pays $39.25.

Mind Boggler

   $28.2 ; $18.2

4   More about Basic Operations

1. 90   2. 120
3. 300   4. 170
5. 3920   6. 13 700
7. 40 ; 70 ; 2800   8. 30 ; 100 ; 3000
9. 60 ; 40 ; 2400   10. 20 ; 80 ; 1600
11. 700   12. 800 − 200 + 100 ; 700
13. 1500 − 400 − 700 ; 400   14. 300 − 100 + 200 + 0 ; 400
15. 2600 ÷ 2 ; 1300   16. 3000 ÷ 6 ; 500
17. 1200 ÷ 4 ; 300
18. Number of desks : 4 x 6 + 2 x 5 = 24 + 10 = 34
    34
19. Total number of seats : 50 x 35 = 1750
    Number of people in the hall : 1750 + 32 = 1782
    There are 1782 people in all.
20. Number of students going by van : 69 − 45 = 24
    Number of vans needed : 24 ÷ 6 = 4
    4 vans are needed.
21. Total number of seats : 5 x 8 + 7 x 6 = 40 + 42 = 82
    Number of empty seats : 82 − 78 = 4
    There are 4 empty seats.
22. Number of lengths Anna swims in 30 minutes : 30 ÷ 5 x 9 = 54
    She can swim 54 lengths in 30 minutes.
23. Distance Anna swims in 30 minutes : 25 x 54 = 1350
    Anna swims 1350 metres in 30 minutes.
24. 500 ; 500   25. 9 ; 4.5 ; 4.5
26. 7 ; 42 ; 42   27. 42 ; 0.70 ; 29.40 ; 29.40
28. 2.80 ;   29. 1300 ; 91 ; 63.70 ;
    24 ; 16.80 ;   1300 ; 52 ; 36.40
    42 ; 29.40 ;
    29.40 − 16.80 ; $12.60
30. $32.00   31. 200 cards
32. 5 packs   33. $1.05
34. $0.74   35. Exact amount : $167
36. $33   37. 8 bags

Mind Boggler

   10

5   Units of Measure

1. 9.5 ; 12.6   2. 3.0 ; 4.0
3.-6. (Suggested answers)
3. 20.9   4. 36.4
5. 23.5   6. 23.5
7. 3 m   8. 7 m
9. 8 m   10. 1943 11 29
11. 2001 02 05   12. September 24, 2002
13. March 20, 2003   14. 40

15. 37

16. 7 : 05

17. 8 : 50

18.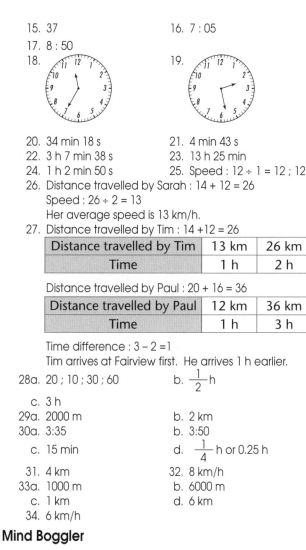

19.

20. 34 min 18 s

21. 4 min 43 s

22. 3 h 7 min 38 s

23. 13 h 25 min

24. 1 h 2 min 50 s

25. Speed : 12 ÷ 1 = 12 ; 12

26. Distance travelled by Sarah : 14 + 12 = 26
Speed : 26 ÷ 2 = 13
Her average speed is 13 km/h.

27. Distance travelled by Tim : 14 +12 = 26

Distance travelled by Tim	13 km	26 km
Time	1 h	2 h

Distance travelled by Paul : 20 + 16 = 36

Distance travelled by Paul	12 km	36 km
Time	1 h	3 h

Time difference : 3 – 2 =1
Tim arrives at Fairview first. He arrives 1 h earlier.

28a. 20 ; 10 ; 30 ; 60

b. $\frac{1}{2}$ h

c. 3 h

29a. 2000 m

b. 2 km

30a. 3:35

b. 3:50

c. 15 min

d. $\frac{1}{4}$ h or 0.25 h

31. 4 km

32. 8 km/h

33a. 1000 m

b. 6000 m

c. 1 km

d. 6 km

34. 6 km/h

Mind Boggler

22 ;

Within 12 hours the minute hand moves 12 complete turns while the hour hand moves only 1 complete turn, so the two hands overlap 11 times. They overlap 22 times in 24 hours.

6   Perimeter and Area

1. 12

2. 12

3. 10

4. 13

5. 10

6. 12 cm

7. 27 m

8. 30 dm

9. 20 dm

10. 32 cm

11. 18 m

12. 39 mm

13. 12

14. 10

15. 12

16. 12

17. 6

18. 10

19. 28 cm ; 49 cm²

20. 13.2 m ; 9.2 m²

21. 20 m ; 25 m²

22. 46 cm ; 96 cm²

23a. 26 cm by 18 cm

b. 88 cm

c. 468 cm²

24a. Small screen : 100 cm ; 600 cm²
Large screen : 200 cm ; 2400 cm²

b. 2 times

c. 4 times

25a. 29 cm

b. 21cm

c. 100 cm

d. 609 cm²

26. (Suggested drawings)

A : area = 12 cm² ; perimeter = 14 cm
B : area = 12 cm²
C : perimeter = 14 cm

27. 12 m²

28. 1.3 m²

29. 2.2 m²

30. 14 m

31. 13 m

32. 9.6 m²

33. 12.8 m²

34. 41.3 m²

Mind Boggler

7   Volume, Capacity and Mass

1. 24

2. 18

3. 28

4. 36

5. 900 cm³ ; 150 cm³ ; 3000 cm³

6. 900 mL ; 150 mL ; 3000 mL

7. 3 L

8. 20

9. 6 times

10. 25 cm x 25 cm x 20 cm

11. 12 500 cm³

12. 40 m³

13. 80 boxes

14. 100 ; 100

15. 250

16. 5 ; 30 ; 30 ; 4500 ; 4500

17. kilogram

18. tonne

19. gram

20. kilogram

21. tonne

22. 4.4

23. 200

24. 20

25. 1.6

26. 250

27. 400

28. 1500

29. 1.50

30a. 20 000 cm³

b. 8000 cm³

c. 1875 cm³

31. 576 cm³

32. 3 cm x 3 cm x 4 cm

33. 36 cm³

34. 40 g

35a. 25 slices

b. 25 000 slices

36a. 4000 cm³

b. 500 cm³

Mind Boggler

3

Progress Test

1.
```
    5984
  + 2079
    8063
  - 3475
    4588
```

2.
```
      53
    x 69
     477
    3180
    3657
```

3.
```
      76
    x 98
     608
    6840
    7448
```

4.
```
        787
    8 )6296
        56
        69
        64
        56
        56
```

5. 3
6. 54
7. 11
8. 0.57
9. 0.79
10. 0.38
11. >
12. <
13. <
14. 13.21
15. 4.19
16. 49.84
17.
```
    0.7 9
8 ) 6.3 2
    5 6
    ‾‾‾
      7 2
      7 2
      ‾‾‾
```
18. 1593
19. 0.608
20. 780
21. 300
22. 1700
23. 3200
24. 1200
25. 2700
26. 1600
27. 1200
28. 7
29. 10
30. 10
31. 12
32. 32 cm ; 64 cm²
33. 12.6 cm ; 9.2 cm²
34. 16 m ; 13 m²
35. 1701 cm³
36. 1960 m³
37. 1500 cm³
38. 11 : 59 : 04
39. May 16
40. C
41. D
42. C
43. B
44. B
45. D
46. B
47. A
48. B
49. D
50a. 30 x 50 x 20 = 30 000
    The volume of water is 30 000 cm³.
  b. 30 x 50 x 5 = 7500
    The volume of the stones is 7500 cm³.
  c. 30 x 50 x 40 = 60 000
    60 000 cm³ = 60 000 mL = 60 L
    The capacity of the aquarium is 60 L.
51a. 17 x 18 + 3 x 15 = 306 + 45 = 351
    351 students can be seated in the hall.
  b. 360 – 351 = 9 ; 9 students have to stand.
  c. 360 ÷ 20 = 36 ÷ 2 = 18
    There are 18 teachers in the hall.
  d. 11 h 7 min – 9 h 15 min = 1 h 52 min
    The assembly lasts for 1 h 52 min.

8 Angles and 2-D Figures

1. 90˚ ; 45˚ ; 120˚ ; 180˚ ; 75˚ ; 150˚
2. Right ; Acute ; Obtuse ; Straight ; Acute ; Obtuse

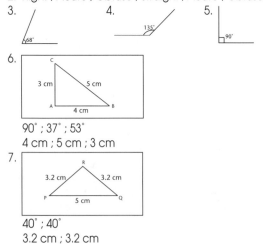

3. (68˚)
4. (135˚)
5. (90˚)
6.

90˚ ; 37˚ ; 53˚
4 cm ; 5 cm ; 3 cm

7.

40˚ ; 40˚
3.2 cm ; 3.2 cm

8. Scalene ; Isosceles
9. Right-angled ; Obtuse-angled
11.-12. (Suggested answers)

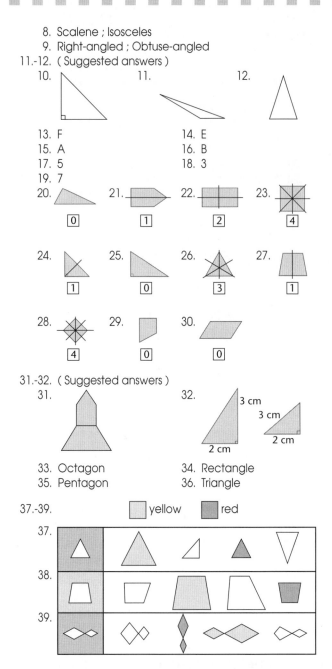

13. F
14. E
15. A
16. B
17. 5
18. 3
19. 7
20. 0
21. 1
22. 2
23. 4
24. 1
25. 0
26. 3
27. 1
28. 4
29. 0
30. 0
31.-32. (Suggested answers)
33. Octagon
34. Rectangle
35. Pentagon
36. Triangle
37.-39. ☐ yellow ☐ red

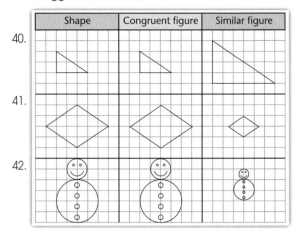

40.-42. (Suggested answers)

	Shape	Congruent figure	Similar figure
40.			
41.			
42.			

ISBN: 978-1-897164-15-0

Mind Boggler

14

9 3-D Figures

1. Square
2. 6
3. Rectangle
4. 5 ; Triangle, Rectangle
5. Cone, Cylinder
6. Circle
7. 8
8. 12
9. 3
10. Cube, Rectangular prism, Rectangular pyramid
11. A ; E
12. 4 ; 5 ; 6 ; 7
13. 6 ; 8 ; 10 ; 12
14. 4 ; 5 ; 6 ; 7
15. 4 ; 4 ; 5 ; 6
16. Triangle ; Rectangle ; Pentagon ; Hexagon
17. vertices ; faces
18. triangular faces
19. edges
20. 1
21. A ; B ; D
22. Tetrahedron or Triangular pyramid
23. Cube
24. Sphere
25. Cylinder
26. Hexagonal pyramid
27. Triangular prism
28. Rectangular prism
29. Cube
30. Rectangular prism
31. Triangular prism
32. Square pyramid
33. Tetrahedron or Triangular pyramid
34. Tetrahedron
35. Cone
36. Cube
37. Triangular prism
38. Rectangular prism

	Top view	Front view	Side view
39.	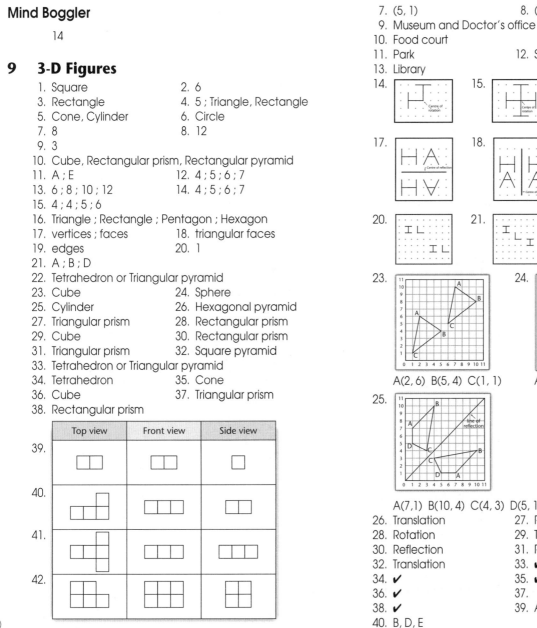		
40.			
41.			
42.			

Mind Boggler

stick

The common base of the two triangular pyramids is also a triangle.

10 Coordinates and Transformations

1.-8.
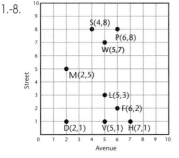

7. (5, 1)
8. (5, 7)
9. Museum and Doctor's office
10. Food court
11. Park
12. School
13. Library

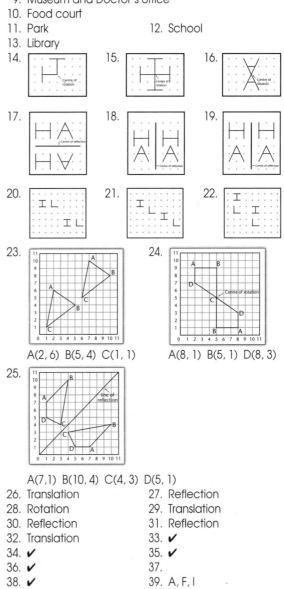

14. 15. 16.
17. 18. 19.
20. 21. 22.
23. 24.

A(2, 6) B(5, 4) C(1, 1)   A(8, 1) B(5, 1) D(8, 3)

25.

A(7,1) B(10, 4) C(4, 3) D(5, 1)
26. Translation
27. Reflection
28. Rotation
29. Translation
30. Reflection
31. Reflection
32. Translation
33. ✔
34. ✔
35. ✔
36. ✔
37.
38. ✔
39. A, F, I
40. B, D, E

Mind Boggler

1.
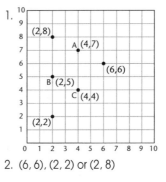
(2,8)
A (4,7)
(6,6)
B (2,5)
C (4,4)
(2,2)

2. (6, 6), (2, 2) or (2, 8)

11 Patterns

1. 2.

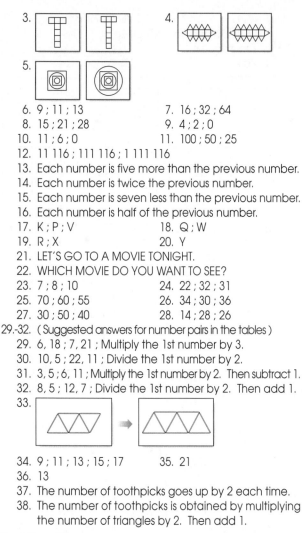

3.

4.

5.

6. 9 ; 11 ; 13
7. 16 ; 32 ; 64
8. 15 ; 21 ; 28
9. 4 ; 2 ; 0
10. 11 ; 6 ; 0
11. 100 ; 50 ; 25
12. 11 116 ; 111 116 ; 1 111 116
13. Each number is five more than the previous number.
14. Each number is twice the previous number.
15. Each number is seven less than the previous number.
16. Each number is half of the previous number.
17. K ; P ; V
18. Q ; W
19. R ; X
20. Y
21. LET'S GO TO A MOVIE TONIGHT.
22. WHICH MOVIE DO YOU WANT TO SEE?
23. 7 ; 8 ; 10
24. 22 ; 32 ; 31
25. 70 ; 60 ; 55
26. 34 ; 30 ; 36
27. 30 ; 50 ; 40
28. 14 ; 28 ; 26
29.-32. (Suggested answers for number pairs in the tables)
29. 6, 18 ; 7, 21 ; Multiply the 1st number by 3.
30. 10, 5 ; 22, 11 ; Divide the 1st number by 2.
31. 3, 5 ; 6, 11 ; Multiply the 1st number by 2. Then subtract 1.
32. 8, 5 ; 12, 7 ; Divide the 1st number by 2. Then add 1.
33.

34. 9 ; 11 ; 13 ; 15 ; 17
35. 21
36. 13
37. The number of toothpicks goes up by 2 each time.
38. The number of toothpicks is obtained by multiplying the number of triangles by 2. Then add 1.

Mind Boggler

1. 6.25
2. 6.25
3. No

12 Using Patterns and Simple Equations

1. 50 ; 60 ; 70 ; 80 ; 90
2. 9
3. 1.30
4. 70 ; 75 ; 80 ; 85 ; 90
5. 10
6. 1.10
7. 8 ; 10 ; 12
8. 2.0 ; 2.5 ; 3.0
9. 16
10. 12
11. 9
12. 4
13. 16 ; 20 ; 22 ; 26
14. Number of items collected goes up by 2, and then 4 in alternate weeks.
15. 122 items
16. 500 ; 1000 ; 2000 ; 4000
17. 26 ; 32 ; 38 ; 3000 ; 6000 ; 12 000 ; 24 000
18. (Suggested answer)
The account which doubles every 5 years is a better investment. The amount invested grows 8 times in 18 years if it doubles every 6 years whilst it needs only 15 years to grow 8 times if it doubles every 5 years.
19. 60 ; 65
20. Mass of Gerry increases by 5 g and then 10 g in alternate weeks.
21. Week 9
22. (Suggested answer)
No. Its mass is 35 g at week 2, but it is only 50 g at week 4.

23a. 5 min 12 s
b. The 7th day
24a. 6 min 40 s
b. The 7th lap
25a. 2.7 m
b. On day 11
26a. 1.46 m
b. On the 9th attempt
27. 9
28. 28
29. 10
30. 2
31. 116
32. 30
33. 20
34. 50
35. 90
36. 34
37. 92
38. 0.5
39. 0.1
40. 0.01
41. 10
42. 2
43. 1.2
44. 0.1
45. 1.4
46. 5.9
47. 11.2
48. 5
49. 100
50. 10
51. 6
52. 96
53. 12
54. B
55. C
56. A

Mind Boggler

30

13 Data and Graphs

1. American
2. Japanese
3. Korean
4. 15
5. 30
6. 45
7. 20
8. 75
9. Japanese
10a. American
b. Japanese
c. Korean
d. European
11. Hockey
12. Tennis
13. 4
14. 19
15. 6
16. 6
17. 3
18. 30
19. 45
20. $\frac{2}{9}$
21. $\frac{1}{4}$
22. Bar graph
23. 65 000
24. 130 000
25. 1994
26. 8000
27. 60 000
28. 1980-1985
29. 1990-1995
30. The population in Bellfield will be about 145 000 in 2010. From the graph, the increase in population between 1985 and 2005 was about 60 000, so the increase for every five years is about 15 000.
31. Line graph. It can show the trend of the population growth.
32. 1.4 ; 2.4 ; 5.4
33. 1 ; 2 ; 5
34. 2
35. 1.6 ; 2

Mind Boggler

4

14 Probability

1.
Tuna (T) — PT
Egg (E) — PE
Cheese (C) — PC
Tuna (T) — ST
Egg (E) — SE
Cheese (C) — SC

ISBN: 978-1-897164-15-0

2. 6

3. $\frac{3}{6}$ or $\frac{1}{2}$

4. $\frac{2}{6}$ or $\frac{1}{3}$

5. $\frac{1}{6}$

6. $\frac{9}{10}$

7. $\frac{1}{100}$

8. $\frac{1}{10}$

9. Green

10. Black and White

11. $\frac{1}{4}$

12. $\frac{1}{2}$

13. $\frac{3}{4}$

14. 75 times

15.

+	1	2	3	4	5	6
1	2	3	4	5	6	7
2	3	4	5	6	7	8
3	4	5	6	7	8	9
4	5	6	7	8	9	10
5	6	7	8	9	10	11
6	7	8	9	10	11	12

16. 36

17. 11

18. 7 ; $\frac{6}{36}$ or $\frac{1}{6}$

19. 2 ; 12 ; $\frac{1}{36}$

20. 5

21. $\frac{5}{12}$

22. A boy

23. $\frac{3}{4}$

24. $\frac{1}{4}$

25. $\frac{1}{6}$

26. No

27. $\frac{4}{5}$

28. $\frac{3}{7}$

29. $\frac{1}{9}$

30. $\frac{1}{5}$

31. $\frac{5}{12}$

32. $\frac{2}{3}$

33. $\frac{7}{12}$

34. $\frac{3}{4}$

35. 0

36. Yes

37. No

38. No

Mind Boggler

1. $\frac{1}{2}$

2. 0

3. 1

Final Test

1. D

2. D

3. B

4. C

5. B

6. C

7. A

8. C

9. B

10. B

11. B

12. A

13. C

14. D

15. A

16. B

17. A

18. D

19. B

20. D

21. C

22. A

23. C

24. D

25. B

26. A

27. B

28. A

29. C

30. C

31. Number of seats : 15 x 13 = 195
   Number of people standing : 200 – 195 = 5
   5 people are standing.

32a. Try : 1.29 x 8 = 10.32 ; 1.29 x 7 = 9.03
   She can get 7 books.

   b. Change : 10 – 9.03 = 0.97
   She can get $ 0.97 change.

33.
```
      8 5 4
  7 ) 5 9 8 2
      5 6
      ---
        3 8
        3 5
        ---
          3 2
          2 8
          ---
            4
```
The remainder is 4.
Check : 854 x 7 + 4 = 5978 + 4 = 5982

34. Approx. amount of water displaced : 580 – 250 = 330
   $1 \text{ mL} = 1 \text{ cm}^3$
   Volume of the rock is about 330 cm³.

35a. He earns : 10.50 x 9 x 5 = 472.50
   He earns $472.50 per week.

   b. His hourly wage on Sunday : 78.75 ÷ 5 = 15.75
   His hourly wage on Sunday was $15.75.

   C. He earned : 78.75 + 472.50 = 551.25
   He earned $551.25 last week.

36.

Population of Greensville

37. 1980 to 1990

38. 1970

39. 80 000

40. It can show the tendency of the growth of population.

41. 9 ; 2 ; 4 ; 5 ; 6 ; 4

42. 30 cars

43. $\frac{1}{5}$

44. $\frac{1}{6}$

45. $\frac{4}{15}$

46. $\frac{7}{10}$

47. 54

48. 50

49. 48

50. No

51. 30

52. 67.5

53. (Answer may vary.)

54. $1

55. 250

56. 300

57. $\frac{1}{2}$

58. $\frac{1}{6}$

59. 150

60. $\frac{3}{11}$

61. 25

62. 450

63. $110

64.-65. (Suggested answers)
   64a. Basketball   b. Hockey
       c. Baseball   d. Football
   65a. Basketball   b. Hockey
       c. Baseball   d. Football

ISBN: 978-1-897164-15-0

Unit 1

1. No. of pencils : 28 x 3 = 84   84
2. No. of books : 28 x 5 = 140   Difference : 140 – 84 = 56
   There are 56 more books than pencils given out at the beginning of the year.
3. No. of chairs : 28 + 2 = 30   No. of stacks : 30 ÷ 5 = 6
   There would be 6 stacks of chairs.
4. No. of pencils belonging to girls : 21 x (3 – 2) = 21
   There would be 21 pencils belonging to the girls.
5. No. of rows : 28 ÷ 7 = 4   There would be 4 rows of chairs.
6. No. of panes of glass : 9 x 8 = 72
   There are 72 panes of glass in the doors.
7. No. of panes of glass : 19 x 2 = 38
   Total no. of panes of glass : 72 + 38 = 110
   There are 110 panes of windows.
8. Cost : 72 ÷ 2 x 3 = 108
   It would cost $108.00 to clean the panes of glass in the doors.
9. Cost : 38 x 5 + 108 = 298
   It would cost $298.00 to clean all the glass in the house.
10. Value : 11 x 34 = 374
    The value of Sally's pennies was 374¢ ($3.74).
11. Value : 135 ÷ 9 = 15   Each nickel was worth 15¢.
12. Value : 14 x 31 = 434
    The value of her collection of dimes was 434¢ ($4.34).
13. Value : 116 x 5 + 76 x (19 – 5) = 1644
    The value of her quarters was 1644¢ ($16.44).
14. Value : 374 + 135 + 434 + 1644 = 2587
    The value of her collection was 2587¢ ($25.87).
15. Value : 25 x (34 + 9 + 31 + 19) = 2325 (2325 < 2587)
    No, it would not be a good idea.
16. No. of hours : 30 x 2 = 60
    She spent 60 hours on doing homework in September.
17. No. of hours : 30 x 2 x 17 = 1020
    The girls spent 1020 hours on doing homework in September.
18. No. of hours : 60 ÷ 20 = 3
    3 hours of homework would be assigned each school day.
19. No. of hours : 25 x 30 ÷ 15 = 50
    Wanda would do 50 hours of homework in September.
20. No. of hours : 50 x 17 = 850
    All the girls would do 850 hours of homework in September.
21. Money spent : 4 x 7 x 3 ÷ 2 = 42
    Lisa spends $42.00 each week on phone calls.
22. No. of phone calls : 4 x 31 = 124
    She would make 124 phone calls in January.
23. Cost : 4 x 31 x 3 ÷ 2 = 186
    Her phone calls would cost $186.00 in October.
24. Money saved : 4 ÷ 2 x 300 – 4 x 46 = 416
    She could save 416¢ ($4.16).
25. Money saved : 4200 – 500 x 7 = 700
    She would save 700¢ ($7.00) each week.
26. Time taken : 936 x 36 = 33696
    It takes 33 696 seconds to dust all the paperback books.
27. Time taken : 882 x 36 = 31752
    It takes 31 752 seconds to dust all the hardcover books.
28. No. of shelves : 936 ÷ 26 = 36
    There will be 36 shelves of paperback books.
29. No. of shelves : 882 ÷ 21 = 42
    There will be 42 shelves of hardcover books.
30. No. of books : 936 + 882 = 1818
    No. of books in each box : 1818 ÷ 6 = 303
    303 books are in each box.
31. Weight : 1242 ÷ 6 = 207
    There are 207 g of raisins in each bag.

32. Weight : 1896 ÷ 8 = 237
    There are 237 g of peanuts in each serving.
33. Weight : 63 x 4 x 15 = 3780   Allan's figs weigh 3780 g.
34. No. of days : (5 x 32) ÷ (4 x 2) = 20   They will last 20 days.
35. No. of cookies : 486 ÷ 6 = 81   Each person gets 81 cookies.
36. In bags of 5 : 486 ÷ 5 = 97...1   In bags of 7 : 486 ÷ 7 = 69...3
    To put in bags of 7.
37. No. of figs : 63 x 4 ÷ 3 = 84   Difference : 84 – 63 = 21
    Each bag holds 21 more figs than before.
38. No. of bags : 1896 ÷ 25 = 75...21   He needs 76 bags.
39. No. of portions of 18 grams : 1242 ÷ 18 = 69
    Cost : 69 x 12 = 828   Allan's raisins cost 828¢ ($8.28).
40. No. of pebbles : 308 ÷ 4 = 77
    She would have to carry 77 pebbles each day.
41. Time spent : 17 x 4 x 1 x 12 = 816
    He would spend 816 hours in a year listening to the CDs.
42. No. of shelves : 1648 ÷ 24 = 68...16
    He would need 69 shelves.
43. No. of plants : 35 x 23 = 805   Peter needed 805 plants.
44. Amount of water : 45 x 31 = 1395   Peter will use 1395 L of water.

Challenge

Day	Mon	Tue	Wed	Thu
No. of ants	100	200	400	800

x2   x2   x2

There might be 800 ants on Thursday.

Unit 2

1. Difference : 19 – 18 = 1   1 m
2. Total distance : 12 + 18 + 14 + 19 + 16 = 79
   They threw 79 m altogether.
3. Mario & Jimmy : 12 + 19 = 31   Sandy & Dolores : 18 + 16 = 34
   Sandy & Dolores threw the ball farther.
4. Danny : 14 + 14 = 28   Difference : 34 – 28 = 6
   The winning team threw 6 m farther than Danny did.
5. Jimmy : 19 x 5 = 95   Sandy : 18 x 3 = 54
   Dolores : 16 x 1 = 16
   Jimmy got the highest number. The number is 95.
6. No. of days : 31 + 29 + 31 + 30 + 31 + 30 + 31 + 31 + 30 + 31 + 30 + 31 = 366   There are 366 days in a leap year.
7. No. of marbles : 56 x 6 = 336   Frank would have 336 marbles.
8. No. of people : 47 x 12 = 564   564 people would fill 12 rows.
9. No. of packages : 1371 ÷ 250 = 5...121
   He must buy 6 packages of paper.
10. Total time : 60 + 20 = 80   No. of times : 80 ÷ 4 = 20
    He can ride around the park 20 times.
11. No. of stamps : 482 + 561 + 398 = 1441
    She has 1441 stamps in all.
12. Cost : 75 x 2 + 34 x 3 = 252   He should pay $252.00.
13. No. of pieces of lumber : 2352 + 598 + 28 = 2978
    They had 2978 pieces of lumber in all.
14. Difference : 2352 – 28 = 2324
    They had 2324 more pieces of pine than maple.
15. Difference : 2352 – 598 = 1754
    They had 1754 more pieces of pine than oak.
16. Length : 2978 x 2 = 5956
    They had 5956 metres of lumber at the lumber yard.
17. Length : (598 – 269) x 2 = 658
    They had 658 metres of oak left to sell.
18.

No. of days	1	2	3
Length of pine sold (m)	1568	3136	4704

It would take 3 days to sell all their pine pieces.

19. No. of pieces of oak left : 414 ÷ 2 = 207
No. of pieces of oak sold : 598 − 207 = 391
391 pieces of oak were sold.

20. Money earned : 2 x 9 x 5 = 90   She earned $90.00.

21. Time taken : 25 + 17 + 28 = 70; (70 min = 1 h 10 min)
He finished at 5:10 p.m.

22. Cost : 15 + 18 = 33
Money Mario had : 20 + 10 + 5 = 35 (35 > 33)   Yes, he could.

23. Time saved : (20 − 14) x 2 x 5 = 60
She could save 60 minutes each week.

24. There are 3 7 years in 21 years.   No. of times : 2 x 2 x 2 = 8
It should be worth 8 times its present value in 21 years.

Challenge

1. There are 3 leap years and 8 years.
No. of days : 366 x 3 + 365 x 8 = 1098 + 2920 = 4018
He is 4018 days old.

2. There are 3 quarters in 9 months.   Charge : 158920 x 3 = 476760
The client would pay them $476 760.00.

Unit 3

1. $6\frac{1}{2} = 6\frac{1 \times 4}{2 \times 4} = 6\frac{4}{8}$; $6\frac{4}{8} > 6\frac{3}{8}$ Peter

2. $\frac{1}{2}$ of an hour = 30 minutes (30 minutes < 42 minutes)
Mary read the chapter faster.

3. Douglas : 25 + 10 + 3 = 38   Jill : 10 + 5 x 6 + 1 = 41
Douglas had $\frac{38}{100}$ of a dollar; Jill had $\frac{41}{100}$ of a dollar. Jill had the larger fraction of a dollar.

4. Cake served : $\frac{2}{7} = \frac{2 \times 4}{7 \times 4} = \frac{8}{28}$
Cake kept : $\frac{1}{4} = \frac{1 \times 7}{4 \times 7} = \frac{7}{28}$
No, she didn't save more cake than she served.

5. Henry ate : $\frac{1}{3} = \frac{1 \times 5}{3 \times 5} = \frac{5}{15}$
Ann ate : $\frac{2}{5} = \frac{2 \times 3}{5 \times 3} = \frac{6}{15}$ ($\frac{6}{15} > \frac{5}{15}$)   Henry ate less.

6. ($1 = 100¢); She had $\frac{63}{100}$ of a dollar.

7. Money Dolores had : 100 + 25 x 7 = 275
(275¢ = 2\frac{75}{100}$) She had 2$\frac{75}{100}$ of a dollar.

8. Money Milly had : 25 + 10 x 4 + 5 x 12 = 125
(125¢ = 1\frac{25}{100}$) She had 1$\frac{25}{100}$ of a dollar.

9. Money Gerry had : 25 x 7 + 10 x 2 + 5 x 6 = 225
(225¢ = 2\frac{25}{100}$) He had 2$\frac{25}{100}$ of a dollar.

10. Dolores raised the most money for charity.

11. Total amount : $\frac{63}{100} + 2\frac{75}{100} + 1\frac{25}{100} + 2\frac{25}{100} = 6\frac{88}{100}$
They raised 6\frac{88}{100}$ for charity in all.

Challenge

1. Sam : $\frac{21}{147} = \frac{1}{7}$ Hindy : $\frac{54}{216} = \frac{1}{4}$
Kelly : $\frac{28}{98} = \frac{2}{7}$ Oliver : $\frac{2}{166} = \frac{1}{83}$
Kelly had the largest fraction of valuable cards.

2. Sam had the second smallest fraction of valuable cards.

3. Kelly, Hindy, Sam, Oliver.

Unit 4

1. Total time : $1\frac{5}{6} + 1\frac{4}{6} + \frac{1}{6} = 3\frac{4}{6}$; $3\frac{4}{6}$

2. Difference : $1\frac{4}{6} - \frac{1}{6} = 1\frac{3}{6}$
Dolores spent 1$\frac{3}{6}$ h more on the project than Mario.

3. Difference : $1\frac{4}{6} + 1\frac{5}{6} - \frac{1}{6} = 2\frac{9}{6} - \frac{1}{6} = 2\frac{8}{6} = 3\frac{2}{6}$
Ann and Dolores spent 3$\frac{2}{6}$ h more on the project than Mario.

4. No. of hours : $1\frac{5}{6} + \frac{1}{6} = 1\frac{6}{6} = 2$
Ann and Mario spent 2 hours on the project in all.

5. Time Dolores spent : $1\frac{4}{6}$ Time Ann and Mario spent : 2
Ann and Mario together spent more time on the project than Dolores.

6. Difference : $1\frac{5}{6} - \frac{1}{6} = 1\frac{4}{6}$
Mario would spend 1$\frac{4}{6}$ hours more.

7. No. of bags : $\frac{3}{7} + \frac{5}{7} + \frac{1}{7} = \frac{9}{7} = 1\frac{2}{7}$
Harry collected 1$\frac{2}{7}$ bags of bottles in all.

8. No. of bags : $\frac{5}{7} + \frac{3}{7} + \frac{2}{7} = \frac{10}{7} = 1\frac{3}{7}$
Barry collected 1$\frac{3}{7}$ bags of bottles in all.

9. No. of bags : $\frac{6}{7} + \frac{6}{7} + 1 = \frac{12}{7} + 1 = 2\frac{5}{7}$
Mary collected 2$\frac{5}{7}$ bags of bottles in all.

10. Mary collected the most bottles.

11. No. of bags : $1\frac{2}{7} + 1\frac{3}{7} + 2\frac{5}{7} = 5\frac{3}{7}$
The children collected 5$\frac{3}{7}$ bags of bottles in all.

12. Difference : $2\frac{5}{7} - 1\frac{2}{7} = 1\frac{3}{7}$
Mary collected 1$\frac{3}{7}$ more bags of bottles than Harry.

13. Difference : $2\frac{5}{7} - 1\frac{3}{7} = 1\frac{2}{7}$
Mary collected 1$\frac{2}{7}$ more bags of bottles than Barry.

14. No. of bags : $2 - 1\frac{2}{7} = \frac{5}{7}$
He needs to collect $\frac{5}{7}$ of a bag of bottles more.

15. No. of bags : $3 - 1\frac{3}{7} = 1\frac{4}{7}$
He needs to collect 1$\frac{4}{7}$ more bags of bottles.

16. No. of bags : $5 - 2\frac{5}{7} = 4\frac{7}{7} - 2\frac{5}{7} = 2\frac{2}{7}$
She needs to collect 2$\frac{2}{7}$ more bags of bottles.

17. Total amount : $\frac{2}{5} + \frac{4}{5} + \frac{3}{5} = \frac{9}{5} = 1\frac{4}{5}$
He had 1$\frac{4}{5}$ boxes of cereal in all.

18. Difference : $\frac{4}{5} - \frac{2}{5} = \frac{2}{5}$
He had $\frac{2}{5}$ of a box more bran flakes than corn flakes.

19. Difference : $\frac{3}{5} + \frac{2}{5} - \frac{4}{5} = \frac{5}{5} - \frac{4}{5} = \frac{1}{5}$
He had $\frac{1}{5}$ of a box more rice and corn flakes than bran flakes.

20. Amount of cereal left :
($\frac{2}{5} - \frac{1}{5}$) + ($\frac{4}{5} - \frac{1}{5}$) + ($\frac{3}{5} - \frac{1}{5}$) = 1$\frac{1}{5}$
1$\frac{1}{5}$ boxes of cereal would be left.

21. Total amount : $1\frac{4}{5} + 1 - \frac{1}{5} = 2\frac{3}{5}$
He would have 2$\frac{3}{5}$ boxes of cereal altogether.

22. Total distance : $2\frac{7}{20} + 3\frac{19}{20} + 2\frac{11}{20} + 5 = 13\frac{17}{20}$
They ran 13$\frac{17}{20}$ km in all.

23. Difference : $5 - 2\frac{7}{20} = 2\frac{13}{20}$ The person who ran the farthest ran 2$\frac{13}{20}$ km farther than the one who ran the shortest distance.

24. Total distance : $2\frac{7}{20} + 2\frac{11}{20} = 4\frac{18}{20}$ Their team ran 4$\frac{18}{20}$ km.

ISBN: 978-1-897164-15-0

25. Distance : $3\frac{19}{20} + 2\frac{11}{20} = 6\frac{10}{20}$

They ran $6\frac{10}{20}$ km in all.

26. Difference : $5 - 3\frac{19}{20} = 1\frac{1}{20}$ Toni ran $1\frac{1}{20}$ km farther than Lori.

27. Difference : $2\frac{11}{20} - 2\frac{7}{20} = \frac{4}{20}$ Freda ran $\frac{4}{20}$ km farther than Kim.

28. New magazines : $1 - (\frac{1}{19} + \frac{9}{19} + \frac{7}{19}) = \frac{19}{19} - \frac{17}{19} = \frac{2}{19}$

$\frac{2}{19}$ of his magazines are new.

29. Fraction of magazines : $\frac{7}{19} + \frac{2}{19} = \frac{9}{19}$

$\frac{9}{19}$ of his magazines were printed between 1980 and the present.

30. Fraction of magazines : $\frac{9}{19} + \frac{7}{19} = \frac{16}{19}$

$\frac{16}{19}$ of his magazines were printed between 1970 and 1990.

31. Fraction of magazines : $\frac{9}{19} + \frac{1}{19} = \frac{10}{19}$

$\frac{10}{19}$ of his magazines need protective envelopes.

32. Fraction of magazines : $1 - \frac{10}{19} = \frac{9}{19}$

$\frac{9}{19}$ of his magazines do not need protective envelopes.

33. Fraction of magazines left : $1 - \frac{3}{8} = \frac{5}{8}$

$\frac{5}{8}$ of his magazines are left.

34. $\frac{113}{190}$ of his magazines are in English.

35. No. of French magazines : $190 - 113 = 77$

$\frac{77}{190}$ of his magazines are in French.

Challenge

$\frac{3}{13} + ? = \frac{9}{13} \longrightarrow ? = \frac{6}{13}$

The fraction under the chocolate stain is $\frac{6}{13}$.

Unit 5

1. Weight : $0.75 + 0.007 + 1.28 + 0.95 + 0.01 = 2.997$; 2.997 kg
2. Weight : $4 - 2.997 = 1.003$

   He could add 1.003 kg more to his dry ingredients.
3. Weight : $0.75 + 1.28 + 0.95 + 0.01 = 2.99$

   This recipe requires 2.99 kg of vegetables.
4. Weight : $0.01 + 1.28 = 1.29$

   This recipe requires 1.29 kg of herbs and spices.
5. Weight : $2.997 + 0.599 = 3.596$

   The entire dish would weigh 3.596 kg before cooking.
6. Money saved : $7.5 - 3.49 - 1.78 - 2 = 0.23$

   She saved $0.23 each week.
7. Money spent : $3.49 + 1.78 = 5.27$

   She spent $5.27 for entertainment and snacks each week.
8. Difference : $3.49 - 2 = 1.49$ She spent $1.49 more for entertainment than transportation each week.
9. Money saved : $0.23 + 0.68 = 0.91$ She would save $0.91 each week.
10. Money left : $3.49 - (2.23 - 1.78) = 3.04$

    She would have $3.04 left for entertainment.

Challenge

1. Distance : $1.97 - 1.78 = 0.19$ He would have to go 0.19 km farther.
2. Final balance : $15.02 + (5.78 - 0.15) + (1.99 - 0.15) - 3.14 - 0.15 - 2.67 - 0.15 = 16.38$ Her final balance was $16.38.

Unit 6

1. Money saved : $5.75 \times 12 = 69$ ($69 < 75.6$);   wouldn't
2. Difference : $75.6 - 69 = 6.6$ He would be short of $6.60.
3. Money saved : $6.45 \times 12 = 77.4$ ($77.4 > 75.6$)

   Yes, that would allow him to buy the game on time.
4. He is short of $6.60. Extra money needed : $6.6 \div 12 = 0.55$

   He would have to save an extra $0.55 each month.

5. Difference : $69 - 59.88 = 9.12$

   Less money saved : $9.12 \div 12 = 0.76$

   He would save $0.76 less each month.
6. Money spent : $2.16 \times 2 = 4.32$ She would spend $4.32 for pine.
7. Money spent : $0.3 \times 4.7 = 1.41$ She would spend $1.41 for oak.
8. Money spent : $2.4 \times 5.65 = 13.56$

   She would spend $13.56 for walnut.
9. Money spent : $4.32 + 1.41 + 13.56 = 19.29$

   She would spend $19.29 for wood altogether.
10. Total cost : $(2.16 + 0.3 + 2.4) \times 0.5 = 2.43$

    The total cost would be $2.43.
11. Total cost : $19.29 + 2.43 = 21.72$

    The total cost for the wood plus finishing was $21.72.
12. Amount each paid : $21.72 \div 3 = 7.24$ Each person would pay $7.24.
13. Length : $2.16 \div 3 = 0.72$ Each part was 0.72 m long.
14. Length : $(2.4 - 0.04) \div 4 = 0.59$ Each part was 0.59 m long.
15. No. of metres of pine : $16.5 \div 2 = 8.25$

    I can buy 8.25 metres of pine.
16. Travel cost : $305 \times 0.06 = 18.3$

    The travel cost on Day 2 was $18.30.
17. Difference : $271 \times 0.04 - 186 \times 0.05 = 1.54$

    The difference in travel cost was $1.54.
18. Day 1 : $271 \times 0.04 = 10.84$ Day 2 : $305 \times 0.06 = 18.30$

    Day 3 : $652 \times 0.05 = 32.60$ Day 4 : $186 \times 0.05 = 9.30$

    Day 5 : $395 \times 0.04 = 15.80$

    The lowest travel cost was on Day 4. It was $9.30.
19. Day 3 was the highest.   The cost was $32.60.
20. Day 5 : $15.80 > 12.00$

    Yes, it would have exceeded his budget.
21. Day 2 : $18.30 > 12.00$ Day 3 : $32.60 > 12.00$

    Day 5 : $15.80 > 12.00$

    Days 2, 3 and 5 exceeded his travel budget.
22. Cost per km : $4 \div 100 = 0.04$ The cost per km would be $0.04.
23. Cost per km : $(4 + 2) \div 100 = 0.06$ The cost per km would be $0.06.
24. Cost : $8.76 \div 4 = 2.19$ Each box of juice costs $2.19.
25. Capacity : $1.25 \div 5 = 0.25$ The capacity of each glass is 0.25 L.
26. Capacity : $1.25 \times 7 = 8.75$ There is 8.75 L of juice in 7 boxes.
27. Regular size : $1.38 \div 2 = 0.69$ Jumbo size : $5.90 \div 10 = 0.59$

    Jumbo size is the better buy.
28. Cost : $1.38 \times 8 = 11.04$ He should pay $11.04.
29. Amount of water : $1.75 \times 7 = 12.25$

    He will drink 12.25 L of water in a week.

Challenge

Area : $16.8 \times 2.4 = 40.32$ Amount of paint : $40.32 \div 32 \times 2 = 2.52$

She will need 2.52 L of paint for the wall.

Midway Review

1. No. of helpers : $9 \times 4 + 12 \times 4 = 36 + 48 = 84$

   There were 84 helpers.
2. No. of pieces of cake : $64 \times 8 = 512$ She made 512 pieces of cake.
3. Cost : $0.75 \times 8 = 6.00$ A cake cost $6.00.
4. Cost : $2.16 \times 64 = 138.24$

   The total cost for baking all the cakes would be $138.24.
5. No. of doughnuts : $1064 + 898 = 1962$

   There were 1962 doughnuts in all.
6. No. of packages : $1064 \div 4 = 266$

   There were 266 packages of chocolate doughnuts.
7. No. of honey doughnuts sold : $898 - 159 = 739$

   739 honey doughnuts had been sold.
8. Cost : $5.04 \div 8 = 0.63$ 1 honey doughnut cost $0.63.
9. No. of cookies : $4 \times 6 \times 15 = 360$ There were 360 cookies.
10. No. of cookies left : $360 - 218 = 142$ 142 cookies were left.
11. Weight : $486.5 \div 5 = 97.3$ 1 cookie weighed 97.3 grams.

ISBN: 978-1-897164-15-0

12. Amount of cake : $\frac{1}{8} + \frac{5}{8} = \frac{6}{8}$

They bought $\frac{6}{8}$ of the cake in all.

13. Difference : $\frac{5}{8} - \frac{1}{8} = \frac{4}{8}$

Sally bought $\frac{4}{8}$ more of the cake than Gary.

14. Change : 10 − 4.16 = 5.84   Her change was $5.84.

15. A bag of 5 bagels : 1.30 ÷ 5 = 0.26

A bag of 8 bagels : 1.76 ÷ 8 = 0.22

A bag of 8 bagels is a better buy.

16. Money collected : 459 x 8 = 3672

The stalls collected $3672.00 in all.

17. Money donated : 3672 ÷ 2 = 1836

Mr Stanley donated $1836.00 to the Children's Hospital.

18. Money Mr Stanley had : $1836 ($1836 > $1285)

Yes, he made a profit after the donation.

19. Profit : 1836 − 1285 = 551   He gained $551.00.

20. Amount of paint : 3.48 x 4 = 13.92

13.92 L of paint are needed for all the bedrooms.

21. No. of cans : 13.92 ÷ 4 = 3.48   She needs 4 cans.

22. No. of boxes of tiles needed : $1\frac{3}{5} + 1\frac{3}{5} + 1\frac{3}{5} = 4\frac{4}{5}$

$4\frac{4}{5}$ boxes of tiles are needed.

23. She needs to buy 5 boxes.

24. No. of boxes left : $5 - 4\frac{4}{5} = \frac{1}{5}$

$\frac{1}{5}$ of a box of tiles will be left over.

25. Money spent : 798.65 + 268.47 = 1067.12

They spend $1067.12 in all.

26. Store A : 102 x 6 = 612   Store B : 621 (621> 612)

Stores A offers a better buy.

27. Cost : 1295 + 612 = 1907   She will pay $1907.00.

28. B   29. C   30. D   31. A   32. C

33. A   34. D   35. C   36. A

Unit 7

1. Cost : 12.37 x 3 + 14.62 = 51.73; $51.73

2. Amount saved : (19.99 − 14.62) x 5 = 26.85

She would save $26.85.

3. Cost : 12.37 + 227.36 = 239.73 (239.73 > 230)   No, he cannot.

4. Change : 150 − 67.99 x 2 = 14.02   Her change was $14.02.

5. Average price : (12.37 + 14.62 + 67.99) ÷ 3 = 31.66

The average price is $31.66.

6. Money spent : 5.88 + 3.35 + 4.32 + 8.37 = 21.92

They spent $21.92 in all.

7. Change : 50 − 21.92 = 28.08   They should receive $28.08 change.

8. Amount each paid : 21.92 ÷ 2 = 10.96

Each person should pay $10.96.

9. They spent $21.92; there were 2 ten dollars.

Cost : 21.92 − 1.05 x 2 = 19.82   They would have paid $19.82.

10. Cost : 5.88 ÷ 6 = 0.98   The cost of 1 kg of apples was $0.98.

11. Cost : 8.37 ÷ 3 = 2.79   The cost of 1 kg of candies was $2.79.

12. Cost : 3.35 ÷ 5 = 0.67   The cost of 1 head of lettuce was $0.67.

13. 5-pound bag : 6.45 ÷ 5 = 1.29   8-pound bag : 9.28 ÷ 8 = 1.16

An 8-pound bag is a better buy.

14. Distance : 0.3 x 1000 = 300

Rachel lives the closest to the school. The distance is 300 m.

15. Distance : 1620 ÷ 1000 = 1.62

The distance between Sandra's house and Paul's house is 1.62 km.

16. Distance : 1.57 + 0.89 = 2.46

The distance from Debbie's house to the school is 2.46 km.

17. Shortest distance : 0.93 + 1.35 = 2.28 (via Sandra's house)

The shortest distance from Debbie's house to the school is 2280 m.

18. Rachel → School → Virginia → Debbie : 0.3 + 0.89 + 1.57 = 2.76

Rachel → School → Sandra → Debbie : 0.3 + 1.35 + 0.93 = 2.58

The shortest distance is 2.58 km.

19. Distance walked per minute : 1.35 ÷ 5 = 0.27

The average distance she walked per minute was 0.27 km.

20. Distance travelled per minute : (1.57 + 0.89) ÷ 6 = 2.46 ÷ 6 = 0.41

The average distance she travelled per minute was 0.41 km.

21. Distance travelled per minute : (2.82 + 1.32) ÷ 9 = 0.46

The average distance she travelled per minute was 0.46 km.

22. Distance travelled : 1.35 x 4 x 5 = 27

She will travel 27 km in 5 days.

23. Distance travelled : 0.89 + 1.35 + 0.3 x 2 = 2.84

They walk 2.84 km in total.

24. Actual distance : 2.5 x 0.3 = 0.75   The actual distance is 0.75 km.

Challenge

1. Cost : 3.75 x 25 + 6.90 = 93.75 + 6.90 = 100.65

They would have to pay $100.65 in total.

2. Cost : 3.75 x 35 − 12.60 = 118.65

They would have to pay $118.65 in total.

Unit 8

1. No. of seats : 26 x 48 = 1248

No. of empty seats : 1248 − 952 = 296   296

2. Total amount from children's tickets : 2475 − 462 x 4.5 = 396

No. of children's tickets : 396 ÷ 3 = 132

132 children's tickets were sold.

3. Amount each child paid : 3 + 2 = 5

Money collected : 1248 x 5 = 6240

$6240.00 would be collected for that show.

4. Amount each adult paid : 4.5 + 2 = 6.5

Money collected : 1248 x 6.5 = 8112

$8112.00 would be collected for that show.

5. She would have to buy 1 adult ticket, 4 children's tickets and 3 pop corns. Cost : 4.5 + 3 x 4 + 2 x 3 = 22.5   She would pay $22.50 in all.

6. Cost : 9 + 14 = 23   He would pay $23.00 for his purchases.

7. Cost : (18 ÷ 3 x 6 + 19) − 4 = 51   Change : 100 − 51 = 49

She would get $49.00 change.

8. Cost : (9 ÷ 2 x 4 + 18) − 4 = 32

Money needed : 32 − 20 − 10 = 2   She would need $2.00.

9. Cost : (14 x 2 + 9 ÷ 2 x 4) − 4 = 42

He would pay $42.00 for his purchases.

10. Cost : (18 ÷ 3 x 9 + 14 x 3) − 4 x 2 = 88

She would pay $88.00 for her purchases.

11. Cost : 19 x 4 = 76   Money needed : 76 − 50 = 26

She would need to borrow $26.00.

12. Price of 6 blouses : 18 ÷ 3 x 6 − 4 = 32   Price of 4 dresses : 19 x 4 = 76

Difference : 76 − 32 = 44   The price difference was $44.00.

13. Amount spent on dresses : 71 − 14 = 57

No. of dresses : 57 ÷ 19 = 3   She bought 3 dresses.

14. No. of shirts : 128 + 224 = 352   No. of packages : 352 ÷ 4 = 88

He made 88 packages of 4 in all.

15. No. of packages : 352 ÷ 3 = 117...1

He made 117 packages of 3 in all.

16. Time for ads and music in an hour : 8 x 2 + 16 x 2 = 48

Time for talk : 60 − 48 = 12 There will be 12 min of talk every hour.

17. There are 16 min of ads in an hour; 16 min have 32 30 seconds.

Cost : 120 x 32 = 3840   The station will earn $3840.00 per hour.

18. No. of songs in an hour : 16 x 2 ÷ 4 = 8

No. of songs between 4:00 p.m. and 9:00 p.m. : 8 x 5 = 40

40 songs can be played between 4:00 p.m. and 9:00 p.m.

19. Non-ad time in an hour : 60 − 8 x 2 = 44

Non-ad time in a day : 44 x 16 = 704

There will be 704 min of non-ad time in a day.

20. There are 12 min of talk in an hour; there are 72 10 seconds in 12 min.
No. of words in an hour : 12 x 72 = 864
He will say 864 words in each hour's talk time.

21. Cost : 0.46 x 4 = 1.84   Change : 5 – 1.84 = 3.16
She would get $3.16 change.

22. Cost for Anna's friends : (0.46 x 4) x 4 = 7.36
Total cost : 0.46 x 4 + 7.36 = 9.2
They would have spent $9.20 in postage.

23.
No. of people involved: 1 + 4 + 16 = 21
21 people were involved in the chain.

24. Cost : 85 x 0.46 = 39.1   They would pay $39.10 for postage.

25. Time each person spent on sending a letter : 6 + 2 = 8
Total time spent : (4 + 16) x 8 = 160
They would spend 160 minutes.

Challenge

1.

Day	Mon	Tue	Wed	Thu
No. of pages read	38	67	67	29

No. of pages left : 249 – 38 – 67 – 67 – 29 = 48
She would have 48 pages left to read on Thursday at noon.

2. Total amount for the payments : 92.6 x 24 = 2222.4
Difference : 2222.4 – 2120.5 = 101.9
Wayne pays $101.90 more by purchasing it on the instalment plan.

Unit 9

1. 1st : 4 + 2 = 6   2nd : 6 x 3 = 18   18

2. 1st : 6 + 2 = 8   2nd : 8 x 3 = 24   Dorothy would answer 24.

3. 1st : 5.5 + 2 = 7.5   2nd : 7.5 x 3 = 22.5
Dorothy would answer 22.5.

4. A : 4 ÷ 2 = 2; 2 + 10 = 12 ✗   B : 4 x 6 = 24; 24 – 10 = 14 ✓
C : 4 – 3 = 1; 1 x 10 = 10 ✗   D : 4 + 8 = 12; 12 ÷ 2 = 6 ✗
B is correct.

5. 1st : 2.4 x 6 = 14.4   2nd : 14.4 – 10 = 4.4
Gladys would answer 4.4.

6. Yes. He scored 2 more baskets each day.

7. $1 \xrightarrow{+2} 3 \xrightarrow{+2} 5 \xrightarrow{+2} 7 \xrightarrow{+2} 9$
The numbers increase by 2 each time.

8. Billy would score 11 baskets on the 6th day.

9.
Billy would score 19 baskets on the 10th day.

10. Total no. of baskets : 1 + 3 = 4
Billy scored 4 baskets in the first 2 days.

11. Total no. of baskets : 1 + 3 + 5 = 9
Billy scored 9 baskets in the first 3 days.

12. Total no. of baskets : 1 + 3 + 5 + 7 = 16
Billy scored 16 baskets in the first 4 days.

13. Total no. of baskets : 1 + 3 + 5 + 7 + 9 = 25
Billy scored 25 baskets in the first 5 days.

14.

Day	1	2	3	4	5	6	7	8	9
No. of baskets in all	1	4	9	16	25	36	49	64	81

Billy would score 81 baskets in the first 9 days.

15.

Day	9	10	11
No. of baskets in all	81	100	121

Billy would take 11 days.

16. $1 \xrightarrow{x3} 3 \xrightarrow{x3} 9 \xrightarrow{x3} 27 \xrightarrow{x3} 81 \xrightarrow{x3} 243$
Each number is 3 times the previous number. The next 2 numbers are 81 and 243.

17. $1 \xrightarrow{+0.9} 1.9 \xrightarrow{+0.9} 2.8 \xrightarrow{+0.9} 3.7 \xrightarrow{+0.9} 4.6 \xrightarrow{+0.9} 5.5$
The numbers increase by 0.9. The next 2 numbers are 4.6 and 5.5.

18.
The letters skip 1 more letter than before. The next 2 letters are o and u.

19. $3 \xrightarrow{+3} 6 \xrightarrow{+4} 10 \xrightarrow{+5} 15 \xrightarrow{+6} 21 \xrightarrow{+7} 28$
The numbers increase by 1 more each time. The next 2 numbers are 21 and 28.

20.
1, 1, 2, 2, 2, 4, 3, 3, 6, 4, 4, 8, 5, 5, 10
3 numbers are in a group.   The first 2 numbers in the group increase by 1, the last numbers increase by 2.
The next 6 numbers are 4, 4, 8, 5, 5, and 10.

21.
1 , 2 , 3 , 5 , 8 , 13 , 21 , 34 , 55
(1+2, 2+3, 3+5, 5+8, 8+13, 13+21, 21+34)
Each number is the sum of the previous 2 numbers.
The next 2 numbers are 34 and 55.

22.

Day	1	2	3	4	5	6	7
Allowance	0.1	0.2	0.4	0.8	1.6	3.2	6.4

Total allowance in a week :
0.1 + 0.2 + 0.4 + 0.8 + 1.6 + 3.2 + 6.4 = 12.7 (12.7>12)
To give $12.00 per week is a better deal for Hortense's parents.

23. Improvement : 58 – 52 = 6;   Final mark : 58 + 6 x 2 = 70
Mr Finley would give Karen 70 for her next test.

24.

Age	12	22	32	42	52	62	72
Value of bond	25	50	100	200	400	800	1600

It will be worth $1600.00 when Jerry is 72 years old.

Challenge

1. 40   2. Subtraction   3. Addition

Unit 10

1. 62.50, 125.00, 500.00, 2000.00, 4000.00

2.

Year	2000	2010	2020
Price ($)	4000.00	8000.00	16000.00

The price of the savings bond in 2020 would be $16 000.00.

3.

Year	2000	2010	2020	2030	2040
Price ($)	4000.00	8000.00	16000.00	32000.00	64000.00

It would be worth $64 000.00 in 2040.

4. No. of times : 250 ÷ 62.5 = 4   It was 4 times more.

5. Money earned : 16000 – 1000 = 15000
I would have earned $15 000.00.

6. 6, 8, 5;   2.25, 3.60;   19, 24, 30, 38, 43

7.

Week	1	2	3	4	5	6	7	8	9
No. of cards	5	6	8	5	6	8	5	6	8

He will buy 8 cards.

8.

Week	7	8	9	10
Money spent	2.25	2.70	3.60	2.25

He will spend $2.25.

9. He will collect 19 cards.   10. He will collect 38 cards.

11.

Week	7	8	9
No. of cards bought	5	6	8
No. of cards in collection	43	49	57

He will collect 57 cards.

12. No. of cards collected in 3 weeks : 5 + 6 + 8 = 19
No. of cards collected in 30 weeks : 19 x 10 = 190
He will collect 190 cards.

13. Following the pattern, Matthew should buy 6 cards next week.
He will buy 6 cards in week 23.

14. Total amount : 2.25 + 2.7 + 3.6 = 8.55   He will spend $8.55.

15. Money spent : (2.25 + 2.7 + 3.6) x 2 = 17.1
He will spend $ 17.10.

16. 14, 16, 18, 20, 22;   8, 11, 14, 17, 20

17. No. of yellow marbles : 22 + 2 = 24; 24

18. No. of blue marbles : 20 + 3 = 23
Tony has 23 blue marbles on the 7th day.

19.

Day	6th	7th	8th	9th	10th	11th
No. of yellow marbles	22	24	26	28	30	32

Tony takes 11 days to have 32 yellow marbles.

20.

Day	6th	7th	8th	9th	10th
No. of blue marbles	20	23	26	29	32

Tony takes 10 days to have 32 blue marbles.

21.

Day	6th	7th	8th
No. of yellow marbles	22	24	26
No. of blue marbles	20	23	26

The yellow and blue marbles will be the same in number on the 8th day.

22. No. of marbles : 22 + 20 = 42
Tony has 42 marbles in all in the first 6 days.

23. The number of yellow marbles increases by 2 every day. The number of blue marbles increases by 3 every day. The total number of marbles increases by 5 every day.

24. 0, 0;   6, 10;   4, 8, 12, 16, 24;   6, 12, 24, 30;
16, 24, 48;   40, 50

25. The numbers increase by 6 each time.
The next 3 numbers would be 36, 42 and 48.

26. The numbers increase by 4 each time.
The next 3 numbers would be 28, 32 and 36.

27. Column 5 has the same pattern as that in row 6.
The numbers increase by 10 each time.

28. Row 6 can show the counting pattern of Joe's cards.
He will have 50 cards after 5 days.

29. Row 5 can show the amount of money Raymond has spent.
He will have spent $32.00 after 4 days.

30. 4, 9, 14, 19, 24, 29   31. 2.50, 3.00, 3.50, 4.00, 4.50, 5.00

32.

Hour	6	7	8	9	10
Charge ($)	29.00	34.00	39.00	44.00	49.00

The charge was $49.00.

33. Charge : 19 + 3.5 = 22.5   The twins earned $22.50 for the service.

34. Cost : 4 + 2 x 4 = 12   Lily's bill was $12.00.

35. Charge for 8 hours of simple care : 29 + 5 + 5 = 39
Total bill : 39 + 39 x 2 = 117   Their total bill was $117.00.

36. $3.50, $4.50, $5.00

37. Cost : 12.50 + 12.00 + 0.75 x 6 = 29
His total bill was $29.00.

38. Charge for 7 hours' care : 17 + 4.5 + 4.5 + 4.5 = 30.5
Total bill : 30.5 + 10 = 40.5   Their total bill was $40.50.

Challenge

Hour	1	2	3	4	5
Charge ($) for children over 3	1	2.5	4	5.5	7
Charge ($) for children under 3	3	4.5	6	7.5	9

Cost : 7 + 9 = 16   Their bill would be $16.00.

Final Review

1. Area : 1.96 x 4 = 7.84   The area is 7.84 km².

2. Distance travelled : 1.4 x 3 = 4.2   She walked 4.2 km.

3. Distance travelled : 1.4 x 4 = 5.6   He walked 5.6 km.

4. Distance travelled : 1.4 x 3 x 2 = 8.4   They travelled 8.4 km in all.

5. Difference : 1.4 x 2 – 1.86 = 0.94   She would have to walk 0.94 km.

6. Distance travelled in 1 min : 1.4 ÷ 5 = 0.28
He would travel 0.28 km in 1 min.

7. Difference : 1.4 ÷ 4 – 1.4 ÷ 5 = 0.35 – 0.28 = 0.07
Doris would walk 0.07 km more than Bobby in 1 min.

8. 4.2, 5.6, 7, 8.4;   9, 12, 15, 18

9. The time taken increases by 3 minutes.

10. The distance travelled increases by 1.4 km.

11.

No. of blocks	6	7	8
Time (min)	18	21	24

He would take 24 min to travel 8 blocks.

12.

No. of blocks	6	7	8	9	10	11	12
Time (min)	18	21	24	27	30	33	36

He would pass 12 blocks.

13.

No. of blocks	6	7	8	9
Distance travelled (km)	8.4	9.8	11.2	12.6

He would travel 12.6 km.

14.

Time (min)	15	30	45	60	75
Water drunk (L)	$\frac{1}{4}$	$\frac{2}{4}$	$\frac{3}{4}$	1	$1\frac{1}{4}$

He would drink $1\frac{1}{4}$ L of water.

15.

Time (min)	75	90	105
Water drunk (L)	$1\frac{1}{4}$	$1\frac{2}{4}$	$1\frac{3}{4}$

He would have travelled 105 minutes (1 h 45 min) on his bike.

16. Cost : 29.45 – 7.15 = 22.3   I have to pay $22.30.

17. Price : 53.25 + 15.5 = 68.75   Its price is $68.75.

18. Cost : 10.8 x 3 = 32.4   He can save $7.15.

19. Cost before discount : 15.99 x 2 = 31.98
Cost after discount : 31.98 – 7.15 = 24.83   He will pay $24.83.

20. Cost before discount : 22.99 x 2 = 45.98
Change : 50 – (45.98 – 15.5) = 19.52   He will get $19.52 change.

21. Cost before discount : 59.99 + 3.99 = 63.98
Change : 60 – (63.98 – 15.5) = 11.52   She will get $11.52 change.

22. Cost after discount : 19.87 – 3.25 = 16.62
Money Gary has : 10 + 2 x 3 + 0.25 x 3 = 16.75 (16.75 > 16.62)
Yes. He will have enough money to buy a box of chocolates.

23. No. of male customers : 329 – 251 = 78
There will be 78 male customers.

24. Money collected : 215 x 5 = 1075
$1075.00 can be collected from 215 customers.

25. Sweater A : 34.87 – 7.15 = 27.72
Sweater B : 40.05 – 15.5 = 24.55
Difference : 27.72 – 24.55 = 3.17
The price difference between sweater A and sweater B after the discount is $3.17.

26. Ray should buy sweater B because it is cheaper.

27. B   · 28. C   29. A   30. B   31. D   32. C
33. B   34. A   35. B   36. D   37. C   38. B
39. B   40. D   41. D

Unit 1

1. Cost : 4.98 + 12.49 = 17.47 $17.47
2. Cost : 20.18 + 5.39 = 25.57   His bill would be $25.57.
3. Cost : 4.98 + 2.84 + 12.49 + 20.18 – 4.5 =35.99
   His bill would be $35.99.
4. Change : 100 – 35.99 = 64.01   He would get $64.01 change.
5. Raking leaves : 23.02 – 4.98 = 18.04 ✗
   Sweeping sidewalks : 23.02 – 2.84 = 20.18 (cleaning garage) ✓
   He swept Mrs Winter's sidewalk and cleaned her garage.
6. Change : 50 – 23.02 = 26.98   She would get $26.98 change.
7. Amount earned per hour : 20.18 ÷ 2 = 10.09
   Ben would earn $10.09 per hour.
8. Amount after donation : (37.65 + 35.94 + 31.53) – (37.65 + 35.94 + 31.53) ÷ 4 = 78.84   Ben would have $78.84 after his donation.
9. Change : 100 – (82.97 – 8 x 1.5) = 29.03   Ann's change is $29.03.
10. Change : 100 – (120.45 – 12 x (1.5 + 0.3)) = 1.15
    Tim's change is $1.15.
11. Cost : 16.99 x 3 = 50.97 ; Rebate : 5 x 1.5 = 7.5
    Change : 50 – (50.97 – 7.5) = 6.53   Ray's change is $6.53.
12. Rebate for buying separately : 1.5 x 9 x 2 = 27
    Rebate for buying together : (1.5 + 0.3) x 9 x 2 = 32.4
    Sally can get more rebate by buying them together.
13. Jacket A : 98.27 – (9 x 1.5) = 84.77
    Jacket B : 102.95 – 10 x (1.5 + 0.3) = 84.95
    Eric should buy Jacket A.
14. Cost of 12 lollipops : 0.97 x 12 = 11.64 ;
    Money saved : 11.64 – 10.8 = 0.84   Donna would save $0.84.
15. Change : 25 – (10.8 x 2) = 3.4   Donna's change was $3.40.
16. Cost of 1 package : 3.24 ÷ 6 = 0.54   1 package cost $0.54.
17. Change : 20 – (0.54 x 18) = 10.28   Gary's change was $10.28.
18. Money spent on jellybeans : 23.76 – 10.8 = 12.96

No. of boxes of jellybeans	1	2	3	4
Cost ($)	3.24	6.48	9.72	12.96

   Louis bought 4 boxes of jellybeans.
19. Average cost : (1.26 x 2) ÷ 3 = 0.84
    Each chocolate bar cost $0.84 on average.
20. Cost : 1.26 x 6 = 7.56   Alexander paid $7.56.
21. Cost of 3 jars of candies : 12.96 x 3 = 38.88   (40 > 38.88)
    Yes, Jeffrey would have enough money to buy 3 jars of candies.
22. Money left : 40 – (12.96 x 2) = 14.08
    Jeffrey would have $14.08 left.
23. $570.75 ; five hundred seventy dollars and seventy-five cents.
24. $462.20 ; four hundred sixty-two dollars and twenty cents.
25. $415.40 ; four hundred fifteen dollars and forty cents.
26. $520.23 ; five hundred twenty dollars and twenty-three cents.
27. week 1, week 4, week 2, week 3

Challenge

1. Amount : 20.94 x 12 = 251.28   Mr Tiff will get $251.28.
2. Gain : 251.28 – 187.2 = 64.08   He will gain $64.08.

Unit 2

1. Perimeter : 1.8 + 2.1 + 3 + 2 + 2.5 = 11.4   11.4 cm
2. Perimeter : 3.4 + 3.6 + 1 + 1.8 + 3.4 = 13.2
   Its perimeter is 13.2 cm.
3. Perimeter : 2.5 + 2.5 + 1.3 + 1.2 + 1.2 + 1.3 = 10
   Its perimeter is 10 cm.
4. Perimeter : 2.5 + 3.8 + 2.5 + 1.5 + 1.1 + 1.3 + 1.1 + 1 = 14.8
   Its perimeter is 14.8 cm.
5. Perimeter : (3.4 + 2) x 2 = 10.8   Its perimeter is 10.8 cm.
6. Perimeter : 2.2 x 4 = 8.8   Its perimeter is 8.8 cm.
7. 11.4 m , 13.2 m , 10 m , 14.8 m , 10.8 m , 8.8 m
8. Actual perimeter : (4 + 3 + 6) x 100 = 1300
   The actual perimeter is 1300 cm (13 m).

9. Actual perimeter : (4 + 2 +3.5 + 4) x 100 = 1350
   The actual perimeter is 1350 cm (13.5 m).
10. Actual perimeter : (2 + 3 + 2 + 3) x 100 = 1000
    The actual perimeter is 1000 cm (10 m).
11. Actual perimeter : (3 + 4 + 5) x 100 = 1200
    The actual perimeter is 1200 cm (12 m).
12. Actual perimeter : (6 + 4 + 3.5 + 3) x 100 = 1650
    The actual perimeter is 1650 cm (16.5 m).
13. T, Q, P, S, R
14. Area : 5 x 6.5 = 32.5   Its area is 32.5 m^2.
15. Area : 3 x 7.3 = 21.9   Its area is 21.9 m^2.
16. Area : 7.9 x 7.9 = 62.41   Its area is 62.41 m^2.
17. No. of times : (5 x 13) ÷ (2.6 x 5) = 5
    The area of the dining room is 5 times that of the washroom.
18. Area : (13 + 6.4) x (7.9 + 5) = 250.26   The area is 250.26 m^2.
19. Area : (7.9 x 7.9) + (5 x 6.5) = 94.91
    94.91 m^2 of carpet would cover the living room and the library.
20. Cost : 94.91 x 2 = 189.82   He needs to pay $189.82 for the carpet.
21. Amount of paint : (5 x 2.8 + 6.4 x 2.8) ÷ 4 = 7.98
    7.98 L of paint are needed for the 2 walls.
22. No. of cans : 7.98 ÷ 2 = 3.99   He needs to buy 4 cans.
23. Perimeter : (2.5 + 1.2) x 2 = 7.4   Area : 2.5 x 1.2 = 3
    Its perimeter is 7.4 m and its area is 3 m^2.
24. Perimeter : 60 x 4 = 240 ;   Area : 60 x 60 = 3600
    Its perimeter is 240 cm and its area is 3600 cm^2.
25. Length : 120 ÷ 4 = 30   Each side is 30 cm long.
26. Width : 450 ÷ 25 = 18   Its width is 18 m.
27. Length : (45 ÷ 2) – 5 = 17.5   Area : 17.5 x 5 = 87.5
    Its area is 87.5 cm^2.

Challenge

1. Length : 40 – (2 x 2) = 36   Width : 25 – (2 x 2) = 21
   The length is 36 cm and the width is 21 cm.
2. Area : 36 x 21 = 756 ;   Perimeter : (36 + 21) x 2 = 114
   Its area is 756 cm^2 and its perimeter is 114 cm.

Unit 3

1. Time : 9 h 40 min + 57 min = 10 h 37 min   10:37 a.m.
2. Time : 10 h 37 min + 40 min = 11 h 17 min
   They left the park at 11:17 a.m.
3. Time : 11 h 17 min + 32 min = 11 h 49 min
   They reached the convenience store at 11:49 a.m.
4. Time : 11 h 49 min + 35 min = 12 h 24 min
   They left the store at 12:24 p.m.
5. Time taken : 12 h 42 min – 12 h 24 min = 18 min
   They took 18 min.
6. Time : 1 h 17 min – 26 min = 0 h 51 min
   She started at 12: 51 p.m.
7. No. of days : 29 – 3 = 26   Larry has 26 days.
8. Time taken : (12 h 0 min – 8 h 16 min) + 4 h 5 min = 7 h 49 min
   He has worked for 7 h 49 min.
9. Time : 5 h 32 min – 2 h 20 min = 3 h 12 min
   He started at 3: 12 p.m.
10. Time : 1 h 48 min + 23 min = 2 h 11 min (2:11 p.m.)
    Yes, she will be there on time.
11. Time : 11 h 45 min + 1 h 35 min = 13 h 20 min
    It will be over at 1:20 p.m.
12. Time movie A finishes :   Time movie B finishes :
    11 h 45 min + 1 h 43 min   12 h 10 min + 1 h 16 min
    = 13 h 28 min (1:28 p.m.)   = 13 h 26 min (1:26 p.m.)
    Movie B finishes first.
13. No. of days = 170 ÷ 24 = 7...2   He spent 7 days and 2 hours.
14. Time : 11 h 26 min + 37 min + 16 min = 12 h 19 min
    He reached the theatre at 12:19 p.m.

    ISBN: 978-1-897164-15-0

Challenge

Time Flight A arrives :

11 h 55 min + 2 h 16 min

= 14 h 11 min (2:11 p.m.)

Time Flight B departs :

2 h 11 min – 1 h 45 min

= 0 h 26 min (12:26 p.m.)

Flight B must leave at 12:26 p.m.

Unit 4

1. Time : 600 ÷ 60 = 10   10 hours
2. Time : 880 ÷ 80 = 11   It would take 11 hours.
3. Average speed : 780 ÷ 10 = 78   Their average speed was 78 km/h.
4. Time : 780 ÷ 60 = 13   It would take 13 hours.
5. Time : (600 + 880 + 780) ÷ 80 = 28.25   It would take 28.25 hours.
6. Average speed : (600 + 880 + 780) ÷ 20 = 113
   The average speed was 113 km/h.
7. Time taken : (4 x 2) ÷ 20 = 0.4   She will take 0.4 h (24 min).
8. Time taken : 2.4 ÷ 12 = 0.2   She will take 0.2 h (12 min).
9. Time saved : (2.4 ÷ 12 – 2.4 ÷ 20) x 60 = 4.8   She will save 4.8 min.
10. Time taken : 3.6 ÷ 20 x 60 = 10.8   She will take 10.8 min.
11. Speed : 3.6 ÷ 15 = 0.24   Her cycling speed was 0.24 km/min.
12. Speed : 0.24 x 60 = 14.4   Her cycling speed was 14.4 km/h.

Challenge

No. of days Ricky takes : 180 ÷ 20 = 9

No. of days Raymond takes : 180 ÷ (36 ÷ 2) = 10

No. of days Sam takes : 180 ÷ (15 x 2) = 6

Ricky takes 9 days. Raymond takes 10 days. Sam takes 6 days.
Sam finishes first.

Unit 5

1. Volume of air : 60 x 25 x 40 = 60000   It was 60 000 cm³.
2. Water held : 60000 ÷ 1000 = 60   It could hold 60 L of water.
3. Volume : 60000 – 20 x 1000 = 40000   It would be 40 000 cm³.
4. Volume : 40000 – 15 x 1000 = 25000   It would be 25 000 cm³.
5. Volume : 25000 – 10 x 1000 = 15000   It would be 15 000 cm³.
6. Difference : 60 – (45 x 15 x 20) ÷ 1000 = 46.5
   The new aquarium could hold 46.5 L more than the old one.
7. Volume : 25 x 20 x 10 = 5000   It is 5000 cm³.
8. Water held : 5000 ÷ 1000 = 5   It holds 5 L of water.
9. Water held : 160000 ÷ 1000 = 160   It holds 160 L of water.
10. Volume : 5000 x 8 = 40000   40 000 cm³ of air will be in the tank.
11. Water remained : 160 – (5 x 8) = 120
    120 L of water will remain in the tank.
12. Pailfuls of water : (160 ÷ 2) ÷ 5 = 16
    16 pailfuls of water must be removed.
13. Pailfuls of water : 160 ÷ 5 = 32   32 pailfuls of water must be removed.
14. Height : 160000 ÷ (1 x 100 x 0.25 x 100) = 64
    It would be 64 cm (0.64 m) high.
15. Volume : 75000 ÷ 6 = 12500 cm³   It is 12 500 cm³.
16. Volume : 100 x 50 x 60 = 300000
    It can hold 300 000 cm³ (0.3 m³) of water.
17. Volume : 60 x 50 x 60 = 180000
    It can hold 180 000 cm³ (0.18 m³) of water.
18. Difference : 300000 – 180000 = 120000
    It holds 120 000 cm³ (0.12 m³) more water than the small one.
19. No. of cubes : 180000 ÷ (10 x 10 x 10) = 180
    It can hold 180 cubes.
20. Time taken : 300000 ÷ 25000 = 12   It takes 12 min to fill it up.
21. Amount of water : 180000 ÷ 30 = 6000
    She will pour 6000 cm³ in one minute.
22. Volume : 5.6 x 8.6 x 3 = 144.48
    144.48 m³ of air is in the living room.
23. Volume : 8 x 7 x 3 = 168   168 m³ of air is in bedroom 2.
24. Difference : (4 x 7 x 3) – (2.3 x 2.8 x 3) = 64.68
    64.68 m³ more air is in bedroom 1 than in the washroom.

25. Volume : (4 x 5 x 3) ÷ 8 = 7.5   It is 7.5 m³.
26. Volume : (400 x 500 x 300) ÷ 8 = 7500000.   It is 7 500 000 cm³.

Challenge

1. 6 x 6 x 3 = 108 ;   4 x 4 x 3 = 48
2. 4 x 3 x 6 = 72 ;   2 x 1 x 6 = 12

Unit 6

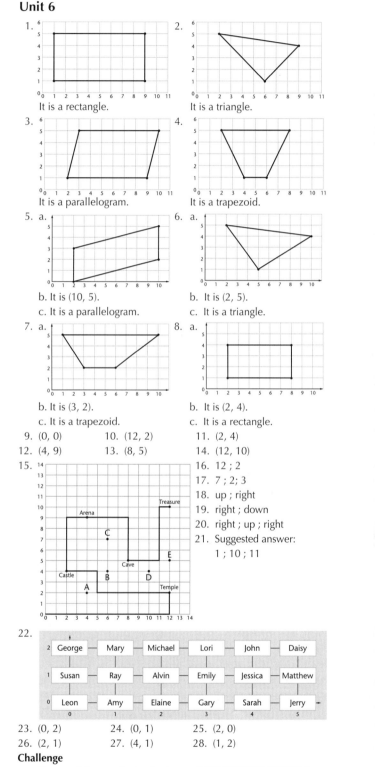

1. It is a rectangle.
2. It is a triangle.
3. It is a parallelogram.
4. It is a trapezoid.
5. a.
   b. It is (10, 5).
   c. It is a parallelogram.
6. a.
   b. It is (2, 5).
   c. It is a triangle.
7. a.
   b. It is (3, 2).
   c. It is a trapezoid.
8. a.
   b. It is (2, 4).
   c. It is a rectangle.
9. (0, 0)
10. (12, 2)
11. (2, 4)
12. (4, 9)
13. (8, 5)
14. (12, 10)
15.
16. 12 ; 2
17. 7 ; 2; 3
18. up ; right
19. right ; down
20. right ; up ; right
21. Suggested answer:
    1 ; 10 ; 11

22.

2	George	Mary	Michael	Lori	John	Daisy
1	Susan	Ray	Alvin	Emily	Jessica	Matthew
0	Leon	Amy	Elaine	Gary	Sarah	Jerry
	0	1	2	3	4	5

23. (0, 2)
24. (0, 1)
25. (2, 0)
26. (2, 1)
27. (4, 1)
28. (1, 2)

Challenge

The possible coordinates for the other two vertices are (0, 1) and (0, 6) or (10, 1) and (10, 6).

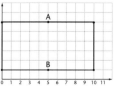

ISBN: 978-1-897164-15-0

Midway Review

1. Time taken : 11 h 11 min – 10 h 47 min = 24 min
   She took 24 min to go from her home to the mall.
2. Distance : 50 x (24 ÷ 60) = 20
   The mall was 20 km from her house.
3. Time : 11 h 11 min + 2 h 18 min + 45 min
   = 14 h 14 min (2:14 p.m.)   She left the mall at 2:14 p.m.
4. Time taken : (20 ÷ 40) x 60 = 30
   Time : 2 h 14 min + 30 min = 2 h 44 min
   She reached home at 2:44 p.m.
5. Change : 100 – 18.27 – 52.49 = 29.24   Her change was $29.24.
6. Difference : 52.49 – 18.27 = 34.22
   It cost $34.22 more than the box.
7. Area : 45 x 60 = 2700   She would need 2700 cm^2 of felt.
8. Length : (45 + 60) x 2 = 210   Her border would be 210 cm.
9. Volume : 45 x 60 x 50 = 135000   It was 135 000 cm^3.
10. No. of boxes : 5 x 3 x 5 = 75   It would hold 75 boxes of tissue.
11. Water held : (20 x 40 x 30) ÷ 1000 = 24
    It could hold 24 L of water.
12. Time taken : 4 h 34 min – 4 h 29 min = 0 h 5 min   It took 5 min.
13. Volume : 20 x 40 x (30 – 5) = 20000
    20 000 cm^3 of water was in the aquarium.
14. Volume : (20 x 40 x 0.5) ÷ 8 = 50
    On average, each pebble was 50 cm^3.
15.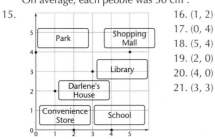
16. (1, 2)
17. (0, 4)
18. (5, 4)
19. (2, 0)
20. (4, 0)
21. (3, 3)
22. Distance : 50 x (15 ÷ 60) = 12.5
    The mall is 12.5 km from the bus stop.
23. Time : 11 h 56 min + 15 min = 12 h 11 min
    She will arrive at 12:11 p.m.
24. Money saved : (1.28 x 10) – 10.4 = 2.4   She will save $2.40.
25. Cost : 10.40 + (2 x 1.28) = 12.96   She pays $12.96.
26. Total amount : 12.84 + 31.39 = 44.23   She spends $44.23 in all.
27. Money she had : 32.97 + 22.81 = 55.78
    She had $55.78 at the beginning.
28. C   29. B   30. A   31. C
32. D   33. D   34. B   35. A

Unit 7

1. a. b. c.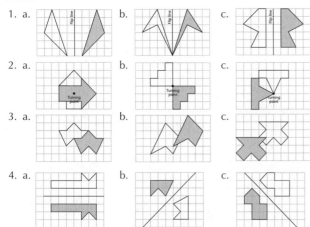
2. a. b. c.
3. a. b. c.
4. a. b. c.

5. a. b.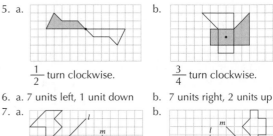

   $\frac{1}{2}$ turn clockwise. $\frac{3}{4}$ turn clockwise.

6. a. 7 units left, 1 unit down   b. 7 units right, 2 units up
7. a. b.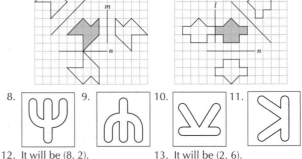

8. 9. 10. 11.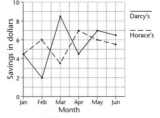

12. It will be (8, 2).   13. It will be (2, 6).
14. He moves it 6 units left and 2 units down.
15. It will be (20, 8).   16. It will be (17, 8).
17. She moves it 1 unit right and 4 units up.
18. It will be (22, 5).

Challenge
   C

Unit 8

1. 80
2. 70 toy cars were produced last Friday.
3. Difference : 85 – 40 = 45
   45 more toy cars were produced on Wednesday than on Thursday.
4. It happened on Thursday because the production dropped that day.
5. It was closed on Saturday and Sunday because there was no production in those two days.
6. No. of toy cars : (80 + 75 + 85 + 40 + 70) ÷ 5 = 70
   70 toy cars were produced each working day.
7. 2000 sports cars were produced.
8. 4000 vans were produced.
9. 7000 jeeps were produced.
10. Difference : 2000 – 1000 = 1000   1000 more vans were produced.
11. Total no. of jeeps : 7000 + 6000 + 7000 + 6000 = 26000
    26 000 jeeps were produced.
12. Total no. of vehicles : 6000 + 6000 + 2000 = 14000
    14 000 vehicles were produced in the 4th quarter.
13. In the 4th quarter.
14. In the 2nd quarter.
15. It indicated a continuous increase in the production of sports cars.
16. Vans should be cut because there was a decrease in the production of vans.
17.

Darcy's and Horace's Savings

18. Difference : 8.5 – 3.5 = 5
    Darcy saved $5.00 more than Horace in March.
19. Difference : 6 – 2 = 4
    Horace saved $4.00 more than Darcy in February.

20. Darcy saved more than Horace in March, May and June.
21. Darcy's savings were more than Horace's in three months.
22. Their savings were the same in January.
23. Amount saved : 4.5 + 2 + 8.5 + 4.5 + 7 + 6.5 = 33
    Darcy saved $33.00 in the six months.
24. Amount saved : 4.5 + 6 + 3.5 + 7 + 6 + 5.5 = 32.5
    Horace saved $32.50 in the six months.
25. Total : 33 + 32.5 = 65.5   (65.5 > 65.39)
    Yes, they would have enough money to buy it.
26.

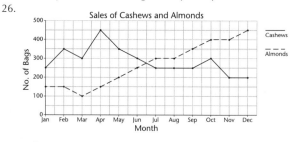

Sales of Cashews and Almonds

27. Difference : 450 − 150 = 300
    300 more bags of cashews were sold than almonds in April.
28. Difference : 350 − 250 = 100
    100 more bags of almonds were sold than cashews in September.
29. Bags of nuts sold : 300 + 250 = 550
    She sold 550 bags of nuts in June.
30. The sales of cashews increased the most in April.

Challenge

The sales of cashews decreased, but the sales of almonds increased.

Unit 9

1. apples
2.
3. Karin spent the least money on grapes.
4.
5. Spending on pears : 100 ÷ 4 = 25
   She would spend $25 on pears.

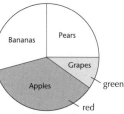

Karin's Spending on Fruit

6. Apples, bananas, pears, grapes
7. Group 4 had the most As.
8. Group 3 had the fewest As.
9. 6 students with an A were in Group 4.
10. 3 students with an A were in Group 1.
11. No. of students in Group 4 : 6 x 2 = 12
    There were 12 students in Group 4.
12. No. of students : 12 x 4 = 48   48 students took the test.
13.

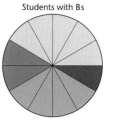

Students with Bs

☐ Group 1
■ Group 2
☐ Group 3
■ Group 4

14. Mario's group raised the second most money.
15. Lori's group raised the least money.
16. Shirley, Mario, John, Lori.
17. Money raised : 24 x 2 = 48   Mario's group raised $48.00.
18. Money raised : 24 x 4 = 96   Shirley's group raised $96.00.
19. Money raised : 24 ÷ 2 = 12   Lori's group raised $12.00.
20. Money raised : 12 + 24 + 48 + 96 = 180
    They raised $180.00 altogether.
21. Shirley's group sold the most number of apples because they raised the most money.
22. Mario's group sold the second most number of apples because they raised the second most money.

23. He spent the most time on video games on Saturday.
24. He spent the second most time on video games on Sunday.
25. He did not play video games on Tuesday and Thursday.
26. Time spent : 1 x 2 = 2
    He played video games for 2 hours on Monday.
27. Time spent : 1 x 3 = 3
    He played video games for 3 hours on Saturday.
28. Difference : 2.5 − 0.5 = 2
    He played 2 more hours on Sunday than on Wednesday.

Challenge

B ; Circle graph B shows that Katie spent the most money on clothing, the second most money on entertainment, the second least money on transportation and the least money on food.

Unit 10

1. Mean : (127+117+120+105+110+105+100) ÷ 7 = 112   112
2. Mean : (110+126+112+104+108+110+121) ÷ 7 = 113
   Her mean running time was 113 s.
3. Mean : (124+106+98+110+106+106+106) ÷ 7 = 108
   Her mean running time was 108 s.
4. Mean : (100+125+105+104+100+104+104) ÷ 7 = 106
   Her mean running time was 106 s.
5. Her mode running time in the 3rd week was 106 s.
6. Her mode running time in the 4th week was 104 s.
7. Amy had the highest allowance in the class.
8. Wayne had the lowest allowance in the class.
9. Mean : (5 + 6.75 + 5.37 + 5) ÷ 4 = 5.53
   Their mean allowance was $5.53.
10. Mean : (3.83 + 7.37 + 3.83) ÷ 3 = 5.01
    Their mean allowance was $5.01.
11. Mean allowance of group B :
    (6.8 + 9.15 + 4.16 + 4.16 + 4.18) ÷ 5 = 5.69
    Mean allowance of group D :
    (4.75 + 8.13 + 4.75 + 4.75 + 8.13 + 0.69) ÷ 6 = 5.2
    Yes, the mean allowance received by the students in group B was higher than that by group D.
12. The mode allowance in group B was $4.16.
13. The mode allowance in group D was $4.75.
14. Mean : (5 + 6.75 + 5.37 + 5 + 4.18) ÷ 5 = 5.26
    Their mean allowance would be $5.26.
15. By systematic trial :
    Mean (Lily in group C) :   Mean (Donny in group C) :
    (3.83 + 7.37 + 3.83 + 4.75) ÷ 4   (3.83 + 7.37 + 3.83 + 8.13) ÷ 4
    = 4.945 (not 5.79) ✗   = 5.79 ✓
    Donny and Mark were the possible students.
16. Mean : (258 + 426 + 426 +678) ÷ 4 = 447
    The mean number of cards was 447.
17. No. of cards : 258, 426, 426, 678
    The mode number of cards was 426.
18. Mean : ((258 + 126) + 426 + 426 + (678 − 126)) ÷ 4 = 447
    The mean number of cards would be 447.
19. No. of cards : 384, 426, 426, 552
    The mode number of cards was 426.
20. Mean : (258 + (426 − 252) + (426 + 252) + 678) ÷ 4 = 447
    The mean number of cards would be 447.
21. No. of cards : 258, 174, 678, 678
    The mode number of cards would be 678.
22. Mean : ((258 − 40) + (426 + 60) + (426 − 60) + (678 + 40)) ÷ 4 = 447
    The mean number of cards was 447.
23. Mean : ((258 + 120) + (426 + 28) + 426 + 678) ÷ 4 = 484
    The mean number of cards would be 484.
24. Mean : (258 + 426 + 426 + (678 −88)) ÷ 4 = 425
    The mean number of cards would be 425.

25. Mean : ((258 + 426 + 426 + 678) − 160) ÷ 4 = 407
    Their mean number of cards would be 407.
26. Mean : ((258 + 12) + 426 + (426 − 48) + 678) ÷ 4 = 438
    The mean number of cards would be 438.
27. By systematic trial :
    Average : (110 + 150 + 120 + 130) ÷ 4 = 127.5 ✗
    Average : (110 + 120 + 130 + 180) ÷ 4 = 135 ✓
    He has boxes A, C, D and E.
28. Mean : (110 + 150 + 120 + 130 + 180) ÷ 5 = 138
    The mean number of cards would be 138.
29. By systematic trial :
    Average : (10.68 + 12.37 + 13.25 + 11.89) ÷ 4 = 12.05 ✗
    Average : (10.68 + 12.37 + 11.89 + 14.46) ÷ 4 = 12.35 ✓
    She has bags A, B, D and E.
30. Mean : (10.68 + 12.37 + 13.25 + 11.89 + 14.46) ÷ 5 = 12.53
    The mean amount in each bag would be 12.53 kg.

Challenge

1. Mark : ((76 x 5) − 78 − 86 − 92 − 68) = 56
   His mark in Math was 56.
2. Mark : ((77 x 5) − 78 − 86 − 92 − 68) = 61
   He would have to get 61 in Math.

Unit 11

1.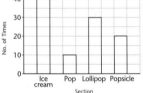

2. No. of times of spinning : 100
   No. of times stopped on 'ice cream' : 40
   Fraction of times : $\frac{40}{100} = \frac{2}{5}$ It was $\frac{2}{5}$.
3. No. of times stopped on 'pop' : 10
   Fraction of times : $\frac{10}{100} = \frac{1}{10}$ It was $\frac{1}{10}$.
4. No. of times stopped on 'lollipop' : 30
   Fraction of times : $\frac{30}{100} = \frac{3}{10}$ It was $\frac{3}{10}$.
5. It is least likely to stop on 'pop'.
6. It is most likely to stop on 'ice cream'.
7. There are 8 marbles altogether; 5 out of 8 marbles are red.
   The probability is $\frac{5}{8}$.
8. There are 10 marbles altogether; 4 out of 10 marbles are blue.
   The probability is $\frac{4}{10}$ ($\frac{2}{5}$).
9. There are 12 marbles altogether; 4 out of 12 marbles are green.
   The probability is $\frac{4}{12}$ ($\frac{1}{3}$).
10. There are 9 marbles altogether; 0 out of 9 marbles are yellow.
    The probability is 0.
11. There are 18 marbles altogether; 4 out of 18 marbles are blue.
    The probability is $\frac{4}{18}$ ($\frac{2}{9}$).
12. No, because there are more blue marbles than red marbles. The most likely marble is blue.
13. 1 out of 4 sections is 'hamburger'. The probability is $\frac{1}{4}$.
14. 2 out of 6 sections are 'sandwich'. The probability is $\frac{2}{6}$ ($\frac{1}{3}$).
15. 1 out of 8 sections is 'pop'. The probability is $\frac{1}{8}$.
16. 3 out of 8 sections are 'hot dog'. The probability is $\frac{3}{8}$.

17. Spinner A : 1 out of 4 sections
    Spinner B : 1 out of 6 sections
    Spinner C : 3 out of 8 sections ($\frac{3}{8} > \frac{1}{4} > \frac{1}{6}$)
    Spinner C has the greatest probability.
18. Spinner A : 1 out of 4 sections
    Spinner B : 1 out of 6 sections
    Spinner C : 1 out of 8 sections ($\frac{1}{8} < \frac{1}{6} < \frac{1}{4}$)
    Spinner C has the least probability.
19. $20.08 has two tens. Michael can spin 2 times.
20. He should spin Spinner C because it has the greatest probability that the spinner will stop on 'hot dog'.
21. The probability is 1.
22. The probability is 0.
23.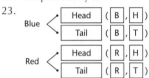

24. There are 6 possible outcomes.
25. They have 1 chance out of 6 to get a red marble and a head.
    The probability is $\frac{1}{6}$.
26. They have 1 chance out of 6 to get a blue marble and a tail.
    The probability is $\frac{1}{6}$.
27. No, it is because both have a probability of $\frac{1}{6}$.
28. They have 1 chance out of 6 to get a yellow marble and a head.
    No. of times : 60 ÷ 6 = 10
    They would get a yellow marble and a head about 10 times.

Challenge

Spinner A :
$P(A) = \frac{2}{12} = \frac{1}{6}$ $P(B) = \frac{4}{12} = \frac{1}{3}$
$P(C) = \frac{2}{12} = \frac{1}{6}$ $P(D) = \frac{4}{12} = \frac{1}{3}$
Spinner B :
$P(A) = \frac{2}{8} = \frac{1}{4}$ $P(B) = \frac{3}{8}$
$P(C) = \frac{1}{8}$ $P(D) = \frac{2}{8} = \frac{1}{4}$
Spinner C :
$P(A) = \frac{1}{6}$ $P(B) = \frac{2}{6} = \frac{1}{3}$
$P(C) = \frac{1}{6}$ $P(D) = \frac{2}{6} = \frac{1}{3}$
Spinner D :
$P(A) = \frac{3}{8}$ $P(B) = \frac{1}{8}$
$P(C) = \frac{1}{8}$ $P(D) = \frac{3}{8}$
Spinner A and Spinner C show the same probability of getting each letter.

Final Review

1. Volume : 20 x 60 x 90 = 108000
   The volume of the carton was 108 000 cm^3.
2. No. of boxes : 4 x 3 x 4 = 48
   It would hold 48 boxes of cereal.
3. Cost : 2.99 x 48 = 143.52
   It would cost $143.52.
4. Boxes of granola : 48 − 18 − 8 − 10 = 12
   There were 12 boxes of granola.
5. 8 out of 48 boxes of cereal were rice flakes.
   The probability was $\frac{8}{48}$ ($\frac{1}{6}$).

     ISBN: 978-1-897164-15-0

6. 38 out of 48 boxes of cereal were not corn flakes.
   The probability was $\frac{38}{48}$ ($\frac{19}{24}$).

7. Bran flakes had the greatest probability because they had the most number.

8.
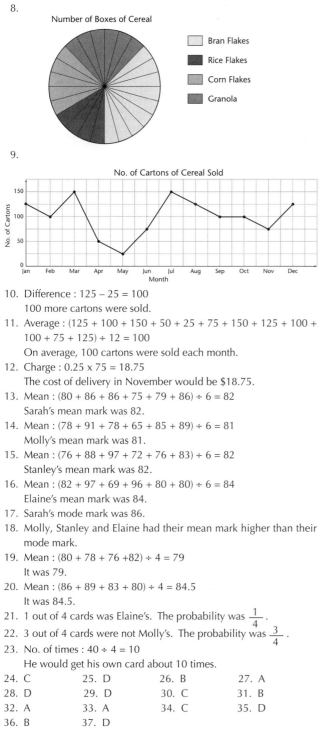

Number of Boxes of Cereal

☐ Bran Flakes
■ Rice Flakes
▨ Corn Flakes
▨ Granola

9.

No. of Cartons of Cereal Sold

10. Difference : 125 − 25 = 100
    100 more cartons were sold.

11. Average : (125 + 100 + 150 + 50 + 25 + 75 + 150 + 125 + 100 + 100 + 75 + 125) ÷ 12 = 100
    On average, 100 cartons were sold each month.

12. Charge : 0.25 x 75 = 18.75
    The cost of delivery in November would be $18.75.

13. Mean : (80 + 86 + 86 + 75 + 79 + 86) ÷ 6 = 82
    Sarah's mean mark was 82.

14. Mean : (78 + 91 + 78 + 65 + 85 + 89) ÷ 6 = 81
    Molly's mean mark was 81.

15. Mean : (76 + 88 + 97 + 72 + 76 + 83) ÷ 6 = 82
    Stanley's mean mark was 82.

16. Mean : (82 + 97 + 69 + 96 + 80 + 80) ÷ 6 = 84
    Elaine's mean mark was 84.

17. Sarah's mode mark was 86.

18. Molly, Stanley and Elaine had their mean mark higher than their mode mark.

19. Mean : (80 + 78 + 76 +82) ÷ 4 = 79
    It was 79.

20. Mean : (86 + 89 + 83 + 80) ÷ 4 = 84.5
    It was 84.5.

21. 1 out of 4 cards was Elaine's. The probability was $\frac{1}{4}$.

22. 3 out of 4 cards were not Molly's. The probability was $\frac{3}{4}$

23. No. of times : 40 ÷ 4 = 10
    He would get his own card about 10 times.

24. C   25. D   26. B   27. A
28. D   29. D   30. C   31. B
32. A   33. A   34. C   35. D
36. B   37. D

ISBN: 978-1-897164-15-0

 ISBN: 978-1-897164-15-0